Wildland Firefighting

Wildland Firefighting

Fire Behavior, Tactics & Command

2nd Edition, Revised and Enlarged

Donald G. Perry

Wildland Firefighting: Fire Behavior, Tactics & Command

2nd Edition Revised and Enlarged

Library of Congress Catalog Card Number: 90-085273

ISBN 0-941943-02-X

Dedicated to Cindy, Megan and Matthew with Love.

Cover photo by Donald G. Perry. Righetti Ranch, Orcutt, CA, 1987

Table of Contents

Foreword

From the initial attack to long-range planning, Donald Perry's book is a comprehensive guide to the vital, yet often misunderstood, subject of wildland firefighting. The chapters on topography, fuel types, weather, tactics and strategy, equipment utilization, urban interface and Incident Command System are particularly valuable.

Chief Perry's unique combination of experience-based technical knowledge and natural instructional ability gives him the perspective and ability to present the material thoroughly, in a readable and intelligible style. He meets the need to understand the complex nature of wildland fire management. This book is a significant contribution to our professional literature.

Wildland fire is a tough, unpredictable adversary. Donald Perry has been there to tell it like it is in *Wildland Firefighting*.

Gene LeBlanc, Fire Chief
Truckee Meadows FPD
Reno, Nevada

Introduction

When I originally wrote *Wildland Firefighting* in 1987 my prime focus was on educating students and firefighters on the issues related to wildland firefighting. Even though I understood this Nation's growth would create an increasing issue in the wildland firefighting area impacting most states, I did not realize it would become the issue it has in just three years. The wildland/urban interface or intermix fire problem is "the" fire problem of the 1990's.

The Paint conflagration in Santa Barbara, California on June 27, 1990 clearly illustrated how important it is for everyone in the firefighting occupation to understand the wildland/urban interface or intermix, the incident command system, mutual aid concepts, strike team resource deployment and tactics, and fire behavior.

Additionally, personnel safety continues to head the list of training priorities and control objectives as far too many firefighter fatalities and serious injuries are still occurring on the fireground. The second addition of *Wildland Firefighting* has been updated to help keep readers abreast of changes and new information in this firefighting speciality.

Donald G. Perry

Chapter 1

Terminology

ADIABATIC A weather term used to describe the expansion of a large parcel of air without loss or gain of heat (See Foehn).
AGE CLASS Indicates relative age, in years, of brush and trees. Some species of vegetation become decadent – and explosive – at a certain age class.
AGENCY REPRESENTATIVE An individual assigned to an incident from an assisting or cooperating agency who has been delegated full authority to make decisions on all matters affecting that agency's participation in the incident. Agency representatives report to the incident liaison officer.
AIR ATTACK Deploying fixed-wing or rotary aircraft on a wildland fire. This can also include using rotary aircraft to shuttle fire crews and supplies to base camp or spike camps.
AIRCO Acronym for "Air Coordinator." A light, fixed-wing aircraft with an experienced officer serving as supervisor for an air tanker attack.
AIR MASS A weather term used to describe a large parcel of air covering 100 to 1,000 square miles that has a consistent air temperature and relative humidity by elevation.
AIR TANKER Any fixed aircraft used to drop fire retardant or water on a wildland fire. Most aircraft used as air tankers are twin or multi-engine.
ALLOCATED A term used to describe personnel and/or resources dispatched to an incident that have not yet arrived.
ANCHOR POINT A term associated with attack methods. Refers to an advantageous location, usually one with a barrier to fire spread, from which to start constructing a fire line. Used to minimize the chance of being "flanked" by the fire while constructing the fire line. Most anchor points originate at or near the area of origin (rear of the fire).
ANEMOMETER A weather instrument used to measure the wind velocity.
AREA IGNITION A fire behavior term for the ignition of a number of individual fires throughout an area, either simultaneously or in close succession and so spaced as to add to and influence the main body of the fire to create a blow-up condition and large con-

tinuous fire spread. Area ignition occurs under adverse weather conditions and/or old age-class fuel types. A condition associated with extreme fire behavior.

ASPECT A topography term for the direction towards which a slope faces.

ASSIGNED Describes personnel and/or resources working an incident.

ASSISTING AGENCY Any agency directly involved with incident command, operations or support.

BACKFIRING When attacking a wildland fire using the *indirect method,* intentionally setting fire to fuels inside the control line to reduce fuel and contain a rapidly-spreading fire. Backfiring provides a wide defense perimeter and may be further employed to change the force of the fire's convective column.

BASE The location where primary logistics functions are coordinated and administered (incident name or other designation is added to the term "base" i.e., "Fox Base"). The incident command post may be co-located with the base. There is only one base per incident.

BERM A term used in conjunction with hand-tool or bulldozer attack. An outside or downhill side of a trench or ditch.

BRANCH That organizational level having functional/geographic responsibility for major segments of incident operations. The branch level supervises up to five divisions/groups. The supervisor in charge of a branch is called a branch director. Branch numbering uses roman numerals, numbered clockwise from origin, i.e., Branch I, II, III, etc.

BRANDS Pieces of burning debris carried aloft into the convective column. Brands may be carried outside the perimeter of the main fire by the wind, causing spot fires.

BRUSH Shrubs and stands of short, scrubby trees that do not reach merchantable size. Generally three to 20 feet in height.

BRUSH PATROL Any light, mobile vehicle having limited pumping and water capacity designed for initial-attack knockdown of a small wildland fire.

BURNING OUT When attack on the wildland fire is *direct,* or parallel with the control line, intentionally setting fire to unburned islands of fuel inside the control line to strengthen the line. The control line is not said to be complete until all fuel is "burned out" to where no fuel remains between the fire and control line. Gives rise to saying, "The only safe line is a 'black line.' "

CAMP A geographic site within the general incident area, equipped and staffed to provide food, water, sleeping and sanitary services to incident personnel. If fire size and topography warrant, "spike camp(s)" may be utilized. Incident name or designator is added to camp, i.e., "Fox Camp." If multiple camps are used, designate nearby ridge or landmark name.

CANDLING Burning aerial canopy of one single tree from ground up.

CANOPY In heavy fuel types (example: chaparral), the foliage or leaf covering on fuel stock. Usually heavily laden with waxes, turpines and resins that, when preheated, are very flammable and will add tremendous thermal outputs to a fire.

CAT LINE A fireline constructed by a bulldozer.

CAT PILE A berm left by a bulldozer that might contain smoldering fuel. Cat piles associated with direct attack must be checked.

CAT TEAM Cost apportionment team. Works with incident finance chief to develop appropriate incident cost responsibilities by agencies involved.

CHAIN A fire behavior term used to figure fire-perimeter size and rate of spread. Equals 66 feet.

CHAPARRAL A highly-flammable, seasonal plant community consisting of scrubs, trees and brush species found in the west and southwestern states.

CHECK-IN Locations where assigned resources check in at an incident. These consist of: Resources Unit (RESTAT) Base, Camp, Staging Areas Division, Helibase. Resource should check in at one location only, then complete ICS form 211.

CLASS OF FIRE (Size of wildland fire)

Class A: A fire of one-fourth acre or less.

Class B: A fire of at least one-fourth acre but less than 10 acres.

Class C: A fire of at least 10 acres, but less than 100 acres.

Class D: A fire of at least 100 acres, but less than 300 acres.

Class E: A fire of at least 300 acres, but less than 1,000 acres.

Class F: A fire of at least 1,000 acres, but less than 5,000 acres.

Class G: A fire of 5,000 acres or greater.

CLEAR TEXT Use of plain language in radio communications transmissions. Ten codes or agency specific codes do not constitute clear text. Example: Instead of saying "10-4," you use "okay" or verbal acknowledgement.

COLD FRONT A cold, dense air mass displacing warmer air. This condition can create major problems for an incident commander if it passes through the fire area. Erratic wind shift between 90 and 180 degrees can be expected and winds may reach 70 miles per hour. Usually associated with a low pressure system.

A good reason to have fire weather forecasters at the incident command post during a major wildland fire.

COLD TRAILING A key to control a partly-dead fire's edge by carefully inspecting and feeling with bare hands for any remaining embers or coals.

COMMAND The act of directing, managing and/or controlling personnel and resources by virtue of explicit legal, agency or delegated authority. The term "command" is also used to describe the incident commander managing the incident, i.e., "Fox Command."

COMMAND STAFF An incident command system term. Command staff consists of the information officer, safety officer and liaison officer. The command staff reports directly to the incident commander.

COMMUNICATIONS UNIT A trailer or mobile van used to provide the major part of an incident communications center. Once in service at an incident, it will assume the incident's name, i.e., "Fox Communications."

COMPANY Any piece of equipment having a full complement of personnel.

CONDUCTION The transfer of heat from one place to another without movement of the medium. For example, a down-dead log provides a medium to transfer heat from one point to another.

CONFLAGRATION A raging, destructive fire. Often used to describe a fire burning under extreme fire weather. The term is also used when a wildland fire burns into a wildland/urban interface, destroying many structures.

CONTAIN FIRE When fire crews and/or resources stop the forward progress of a fire but have not put in all control lines.

CONTROL LINE A term used for all constructed or natural fire barriers used to control a fire.

CONTROL OF FIRE When fire crew(s) and/or resources completely surround and leave no open line on the fire perimeter.
cloud development.

CONVECTION The transfer of heat by physical movement of a heated medium from one place to another. The convective column of a wildland fire can provide the medium.

CONVERGENCE A weather term associated with horizontal wind flows. Refers to when areas of higher barometric air pressures flow towards the center of low barometric pressure, resulting in a vertical

COOPERATING AGENCY Any agency or community organization that provides assistance other than direct command, operational or support functions, i.e., law enforcement, utility companies, Red Cross, National Guard, road departments, public works, etc.

COORDINATIONS The process of systematically analyzing a situation, developing relevant information and informing appropriate command authority of viable alternatives. The coordination process (which can be either intra- or inter-agency) does not, in itself, involve command dispatch actions. Personnel responsible for coordination may perform command or dispatch functions within limits, as established by specific agency delegations, procedures, legal authority, etc.

CREW TRANSPORT Any vehicle capable of transporting personnel.

CROWN FIRE Any fire that advances from top to top of trees or brush that is more or less independent of the surface fire. A crown fire is sometimes classified as either running, or dependent, to distinguish the degree of independence from the surface fire.

DEMOB An acronym for demobilization. The systematic release of personnel and resources from an incident. Demob should start during the incident's mobilization phase.

DEW POINT A weather term. The air temperature at which condensation forms (100-percent relative humidity).

DIRECT ATTACK Using either brush trucks, dozers or hand crews, attacking the fire on its burning edge or close to it. A direct attack is usually made on a wildland fire that is moving slowly and is not too hot for fire personnel to get in close with equipment. Crews, as they put in control lines, "burn out" any islands of unburned fuels to make a "black line."

DIRECT HIT A term used in air attack to describe an air drop made exactly on target.

DIURNAL A weather term to describe the daily heating and cooling cycle of a specific location.

DIVERGENCE A weather term for horizontal wind flows that extend outward from an area of high barometric pressure. Associated with horizontal cloud development.

DIVISION The largest segment of a geographical fire perimeter. Generally, a wildland fire is split into halves (i.e., Division A, Division B). A division supervisor is in charge of operational activities within the division. Letters are assigned to describe a division, i.e., A, B, C, D, etc. Division lettering starts clockwise from origin area.

DOZER A heavy piece of construction equipment used to construct a fire line by clearing brush, trees, grass, etc. Often utilized in tandem with a hot shot crew to burn out unburned islands of fuel. Also called a "cat" or "bulldozer."

DRIFT SMOKE Smoke that has drifted from its point of origin and lost its original billowing form. Drift smoke can fill in canyons under stable air masses and make it difficult to see spot fires.

DROP A term associated with air attack. Refers to dropped cargo, personnel or retardant (i.e., "The drop was successful").

DRY RUN When AIRCO sends a lead plane or an air tanker over the target prior to the final drop for a mock run. Can be used by an air tanker pilot to warn personnel on the ground to clear out of the target area or to check on air turbulence in a canyon.

DRY STORM A lightning storm where little or no rain reaches the ground.

DUFF The mat of partly-decomposed dead leaves, twigs and bark under brush or trees.

DUST DEVIL A term used to describe a small whirlwind. A dust devil can indicate a fire-behavior change or unstable condition. It throws brands and embers across the fire line into unburned areas.

EARLY A term used in air attack to describe an air drop that falls short of a target area.

EDDY A weather term for micro-wind currents flowing against general wind direction.

ENGINE Any fire vehicle providing specified pump, water and hose capacities.

ENGINE COMPANY Any fire vehicle providing specified pump, water, hose and a minimum of three personnel.

EXTREME FIRE BEHAVIOR When a wildland fire is influenced by adverse winds, old age class fuel, adverse topography or any combination of the above. High rates of spread, spotting and thermal outputs are associated with extreme fire behavior.

FINAL RUN Actual run on drop target by air tanker or helicopter.

FINE FUEL MOISTURE (FFM) A term expressing the moisture level (in percentage) found in fine fuels (grass).

FINGERS OF A FIRE The long, narrow "tongues" projecting from the main body of a fire.

FIRE BEHAVIOR The manner in which a wildland fire develops: how fuels ignite, flame development and fire spread.

FIRE BREAK An existing barrier, man-made or natural, that will stop or slow an oncoming wildland fire.

FIRE FLANK The part of a wildland fire roughly between the head and the rear. Described as either a "hot" or "cold" flank, depending on wind and fire spread. A flank running with the wind is a hot flank. A flank backing into the wind is a cold flank. In a situation with little or no wind, a compass direction can be used, i.e., "east flank."

FIRE LINE The part of a control line that is scraped or dug down to mineral soil.

FIRE PERIMETER The entire length of the outer edge of the fire. The perimeter is described as ''approximate chains of line.''

FIRE RETARDANT Any substance or chemical applied to wildland fuels to slow the rate of combustion or reduce flammability. Generally expressed as long-term or short-term. Long-term retardants are generally chemical base, whereas short-term are primarily thickened water.

FIRE SEASON The period of the year when wildland fires are most likely to occur.

FIRESCOPE Acronym for ''Firefighting Resources of Southern California Organized for Potential Emergencies.'' After the disastrous 1970 fires in Southern California that burned 500,000-plus acres, destroyed 700 structures and killed 16 persons, many fire agencies in California, the aerospace industry, state and federal agencies decided to cooperate to prepare and cope with disasters such as wildland fires. The FIRESCOPE program developed the Incident Command System (ICS) and Multi-Agency Coordination System (MACS) presently being used nationwide as an all-risk management system. (See NIIMS.) In 1988 FIRESCOPE was adopted statewide as the all risk incident command system. The acronym was slightly altered to reflect this adaptation. FIRESCOPE now stands for ''Firefighting Resources of California Organized for Potential Emergencies.''

FIRE STORM Violent convective columns caused by large continuous areas of fire often appearing as tornado-like whirls. Can also occur from uneven terrain as fire spreads through an area. Associated with extreme fire behavior.

FIRE TROL An air attack term. A product name used to describe a long-term retardent using ammonium sulfate (AS) as its base.

FIRE WEATHER FORECAST A weather prediction made for a plans chief on a wildland fire with special emphasis given to weather fronts, humidity changes and recovery, winds and air temperatures. A fire weather forecast is an important element of the incident action plan.

FIRING OUT Also called ''firing.'' The intentional setting on fire of fuels between the control line and the main body of fire in either a backfiring or burning-out operation. The firing boss is responsible for the firing sequence.

FIRING TEAM Experienced wildland firefighters and firing boss in charge of carrying out backfiring or burn-out function.

FLANKING Attacking a wildland fire by working the sides of the fire between the head and rear.

FLASH FUELS Fuels like grass, leaves, pine needles and tree moss that ignite readily and burn rapidly. Also called fine fuels.

FOEHN WIND (A German word pronounced "Fern") Winds created by a well-established high pressure system over the Great Basin states and a low-pressure system off Baja, California. Very cold winds aloft "fall" toward California and the low-pressure system. As the wind crosses the desert, it is warmed through adiabatic heating of the air. This wind is most famous in California, particularly Southern California, where it has names like "Devil Wind," "Santa Ana," or "Santana." These winds are responsible, in part, for most of California's disastrous, large-life-loss wildland fires. Erratic winds and wind speeds of 50 to 70 miles per hour are not uncommon. (Gusts of 95 to 100 miles per hour occurred during the major California wildland fires of 1970.) Relative humidities drop below 10 percent and air temperatures exceed 100 degrees F. The Foehn wind condition on the eastern slopes of the Rocky Mountains is called "Chinook."

FRONT A weather term describing the transition zone between two parcels of air with different characteristics of temperature and air stability.

GENERAL STAFF The group of incident management personnel comprised of: Incident Commander, Operations Chief, Planning Chief, Logistics Chief, Finance Chief.

GRADIENT WIND Wind created by differing barometric pressures between high- and low-air-pressure systems. This condition can cover 100 to 300 miles. Velocity is generally five to 30 miles per hour, and wind shifts are usually gradual as systems move and shift.

GROUND FIRE A fire that consumes the organic material beneath surface fuels such as duff and peat moss.

GROUP Resources assembled at an incident to perform a special function not necessarily within a single geographic division. Groups will be managed by a group supervisor. Once the special function is completed, the group is disassembled. Groups are often used for structural protection and firing operations.

HAULING CHART A fire-behavior term for the graph that shows fire behavior characteristics and limits of attack resources and personnel.

HEAD OF A FIRE The most-active part of a wildland fire. A developing wildland fire can have multiple heads.

HEAVY FUELS Fuels of large diameter, such as logs, snags and large tree limbs. These ignite slowly and burn slow but hot.

HEEL See "Rear of Fire."

HELIBASE A location within the general incident area for parking, fueling, maintenance and loading of helicopters. A helibase is managed by a helibase manager.

HELIPORT A permanent or semi-permanent base for helicopters.

HELI-SHOT CREW An intensively-trained fire crew that travels to a fire in a rotary aircraft. On arrival it becomes a hot-shot crew. A helicopter assigned with a heli-shot crew should be assigned to support that crew.

HELISPOT On or near the fireline, a temporary area cleared of brush, trees and debris so helicopters can land and drop fire crews or supplies. Helispots can also be used as safety zones for personnel.

HELITANKER A helicopter equipped with tank(s) to carry water or fire retardant.

HIGH DROP An air attack term used to describe an air drop where the retardant or water does not effectively reach the surface fuels.

HIT 'N' GO A term used by hand crews to indicate each crew person is to take several quick strokes and bump forward. A technique used in light fuel types when a small fire is threatening to escape initial attack.

HOSE LAY Connecting sections of fire hose together from the fire pump to the fire location with designated sections of line controlled by use of water. Usually a 1½-inch cotton jacket line is branched down with 1-inch cotton jacket hose.

HOT-SHOT CREW An extensively-trained firefighting crew used primarily in hand-line construction. Crews can consist of anywhere from 10 to 20 persons, plus crew leader.

HOT SPOTTING Taking control action against points around the control line where a spot fire might occur or where a problem could develop. Specially-trained hand crews are usually required if an open line exists where the hot spots are developing.

HYGROTHERMOGRAPH A sensitive weather instrument for automatically recording continuous air temperature and relative humidity.

IGNITION TEMPERATURE The temperature at which wildland fuels ignite (usually 400 degrees to 700 degrees F).

INBOUND An air-attack term for aircraft approaching the fire. Aircraft will advise if it is inbound and estimate minute(s) from arrival and direction of the approach.

INCENDIARY FIRE A wildland fire willfully set by anyone to burn wildland or property not owned or leased by this person.

INCIDENT ACTION PLAN (IAP) The incident action plan contains objectives for the overall incident strategy and specific control actions for the next operational period of an incident. When complete, the incident action plan will have a number of attachments. (See Incident Command System.)

INCIDENT COMMANDER The officer in charge of the overall management of the incident. He/she is responsible for building management organization based on a span of control and incident complexity. There is only one incident commander per incident.

INCIDENT COMMAND POST (ICP) Location at which the primary command function is executed. Usually co-located with the incident base. There is only one ICP per incident.

INCIDENT COMMAND SYSTEM (ICS) A broad term used to describe a management system for all risk incidents. It involves a combination of facilities, equipment, personnel, procedures and communications operating within a common organizational structure. It outlines responsibility for the management of assigned personnel and resources utilizing cost-effective procedures.

INDIRECT ATTACK A method of attack in which the control line is located along a natural barrier, firebreak, creek, river or paved road. This attack method may be used in conjunction with backfiring.

INITIAL ATTACK (IA) The first-alarm assignment (resources and personnel) dispatched to a wildland incident.

INITIAL ATTACK ACTION Suppression action and size-up by first-arriving fire crews.

INITIAL ATTACK PRINCIPLES Initial ground or air attack deployed for fast, aggressive action on flanks and head and rapid containment and control. Provide for safety first. Start all actions with a good anchor point. (See SQQT.)

INITIAL PASS A term used in air attack to indicate the pilot is making a run over the target area to test air turbulence and outbound exit. (See Dry Run.)

INSTABILITY A weather term that describes when a parcel of air rapidly leaves its original level (elevation).

INTERMIX Unlike the wildland/urban interface which has an easily defined boundary between the wildland fuel and structures, the intermix is where structures are more widely dispersed in the fuel bed.

INVERSION A weather term used to describe when, in a given parcel of air, the air temperature increases with altitude.

JET STREAM A weather term used to describe a high-altitude, high-speed wind band located 40,000 feet-plus above sea level that influences frontal system movement. Wind speeds can reach 250 mph at the jet stream core.

JOINT COMMAND Two agencies working an incident both with jurisdictional authority. Each agency has an incident commander. Both incident commanders stay co-located developing one common list of control objectives. They also jointly conduct media briefing, planning and logistical support. One agency assumes responsibility for the unified ordering point. Neither agency compromises jurisdictional authority.

LATE An air-attack term used to describe an air drop that falls beyond the target area.

LEAD PLANE A fixed wing plane with the same basic job responsibilities of AIRCO. Used by the USFS officer in charge of air attack supervision.

LENTICULARIS A weather term for a cloud that indicates high speed winds aloft.

LIAISON OFFICER A member of the command staff responsible for interacting with representatives from assisting and cooperating agencies.

LINE FIRING A firing technique where one strip is set along the inside of a road, break or a cat line to widen the line.

LITTER Freshly-fallen leaves on top of a dull layer that eventually add to the layer through decomposition of organic material.

LIVE FUEL MOISTURE (LFM) A term describing moisture levels (expressed in percentage) found in brush and trees.

LOCAL WIND A wind whose velocity and direction is determined by local heating and cooling (diurnal cycle). Local winds are low-velocity winds averaging less than 10 mph.

LONG-TERM RETARDANT A term used in air attack. This retardant uses a chemical base to coat or treat the canopy, ground fuel foliage and stocks to slow the combustion process. It has a 60-minute-or-less holding characteristic.

LOW DROP An air attack term used to describe an air drop made too close to ground personnel for safety.

MAJOR FIRE Generally, a fire of the size and/or complexity that it requires a large force of fire resources, personnel and several days to control.

MILLIBAR A weather term used to express barometric pressure. A millibar is a unit of atmospheric pressure. At sea level there are 1,013.2 millibars of atmospheric pressure, or 29.92 inches of mercury or 14.7 pounds of pressure.

MONSOON A bucket, usually 60 to 300 gallons, slung under a helicopter to carry water or fire retardant to a fire. It can be loaded without the helicopter landing.

MOP-UP After the fire has been controlled, all actions required to make the fire "safe." This includes trenching, falling, snags and checking all control lines.

MULTI-AGENT COORDINATION SYSTEM (MACS) The MACS component of ICS is especially valuable when multiple fires require priorization of aircraft, bulldozers and hand crews. (These resources will become depleted and committed more rapidly than engines or brush trucks.) With the system, a matrix is developed for each major incident, evaluating life, property or watershed damage potential.

Also, a generalized term describing a combination of facilities, equipment, personnel, procedures and communications integrated into a common system with responsibility for coordination of assisting agency resources and support.

NATIONAL INTERAGENCY INCIDENT MANAGEMENT SYSTEM (NIIMS) NIIMS consists of five major sub-systems that collectively provide a total systems approach to all risk incident management. Sub-systems include: the Incident Command System, Training, Qualifications and Certification, Supporting Technologies, Publications Management.

NOAA WEATHER STATION A mobile weather data-collection and forecasting facility (with personnel) provided by the National Oceanic and Atmospheric Administration that can be utilized at the incident.

ONE-LICK METHOD A progressive method of constructing a fire line with a hand crew. Crew members take several strokes at clearing fuel or widening break and then move forward a specific distance.

OPERATIONAL PERIOD The period of time scheduled for execution of a given set of operation objectives as specified in the Incident Action Plan.

OPERATIONS COORDINATION CENTER (OCC) The primary facility of the Multi-Agency Coordination System. It houses the staff and equipment necessary to perform the MACS functions. Located in Riverside for Southern California, Sacramento for Northern California.

ORBIT A term used in air attack to indicate that air resources are holding in a fixed elevation, circling the incident.

OROGRAPHIC A topography term pertaining to mountains.

OUTBOUND An air attack term for aircraft leaving the fire to return to base or reload. Generally the air attack supervisor upon hearing the aircraft outbound will advise the pilot to reload and return, or return to base and hold.

OVERHEAD PERSONNEL Personnel who are assigned to supervisory positions. This includes Incident Commander, Command Staff, General Staff, Directors, Supervisors and Unit Leaders.

PALMER DROUGHT SEVERITY INDEX (PDI) A graphic utilized by fuel and fire managers to forecast vegetation stress levels due to moisture changes in soil and vegetation. First developed around 1900, this tool shows long range relationships between vegetation and potential fire severity.

PARALLEL METHOD A method where hand-tool crews operate 100 yards parallel to the fire's edge and burn out as they complete the fire line.

PHOS CHEK An air-attack term referring to the product name of a long-term retardant that has diammonium phosphate (DAP) as its base.

PLANNING MEETING One of the meetings held as needed throughout the duration of an incident to select specific strategies and tactics for incident control operations and service and support planning. The plans chief is responsible for coordinating the planning meeting schedule. Planning meetings are a key part of developing an incident action plan (IAP).

PRESCRIBED BURNING The intentional burning of heavy fuel types to break up continuous fuel beds for conversion to a lighter fuel type that is easier to control should a fire start in it.

PROGRESSIVE HOSE LAY A hose lay used on a wildland fire, usually on the flanks, to follow up a hand line made by fire crews or as a means of making a "wet line" along the fire's edge. Major components of this lay include 1½-inch hose as a main feeder line with 1-inch hose branched off it, usually every 100 to 150 feet.

PYROLYSIS Thermal decomposition of matter. The temperature at which wood products start the process of separating flammable and non-flammable products.

RATE OF SPREAD (ROS) A fire behavior term used to express relative horizontal growth of a wildland fire. Expressed in total perimeter growth in chains per hour. (See Chain.)

REAR OF FIRE The portion of a fire opposite the head. The slowest-burning part of a fire.

RELATIVE HUMIDITY A weather term. The amount of moisture in a given parcel of air expressed as a pecentage of the maximum amount that parcel of air could hold at the same air temperature.

RESTAT An acronym for the Resources Unit. A unit within the Planning Section.

RIDGE A weather term describing an elongated parcel of air with high barometric pressure extending outward from the center of a high-pressure system.

SALVO DROP In an air attack, dropping the total retardant load. This is used on larger spot fires and hot spots or to unload for an emergency.

SHORT-TERM RETARDANT A term used in air attack. It refers to retardants using a water base with short-term holding characteristics (30 minutes or less).

SPIKE CAMP A secondary camp used for servicing and supplying fire crews far from the main camp. Larger wildland fires often have two or three of these camps.

SQQT An acronym for Safety first, Quality second, Quantity third, Time last. In other words, pace your work. All attack methods should have SQQT as a goal.

STABILITY A weather term used when a parcel of air resists vertical motion.

STANDARD ATMOSPHERIC PRESSURE A weather term used to describe the weight of the atmosphere. At sea level, standard atmospheric pressure is 1013.25 millibars, or a barometric pressure of 29.92 inches of mercury at 60 degrees F.

STRIKE TEAM Specified combinations of the same kind and type of resources, with common radio communications and leader.

STRIP FIRING Setting fire to more than one strip of fuel and assuring that the strips burn together, thus widening your control line. This method is faster than normal line firing, however, coordination and safety for the firing team are critical.

STRING An air-attack term meaning to drop retardant out of separate compartments or tanks in succession. (See Trail Drop.)

SUBSIDENCE A weather term related to a large mass of air "falling" towards an area of low pressure. The falling air is heated by compression.

SUNDOWNER A weather term used to describe the strong, surfacing down-slope wind that occurs at dusk along the Southern California coastal range.

SURFACE FIRE A fire that burns surface litter like dry pine needles and leaves.

SWAMPER A term associated with dozer operations. A swamper is the person or relief operator assisting dozer operator(s), often by driving a fuel or service truck.

SYNOPTIC A weather term used to describe a large-area weather chart.

TASK FORCE A set of resources with a common leader and communications temporarily assembled for a specific mission. Task forces are generally used for firing operations and structural protection. Assignments are usually to a Group Supervisor rather than a specific division.

T-CARD A T-shaped colored card used by RESTAT to record the status of personnel and resources on an incident and to assist in DEMOB.

TECHNICAL SPECIALISTS Personnel with special skills who are called upon only when needed. Technical specialists may be requested in the areas of fire behavior, water resources, environmental concerns, resources use and training. Technical specialists operate as part of the Planning Section.

THERMAL BELTS In mountainous regions, the middle third of the slopes that remain active with fire during evening hours. This is due to down-canyon "falling" winds that pool cooler air in canyon bottoms but leave the middle part of the slope active.

TOPOGRAPHY An accurate and detailed description of a place, including land surface configuration, both man-made and natural. Topography can be described in terms like "level," "steep," "broken" or "rolling."

TOWNSHIP A topography-related term. A township is a surveyed area of land containing 36 sections. Each section is one square mile, and a township is 36 square miles.

TRAIL DROP In air attack, the dropping of fire retardant in lapping succession to extend the length of the drop. This is a very effective method of laying down a flank fire to cool it for hand crews and bulldozers.

TRENCHING The action of digging trenches on a side slope to catch any material that might roll across the control lines.

TROUGH A weather term describing an elongated parcel of air with low barometric pressure extending out from the center of a low-pressure system.

TWO-FOOT METHOD A suppression action taken within two feet of the fire's burning edge, requiring no burn out.

UNDERCUT LINE A control line constructed below a fire on a slope.

UNIFIED COMMAND A method whereby agencies or individuals who have either geographic or functional jurisdiction at an incident can jointly determine overall objectives, select a strategy and establish common organizational objectives. This may be implemented in a variety of ways and does not compromise the principle of having only one incident commander.

UOP Unified Ordering Point. On a developing incident involving multiple agencies the assignment for one agency to assume responsibility of receiving all incident ordering. This reduces chances for duplicate ordering, and allows for better fiscal tracking.

VIRGA A weather term describing moisture falling from clouds but not reaching the earth's surface.

WARM FRONT A weather condition where warm, less-dense air advances, replacing cold air. Much slower-moving than a cold front, it usually presents few problems, as wind speed and direction changes are slow and predictable.

WET LINE Control line put in by means of a progressive hose lay using1½-inch feeder line with 1-inch branch lines every 100 to 150 feet.

WETTING AGENT A chemical agent added to water to relieve surface tension and allow it to spread and penetrate fuels more easily.

WILDLAND/URBAN INTERFACE Where native vegetation (fuel types) interface with man-made fuel types (structures), that is, human encroachment into wildland areas. Once a term only used in California, it is now a national problem.

WIND The horizontal flow of air relative to the earth's topogaphy and surface.

WYE A hose fitting permitting two or more lines to be taken from a single supply line. Used frequently in progressive hose lays on wildland fires.

Abbreviations and Acronyms

AC Altocumulus
ACA Area Command Authority
AFFIRMS Administrative Forest Fire Information Retrieval and Management System
ASF American Society of Foresters
AT Air Tanker (AT 16, 16 Tail Number)
BIA Bureau of Indian Affairs
BIFC Boise Interagency Fire Center (Boise, Idaho)
BLM Bureau of Land Management
BTU British Thermal Unit
CALFIRMS California Fire Resources Management System
CAT Clear Air Turbulence
CB Cumulonimbus
CCC Civilian Conservation Corp.
CDFFP California Department of Forestry and Fire Protection
CI Cirrus
CSFS Colorado State Forest Service
CU Cumulus
CWCG California Wildfire Coordinating Group
DEMOB Demobilization
EFSA Escape Fire Situation Analysis
ETA Estimated Time of Arrival
ETD Estimated Time of Departure
ETE Estimated Time of Enroute

FBO Fire Behavior Officer (Technical Specialist-Plans Section)
FDF Florida Division of Forestry
FEMA Federal Emergency Management Agency
FFM Fine Fuel Moisture
FIMS Fire Information Management System
FIRECAST Fire Behavior Computer Model (FIRESCOPE)
FIREMOD Fire Behavior Computer Model (FIRESCOPE)
FIRESCOPE Firefighting Resources of Southern California Organized for Potential Emergencies (Riverside, California)
FLIR Forward Looking Infrared
FOG Field Operations Guide (FIRESCOPE)
FSC Finance Section Chief (Finance)
FWS Fish and Wildlife Service
H Designates High pressure air mass
IA Initial Attack
IAP Incident Action Plan (FIRESCOPE)
IC Incident Commander
ICP Incident Command Post
ICS Incident Command System
IR Infrared
JAC Joint Air Coordination
L Low-pressure air mass
LFM Live Fuel Moisture
LSC Logistics Section Chief (Logistics)
MACS Multi-Agency Coordination System
MAFFS Modular Airborne Fire Fighting System (C-130)
NARTC National Advanced Resource Technology Center (Marana, Arizona)
NDF Nevada Division of Forestry
NFA National Fire Academy
NFDRS National Fire Danger Rating System
NIIMS National Interagency Incident Management System
NOAA National Oceanic Atmospheric Administration (mobile weather units) (See NWS)
NPS National Parks Service
NWCG National Wildfire Coordinating Group
NWS National Weather Service
NZ North Zone (Redding, California)
OAS Office of Aircraft Services (BIFC)
OCC Opertions Coordination Center (Riverside, California) or Operations Control Center
ODF Oregon Division of Forestry

OES Office of Emergency Service
OSC Operations Section Chiefs (Operations)
PSC Planning Section Chief (Plans)
RAWS Remote Automated Weather Station
RECONN Reconnaissance (Flight)
RESTAT Resource Status (Plans Section)
R/H Relative Humidity
ROS Rate of Spread
SITSTAT Situation Status (Plans Section)
SMDW Strong Mountain Downslope Wind
ST Stratus
S/T Strike Team (FIRESCOPE)
SZ South Zone (Riverside, California)
T Temperature (degrees F or C)
T/F Task Force (FIRESCOPE)
TFS Texas Forest Service
USDA United States Department of Agriculture
USDI United States Department of Interior
USFA United States Fire Administration
USFS United States Forest Service

SPANISH TERMS USED IN WILDLAND FIREFIGHTING

ABAJO (uh-bah-ho) Down
AGUA (agh-wa) Water
ALTO (al-tow) High
APLANADORA (uh-plan-uh-door-ah) Bulldozer
ARBOL (are-bowl) Tree
ARBOLADO (ar-bo-lah-doh) Wildland
ARRIBA (a-reeb-a) Up
BOMBERO (bohm-bear-oh) Firefighter
BOSQUE (bohs-kay) Forest
CAJON (ka-hone) Canyon
CAMINO (ka-meen-o) Road, trail or way
CAMPO (kam-po) Level field
CERRO (ser-ro) Hill
COCHE DE BOMBEROS (koh-chay day bohm-bear-ohs) Fire engine
CUESTA (kwes-tah) Slope of hill/grade
ENCIMA (en-cee-mah) Summit
ENCINO (en-cee-no) Live oak
INFLAMAR (in-flah-mar) To catch or set on fire, ignite
JUNIPERO (hoo-nee-peh-ro) Juniper
LADERA (lah-de-rah) Slope
LLANO (yah-no) Flat

LOMA (lo-mah) Hill
MADERA (mah-deh-rah) Wood
MANGA (man-gah) Hose
MIRADOR (mere-ah-door) Viewpoint, vantage point
MONTE (mon-tae) Mountain, woodland
MONTE BAJO (mon-tae bah-ho) Brushland, thicket
NOROESTE (no-ro-es-tae) Northwest
NORTE (nor-tae) North
OESTE (oh-es-tae) West
ORIENTE (or-ee-hen-tae) East
PALA (pah-lah) Shovel
PALO (pah-low) Tree trunk
PALOS COLORADOS (pah-lows ko-low-rah-dows) Red poles, describes the redwood trees of California
PASO (pah-so) Pass
PELIGRO (peh-leg-grow) Danger
PINO (pee-noh) Pine
POZO (poh-zoe) Dig a well
PRADERA (pray-deh-rah) Grassland
PRADO (pray-doh) Meadow
ROBLE (roh-blay) Oak
ROCA (roh-ka) Rock, cliff
SEDE (seh-day) Headquarters
SUR (sir) South
VALLE (vie-yay) Valley
VIENTO (be-yen-toh) Wind

Measurements, Tables and Calculations

CHAIN 66 feet
STEP Average person's step = three feet (chain = 22 steps)
10 CHAINS 220 steps, or 660 feet
ACRE 208 feet x 208 feet, or 43,560 square feet or 0.40 hectacre
HECTACRE 2.5 acres, or 107,637 square feet
MILE 5,280 feet, or 80 chains
SQUARE MILE 640 acres
MILLIBAR .0295, or .03 inch
ONE INCH 33.863 millibars, or 25.40 millimeters
ONE MILLIMETER .039, or .04 inch
METER 3.3 feet, or 1.09 yards, or 39.3 inches
SECTION One square mile, or 640 acres
TOWNSHIP 36 sections, or 23,040 acres east to west reference lines on a township map. A township measures six miles by six miles.
RANGES North-south reference lines on a township map. A range

line occurs every six miles.

BTU 0.25 calorie

CALORIE four BTUs

ONE DEGREE FAHRENHEIT (degrees C x 9/5) + 32

ONE DEGREE CELSIUS (degrees F -32) x 5/9

FAHRENHEIT	0	10	20	30	40	50	60	70	80	90	100	110
CELSIUS	-18	-12	-7	-1	4	10	16	21	27	32	38	43

OUNCE 0.0625 lb.

POUND 16 ounces

TON 2,000 lbs.

PINT 0.125 gallon

QUART 0.25 gallon

GALLON four quarts, or eight pints, or 128 ounces

FOOT/SECOND 60 feet per minute, or 0.7 miles per hour (mi/h)

MILES PER HOUR (mi/h) 88 feet per minute (ft/min), or 1.5 feet per second (fps)

KNOT (k) 101 feet per minute (ft/min), or 1.2 miles per hour (mi/h), or 1.7 feet per second (ft/s)

STANDARD ATMOSPHERIC PRESSURES

Altitude (Feet)	Temperature (°F)	Barometric Pressure (mb)
Sea Level	59°F	1,013.2
1,650	53°F	954.6
3,300	47°F	898.8
4,950	41°F	845.6
6,000	36°F	795.0
8,250	29°F	746.9
9,990	23°F	701.2
11,550	18°F	657.8
13,200	12°F	616.6
14,850	6°F	577.5
16,500	0°F	540.0

BAROMETER CONVERSION TABLE

Inches of Mercury	Millibars	
29.30	992.2	
29.40	995.6	
29.50	999.0	
29.60	1002.4	low
29.70	1005.8	pressure
29.80	1009.1	
29.90	1012.5	
30.00	1015.9	
30.10	1019.3	
30.20	1022.7	high
30.30	1026.1	pressure
30.40	1029.5	
30.50	1032.6	

Barometric pressures adjusted to sea level

Chapter 2

Safety

Given the characteristics of a wildland fire, it's not hard to see why several wildland firefighters are killed annually and thousands more injured. During firefighting operations, the wildland firefighter is routinely exposed to heat, smoke and body fatigue. Many fuel types are capable of producing ground temperatures to 400 degrees F. It is not uncommon for these same fuel types to produce aerial temperatures approaching 2,000 degrees F.[1] The human body cannot function at much over 250 degrees F.

Even more than the tremendous heat found at wildland fires, smoke is the critical element in the "firefighter risk triangle" shown in Figure 2a. In addition to burning the eyes and chocking out clean

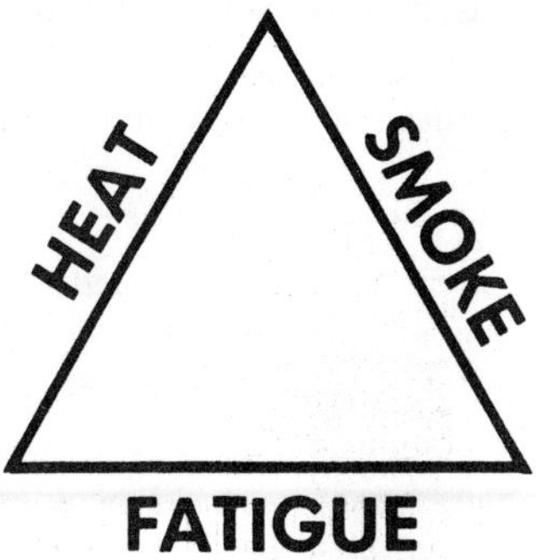

Figure 2a
Firefighter risk triangle

[1]*Donald G. Perry, Wildland Fire Behavior and Fire Spread Tests 1975-1981, Santa Barbara County, CA, 1981.*

air, smoke contains high levels of deadly carbon monoxide.

It is not uncommon for initial attack forces to work four to eight hours at a stretch, and fatigue and stress are often cited when a firefighter is injured. These conditions are directly related to body condition and physical fitness. As C. Raymond Clar and Leonard Chatten, authors of the 1954 *Principles of Forest Fire Management*[2] stated, "The safety of everyone engaged in firefighting is the personal business of everyone, both for himself and his fellows."

PERSONNEL SAFETY

Today, over three decades later, personnel safety is as critical as it was in 1954. Changes in clothing standards have seen the wildland firefighter's blue jeans and t-shirts exchanged for fire-resistive garments. In keeping with Occupational Safety and Health Association (OSHA) requirements, many states like California have written into their general industrial safety order[3] requirements for wildland firefighting clothing and head gear. These orders primarily cover head gear, eye, body and foot protection. A brief review of these requirements will give you an idea of California standards:

Head Protection

Head protection shall be worn by firefighters whenever they are exposed to head-injury hazards. Head protection shall be provided for each firefighter and shall be maintained in a location of ready availability to firefighters. Helmets and liners shall meet ANSI Z89.1 standards and may be Type 1 or 2. Helmets shall be retained by a chin strap. Helmet weight shall not exceed 20 ounces, as specified in section 3403.

As pointed out earlier, heat is the primary reason for fatigue, stress and injuries. In California, head protection is tested in laboratory environments by subjecting it to 250 degrees F for a period of five minutes. During these tests, the helmet cannot soften, melt or shrink.

Eye Protection

Employees exposed to eye-injury hazards shall be protected in accordance to provisions in section 3382.

Most wildland firefighters wear plastic goggles. There are many types on the market, including several with interchangeable colored lenses. Some firefighters even wear ski goggles, saying they seem to have superior straps and flexibility.

Another eye-related concern is the potential for eye injury due

---

[2] *State of California, Sacramento, CA.*

[3] *California Industrial Safety Orders, State of California, Sacramento, CA, 1981.*

to glass lens breakage. This author experienced some anxious moments in an emergency room when a metal object shattered so-called "safety glasses," sending small pieces of glass into my right eye.

After making some inquiries, I learned that there are three basic types of lenses available. "Safety glass" is a term that applies to two types of lenses. Of the two, industrial safety lenses are the most shatter-resistant and have the best protection against glass slivers. Industrial lenses function much like a car windshield that cracks but doesn't shatter into deadly fragments. They are tempered and will take a good drop or blow.

The third alternative is plastic. Plastic's only real drawback is that it scratches easily and is not presently able to change colors like glass. Plastic lenses are much lighter than the glass, however.

The eyeglass-wearing firefighter should wear goggles over glasses, as there is always a potential for a rock, limb or other flying objects to hit his or her face. The eyeglass wearer should also wear a sports strap, so when bending over, or if a tree branch brushes the glasses, they will stay put. It is also advisable to carry an extra pair in your "war bag."

Thermal Protection for Ears and Neck

Protection against burns on the ears and neck shall be provided.

Most departments meet this requirement by using fire-resistive Nomex or fire-resistive cotton cloth shrouds that attach to the helmet and drape the shoulder area. Velcro fasteners attach the shrouds to the helmet.

Body Protection

Clothing directly exposed to the fire environment and subject to flame impingement shall meet the following requirements: Flame resistance, meet Federal Test 191 Standards. Ignition of material shall not produce any melting, dripping, or flaming. Additionally, the material, when exposed to flame impingement, shall not adhere to the skin of the wearer as to cause burns.

Hand Protection

Protective gloves shall be worn by each wildland firefighter. Gloves shall be leather or treated fabric designed to withstand the effects of heat, flame and activities performed by the firefighter. The exterior of the gloves shall be snag-free and shall have an integral knit wristlet at least four inches in length. Wristlet fabric must meet fire-resistive standards.

Foot Protection

Protective footwear shall consist of heavy-duty lace-type boots with non-slip soles and heels. They shall provide firm ankle support. Leather uppers shall be at least six inches in height measured from the bottom of the shoe heel.

Fire Shelters

After March 31, 1983 in California, fire shelters shall be made available for every wildland firefighter. These shelters shall meet federal fire shelter specifications 5100-32D established in 1977.

Shelters generally last for two fire seasons and then must be replaced.

The above California guidelines can be used by any state to establish safety practices for wildland fires. Of course, as important as safety is, cost must be taken into consideration for small or volunteer fire departments. The above items may initially cost $250 or more per person. This high figure is based on about $100 for good boots, $75 for a two-piece Nomex or fire-resistive cotton jump suit and $40 for a fire shelter and case. You can figure that the boots will last for many fire seasons and a well-maintained fire shelter will last about two.

If a department cannot afford the above items it can still require its firefighters to wear the following, at minimal cost:

Head protection: Plastic construction-type helmet with a good liner and chin strap. Face and ear protection can be afforded by wearing a good cotton handkerchief. The handkerchief can be wet down to provide some protection from inhaled smoke.

Eye protection: Goggles with a good strap and flexibility.

Body protection: Many injury and fatality studies have revealed the importance of the "layer effect" in clothing. Wearing cotton or wool undergarments can greatly increase the wearer's ability to withstand heat and burns. Heavy-duty, "workman's" blue jeans are good.

Polyester fabric pants or shorts should not be allowed. The upper body garment should be a good cotton or wool long-sleeve shirt – no short sleeves. Promote the wearing of cotton t-shirts under the shirt and cotton underwear under the pants.

Foot protection: Good lace-up or hiking boots. These will cost between $100 and $200. The importance here is good footing and proper ankle support. A good heavy cotton sock is also very important.

Gloves: If you cannot afford specialized firefighting gloves ($10 to $15) then a good-fitting glove with wrist protection is better than none. Stay away from polyester, plastic or rubber.

Urban firefighters, who are infrequently faced with wildland incidents and do not have special wildland protective clothing should be aware of a couple of pitfalls:

Structure fire turnouts: These can be very bulky on wildland incidents and may cause heat exhaustion.

Rubber turnout boots: Many severe foot injuries and blisters have been caused by these loose-fitting boots. They also make it easy to sprain an ankle. These boots should really not be worn on wildland incidents.

In summary, much research has been done on protective gear. A variety of wildland injuries and fatalities have been analyzed in developing recommendations and standards. Every attempt should be made to reduce injuries and fatalities by utilizing good protective clothing and gear.

FOLLOWING ORDERS

Wildland firefighting tasks are diverse and can range from using a Pulaski tool or a chainsaw to pulling a 1-inch cotton jacket hose line. These and most other tasks require the firefighter to use good safety practices.

Even with modern technological advances in safety clothing, equipment and training fatalities and serious injuries are far too commonplace. For example, United States Forest Service statistics show that between 1978-1988, 147 wildland firefighters died in the line of duty. Of these 147 fatalities, 12 were chief officers, 15 company officers and 120 firefighters. The median age for the fatalities was 42 years. Three of the 147 fatalities were women. The primary causes for the fatalities were stress, physical exertion and contact with an object.

Over 90 percent of these fatalities or injuries can be directly attributed to a violation of one or more standard fire orders. In addition, many injuries are related to a violation of the "watch-out" situations.

Standard Fire Orders[4]

1. **Keep informed of fire weather conditions and forecasts.**
2. **Know what your fire is doing at all times.**
3. **Base all actions on current and expected fire behavior.**
4. **Plan escape routes for everyone and make them known.**
5. **Post a lookout where there is possible danger.**
6. **Be alert, keep calm, think clearly and act decisively.**
7. **Maintain good communications at all times.**
8. **Give clear instructions and be sure they are understood.**
9. **Maintain control of your personnel at all times.**
10. **Fight fire aggressively, but provide for safety first.**

[4]*United States Forest Service, Washington, DC.*

All of the above orders are simple and, to a great extent, based on common sense, but as mentioned earlier, they are often violated.

Standard fire orders can be broken down into categories of **safety, fire behavior** and **communications.** Safety order number one relates to the importance of knowing your weather. Firefighters should have a good knowledge of local conditions, including normal daytime temperatures, relative humidities and basic wind patterns. They should also have an idea of abnormal conditions.

Ask any seasoned firefighter who has been around your area for many years about high temperatures, lowest relative humidities and winds and you'll get a knowledgeable answer. He or she has learned that being able to analyze these factors on a fire line can be extremely beneficial.

For example, in the Santa Barbara coastal region of California, history shows that strong down-slope winds called "sundowners" have been directly responsible for millions of dollars in damages and several firefighter fatalities. Most notable of these fires was the 1990 Paint Fire, which burned 4,900 acres and damaged or destroyed 648 structures in the wildland/urban interface causing an estimated $400 million in damage. These winds occur during summer near sunset.

Firefighters in that area know these conditions and the potential conflagration they can bring. They also realize how important it is not to get too aggressive in their attack methods because of the gusty, erratic nature of these winds.

It is also very important to keep posted on fire weather forecasts. During fire season I like to have personnel review a weather map and forecast when they come on duty. A weather map such as the one featured in many metropolitan newspapers shows barometric pressures, fronts, temperatures and a good satellite photo. Barometric pressures are accurate measures of forecasting frontal activity.

The second fire order points out how important it is to make a good size-up *prior* to deploying personnel and resources. Know what your fire is doing at all times. Never put yourself in a position where you can't adjust your tactics or reach a safety zone.

If you cannot see the total fire situation, ask yourself, "Do we have a good anchor point?" and "Where are there black or burned areas we can use for safety zones or escape routes?" Try and put yourself in a good vantage point and scout ahead. Watch your smoke column – it can be an advance warning of changing conditions.

Maintain control of your personnel at all times. This is important on the fireline, at a staging area or in base. Whether or not a crew stays together while using an escape route or safety zone depends a lot on the leader's ability to keep calm, think ahead and exercise good leadership. This relates back to safety order number 6.

If the leader utilizes good fire behavior forecasting and tactical deployment skills, the crew will be able to leave the area as a team in an orderly manner in plenty of time, with no panic. Panic is the by-product of a lack of planning and situational analysis by the leader.

Wildland fire behavior situations can change instantly. If a leader reacts to change only after it has occurred, judgment may be impaired. This can result in fragmentation of the crew if a blow-up occurs, forcing the crew to evacuate the area.

A professional crew will stay together at the staging area and base. They eat and sleep as a team. The leader does not have to waste valuable time tracking down anyone who wanders off.

The last order is a very key one, as it emphasizes the need to base all actions on safety. Many times we overly stress the word "aggressive" in our attack philosophies. This is especially so on grass fires. It has been pointed out in several fatality studies that taking the small grass fire for granted was the prime contributor to the death. We must stress to all of our firefighters: *first,* anchor; *second,* direct attack, if possible; *third,* no head attacks; and *fourth,* don't take chances.

SOME PRECAUTIONS

During a wildland firefighter's career, he/she will face a variety of fire-behavior conditions. Sometimes he/she will be put into line assignments with high-risk factors. In these situations, it's best to be forewarned.

The following "watch out" situations were developed after analyzing many accidents, injuries and fatalities. They are intended to warn firefighters of potential problems *prior* to their occurrence.

WATCH-OUT SITUATIONS[5]

1. **You are given an assignment not clear to you.**
2. **You cannot see the main body of the fire, and you are not in communication with anyone who can.**
3. **You are getting spot fires over your line.**
4. **You are attempting a head attack on the fire.**
5. **You are in an area where you do not know local fire behavior conditions.**
6. **You are working in an area you have not seen in daylight.**
7. **You are working in steep, broken topography.**
8. **You are working an indirect attack in heavy fuels.**
9. **Weather is getting hotter and drier.**
10. **You notice a wind change.**

---

[5] *United States Forest Service, Washington, DC.*

11. **You notice rolling materials on the slope you're working on.**
12. **You are assigned to construct a line downhill.**
13. **You or your crew complain of headaches, fatigue or drowsiness while working.**
14. **You are assigned to work on a line with dozer or air-attack resources.**
15. **Your line assignment has chutes, chimneys and a saddle to work across.**
16. **You or your crew members are out of condition.**

Watch-Out situation Number 1 is very closely related to Standard Fire Order Number 8: "Give clear instructions and make sure they are understood." If *you* are given an assignment that is unclear or has vague performance objectives, ask questions *prior* to starting that assignment. Assignments must be based on a good size-up and fire behavior forecast and have considerations for safety zones and escape routes in planning assignments.

Make sure you and your crew have the expertise to accomplish the assignment and the resources to support your efforts. This becomes especially critical on large-acreage fires where mutual aid resources are used.

More and more, municipal fire departments traditionally trained in structural firefighting, are getting involved in wildland firefighting. As the wildland/urban interfaces grow, this evolution will continue. Unfortunately, structural firefighters may not have training and experience in wildland tactics, backfiring, air attack, hand crews and dozer operation.

However, municipal firefighters can provide invaluable expertise in providing structural protection. In addition, they may play an important role on holding crews for firing operations.

Conversely, the wildland firefighter with little or no structural firefighting experience should not receive a structural firefighting assignment.

In reality, however, responding personnel and resources are deployed to accomplish the objectives stated in the incident action plan. Given that this is the case, it is paramount to monitor safety and evaluate personnel and equipment. This evaluation should include – but not be limited to – safety gear, physical condition and experience of personnel and equipment carried on resources.

The second watch-out situation makes reference to the indirect attack method, where the fire is allowed to burn towards you and your crew. It says that you are not in communication with anyone who can advise you on the fire's behavior. Rather than allowing this to happen, make sure you have good safety zones, an escape route plan and, if possible, an air-attack aircraft to keep you posted on the fire's progress.

Situation Number 3 concerns spot fires. If you are working a hot flank and notice spot fires, this is an advance warning of changing fire behavior, maybe even a blow-up. Faced with this situation, calmly have your crew pull back to a safety zone. An experienced wildland firefighter will often get a "gut feeling" of a deteriorating situation.

It is extremely important that the crew react to these changes calmly and as a team. If any of the team panics or hesitates to obey the order to pull back, the entire crew's safety could be jeopardized.

Very few firefighters know in advance how they would react in a blow-up or adverse fire-behavior situation. This often means the leader, crew or division supervisor has no idea how personnel might react under adversity.

If you are working on a division with other crews or resources, advise them of your situation, as well as your supervisor. When it comes to spot fires, an important rule of survival is that if you can see spot fires, there are many others out there you don't see. These "quiet" spots will often increase in intensity and size before you notice them. Pulling back your personnel to a safe position and giving up your line may forfeit some acreage, but that is far better than risking a firefighter's life.

Situation Number 4 deals with head attacks. On the small, innocent-looking grass fire, it's very tempting to make a "quick kill" by hitting the head first. How many times have you or someone you know gotten away with it? Far too often, I suspect.

Yet this technique has been a contributing factor in many fireline injuries. Grass fires are used as an example because they can change behavior and rate of spread very rapidly, quickly trapping firefighters. Grass fires have been responsible for many more fatalities than heavy fuel types.

All attack methods should start from an anchor point. The head attack should be taken out of the initial-attack "tactics book" forever.

Situation Number 5 refers back to our discussion of fire behavior. Say you are called as mutual aid into an area where you are not familiar with fuel, weather, topography and fire behavior. If this happens, ask plenty of questions. Make sure you understand when and if the winds change and are apprised of any unusual fire behavior factors (i.e., low humidity, high temperatures, spotting).

As you might infer from Situation 6, nighttime fireline conditions are among the most dangerous. Nighttime fires do not give you helpful visual indicators such as smoke column intensity, color and density. In addition, it is very difficult to estimate the fire's behavior and size. As soon as it gets dark, you lose valuable topographic references, travel can become hazardous and it's hard to judge how your line progress is coming. In steep topography, it is difficult to see rolling rocks or material that can injure you. You may also run into snakes or other wildlife fleeing the fire.

Be very cautious about nighttime assignments. Use topography maps to assist you in locating hazardous chutes, saddles and narrow ridge lines. In addition, firefighters ordered up during daytime hours for a nighttime shift should make sure they get an adequate briefing and overview of the area while it's still light.

The warning in Situation 7 is engendered by the fact that fires that spread into steep, broken topography often create erratic fire-behavior conditions. Rock outcropping allow eddy winds to develop. These eddies can modify fire spread and fire intensity.

Using hand tools can be hazardous in steep, broken topography. Caution all personnel to watch footing and shorten tool swings. They should also look into brush understory prior to swinging, as the tool could come into contact with a rock and glance off towards legs and feet. Remember also to carry hand tools on the downhill side of the slope so, if your footing fails, you can drop the tool away from your body.

As indicated in Situation 8, many times, when a wildland fire is being pushed by winds across tinder dry fuels, direct attack is ineffective. The incident commander may choose to "back off" to a wide ridge line, fuel break or open area, then backfire.

Any time you must back off the direct attack, the fire goes on the offensive and the firefighter must take a defensive stand. If you back off far enough that you can't see the head and hot flank, you should use scouts to get needed fire behavior and fire spread data. Many times, this can only be accomplished using aircraft, as air reconnaissance doesn't expose a scout to the oncoming fire.

Watch-Out Situation Numbers 9, 10 and 11 relate back to knowing the normal and abnormal fire weather conditions of your area. Ambient changes of temperature, relative humidity and winds can be advanced indicators of possible extreme fire behavior or blow-up conditions.

Probably the best example of what can occur in a short time frame took place on the 16,000-acre Romero Canyon Fire in Santa Barbara County, California during October 1971. The time was approximately 1900 hours. The fire was laying down; very few active flames could be seen. Temperature was 66 degrees F and the relative humidity about 68 percent.

Then, at 1915 hours, conditions exploded. The temperature soared to 92 degrees F. Relative humidity dropped to 15 percent. A sundowner wind pushed the fire down-canyon into the urban/interface, over-running a group of dozers and swampers. The result was four fatalities and a serious burn injury.

The cataclysmic conditions of the Romero Fire held until 0500 hours the next morning. It is impossible to describe the magnitude of the fire storms that developed as a result of these changes. At the end count, this arson-caused fire damaged or destroyed nearly 100 homes.

The important point to remember is that, in most blow-ups or extreme fire-behavior, weather and fire-behavior changes occur rapidly. In a 15-minute time frame, a fire can go from no activity to a fire storm.

Fifteen minutes is not very long if you must make decisions concerning safety zones, escape routes and direction of fire spread, all the while transmitting over the radio. The key reason for assignment briefings, planned safety zones and established escape routes is so you can use that 15 minutes to improve your chances of survival.

During the 1980s there has been a marked increase in injuries and fatalities involving wildland fires over-running vehicles. Sedans, brush trucks and engines have been involved. Looking at these incidents, which have involved both personnel who stayed inside the protective confines of the cab or crew compartment and those who didn't, it becomes clear that the best bet for survival if overrun is to stay inside the vehicle or crew cab.

This author was fortunate to survive a wildland (the Honda Canyon Fire) fire overrun during the 1977 fire season. It was a blustery, cool, December day at about 0730 hours. Wind gusts were 30 to 40 miles per hour. Rainfall had been well below normal during the winter of 1976, so the chaparral was extremely dry. The size of the chaparral fuel bed was 30,000 acres with a 40-plus age class.

That morning, a fallen high-tension power line would provide the ignition source for what would be a 10,000-acre fire responsible for four fatalities.

At approximately 0930 hours, winds became erratic and gusty, pushing 80 miles per hour. A peak wind speed of 102 mph was recorded at the highest ridge line of the fire.

The command team was located several drainages away from the fire, which was burning away from the incident command post. At the time, there was a well-developed high-pressure air mass over the Great Basin states. Off the central California coast were three developing low-pressure systems.

At approximately 0945 hours, the fire reversed its direction and began moving with a tremendous rate of spread. The large parcel of high-pressure air moved toward the low-pressure centers offshore. This caused the fire to quickly envelop the incident command post area with dense ground-level smoke, embers and massive flame fronts. Area ignition began to occur.

The command team rapidly loaded up into two vehicles, one four-door sedan and one four-wheel-drive Suburban station wagon. Both vehicles quickly evacuated the command post location, using a sandy, single-lane egress road. The vehicles had traveled not more than one-half mile when the furious fire storm overran both vehicles with horizontal flame lengths estimated at 75 feet.

Those of us in the lead vehicle realized we would not be able to transverse the remaining one mile of road to safety. I pulled the sedan over to the right as far as the sand would allow. The driver of the second vehicle, the Suburban, backed up some distance behind my vehicle.

Inside my vehicle were three additional occupants, including a hotshot crew leader. He suggested we place his fire shelter over the inside of the windshield. This turned out to be a great suggestion, as I'm sure the windshield would have failed and the radiant heat been untenable without it.

It was very hot inside the vehicle and the air was full of the smell of burning tires and wiring. Visibility was zero. Nothing could be seen except dancing embers hitting the windows and white-painted hood surfaces. Then the tires failed and started to burn.

After some time (it seemed like light years), we concluded from the frequent holes in the smoke and drop in temperature that we had survived. The three occupants of the second vehicle were not so fortunate. They had chosen to leave their vehicle and try and outrun the fire storm. They perished in the fire. Additionally, a short distance away a dozer operator lost his life when he attempted to outrun the fire storm.

Damage to my sedan was severe. However, ironically, the Suburban wagon, being a four-wheel-drive with excellent ground clearance, received only minor damage. It was later driven away and used by other command personnel at this incident. Sadly, had the occupants of the second vehicle remained inside, they would have lived.

Some key points and reassurances of this scenario:

Glass — did not fail or shatter.

Fuel tank — did not fail or leak.

Vehicle — did not burn (though paint was scorched).

Tires — did burn and fail, but the fire quickly went out and did not threaten occupants or vehicle.

Electrical system — did fail and burn. Did not threaten occupants or vehicle.

Oxygen — sufficient oxygen inside the vehicle for four occupants to survive for nearly half an hour.

Watch-Out Situations 12 and 14 relate to constructing a fire line. Making a downhill fire line is an extremely-hazardous practice that was directly related to the tragic loss of 12 hand-crew members at the Loop Fire in Southern California. If topography is steep, with a saddle, chimney and chute, and the fire is well below you, don't attempt it. Use an alternate attack plan. Even if the fire looks innocent, situations can change rapidly.

If conditions are such that no adverse topography is involved and the fire is not spreading rapidly, do the following prior to attempting a downhill assignment: (1) Anchor the heel of the fire (2) Establish good communications with ground forces below you (3) Plan for a direct attack, when possible (4) Construct safety zones and make sure they are easily reached and your crew understands the escape-route plan (5) Use only experienced hand crew personnel for assignment.

Situation 13 relates to health hazards. One of the major ones is is carbon monoxide.

CARBON MONOXIDE

Carbon monoxide (CO) is one of several fire gases given off during a wildland fire. Carbon monoxide manifests itself when incomplete combustion is taking place, such as in the following fire scenarios:

1. Early-morning grass fire where fine-fuel moisture level, relative humidity are high.

2. Fire burning in a steep, well-defined drainage with a smoke inversion and little slope winds to circulate fresh air.

3. Early-season wildland fires where live-fuel moisture levels are over 100 percent.

4. Fire creeping through down-dead fuels, leaves and duff.

5. Fire burning in typical northern-slope fuel types (lush green) such as oak, woodland, poison oak-ivy, berry bushes, ferns and riparian zones.

Carbon monoxide, unlike most by-products of smoke, is tasteless, invisible and odorless. The primary effects of exposure are as a result of carbon monoxide's attraction to hemoglobin in the blood. Some studies have shown that carbon monoxide's attraction can also affect the body's enzyme systems.[6]

Most studies I have read do not indicate a high potential for life-threatening levels to wildland firefighters, however, there are numerous instances where low-level exposure occurred. One should not be mislead by the term, "low-level," because even a minimal exposure will affect a firefighter's psychomotor functions. There is evidence to show that behavioral performance, vision impairment, cardiac and pulmonary change, fatigue and headaches can result. (Figure 2b.)

Carbon Monoxide Exposure

CHOb Level Present	Effect to Firefighter
1.0 - 2.0	Some evidence of effect on behavioral performance.
2.0 - 5.0	Affects central nervous system. Impairment to vision affects psychomotor functions.
5.0 - 10.0	Cardiac and pulmonary changes.
10.0 - 80.0	Headaches, fatigue, coma, respiratory failure, and death.

(Source: National Institute for Occupational Safety and Health)

Figure 2b

The Santa Barbara County Fire Department in California conducted tests on wildland firefighters during initial-attack grass and sage fires to measure levels of carbon monoxide exposures. These fires, like the majority of wildland incidents, were initial attack in nature, with exposure time of from five to 60 minutes. The National Institute for Occupational Safety and Health (NIOSH) assisted by sending a certified industrial hygienist to take air samples.

The testing was conducted at an annual wildland fire hand-crew academy and involved hot-shot crew persons and dozer operators. Fourteen non-smoking wildland firefighters were tested during hot drills involving one-to-three-acre initial attack size grass-sage fires. (Figure 2c.) In addition to the firefighters, several hot-fire shelter drills were evaluated. (Figure 2d.)

[6]*Occupational Exposure to Carbon Monoxide, National Institute for Occupational Safety, 1972.*

Figure 2c
Initial-attack grass-sage fires

Figure 2d
Hot-fire shelter drills.

The firefighters provided expired air samples prior to starting firefighting activities. Then they began field exercises involving either firefighting with hand tools, backfiring, burnout or line holding, all in a smoky environment.

The "post-firefighting" samples were collected in the field immediately after conclusion of activities, so they would reflect COHb levels directly generated as a result of exposure to smoke. The breath samples were measured using two analyzers. Each firefighter was asked to inhale and exhale completely and then take a full inhalation. After holding their breath for a measured 20 seconds, firefighters were asked to expel about one-half of the held breath into the air and the remaining into a six-liter aluminized-plastic sampling bag. Each person had to repeat this cycle several times to fill the sample bag. Then the valve on the bag was shut and the sample evaluated for CO.

The air samples were analyzed using two different instruments. The primary instrument was an Interscan Corporation COTECH Carbon Monoxide Analyzer. Air from the sample was also run through a Foxboro Corporation Wolkes-Miran #103 Carbon Monoxide Filter.

The resultant carbon monoxide readings were recorded and studied by NIOSH. Readings from the Interscan and the Wilkes-Miran were compared to determine the feasibility of using the Wilkes-Miran for carbon monoxide analysis in the field. However,

SAMPLE NUMBER	PRE CO P.P.M.	PERCENT COHb	POST CO P.P.M.	PERCENT COHb	DIFFERENCE PERCENT CHOb
1	6	1.3	8	1.6	+0.3
2	7	1.4	8	1.6	+0.2
3	7	1.4	10	2.0	+0.6
4	5	1.0	NO POST SAMPLE		
5	24	4.8	12	2.4	−2.4*
6	5	1.0	NO POST SAMPLE		
7	10	2.0	NO POST SAMPLE		
8	5	1.0	9	1.8	+0.8
9	5	1.0	7	1.4	+0.4
10	14	2.8	17	3.4	+0.6
11	16	3.2	NO POST SAMPLE		
12	4	0.8	4	0.8	0.0
13	9	1.8	NO POST SAMPLE		
15	5	1.0	5	1.0	0.0

June 21, 1983 Carbon Monoxide levels and calculated COHb percent in expired air samples, Wildland Fire Hand Crew Academy, Santa Barbara County, California.
Percent COHb calculations based on CO p.p.m./5.

SAMPLE NUMBER	PRE CO P.P.M.	PERCENT COHb	POST CO P.P.M.	PERCENT COHb	DIFFERENCE PERCENT CHOb
1	6	1.2	16	3.2	+2.0
2	7	1.4	9	1.8	+0.2
3	10	2.0	11	2.2	+0.2
4	9	1.8	6	1.2	−0.6
5	15	3.0	9	1.8	−1.2
6	8	1.6	9	1.8	+0.2
7	6	1.2	14	2.8	+1.6
8	4	0.8	8	1.6	+0.8
9	6	1.2	8	1.6	+0.4
10	4	0.8	9	1.8	+1.0
11	15	3.0	NO POST SAMPLE		
12	6	1.2	15	3.0	+1.8
13	8	1.6	9	1.8	+1.2
14	5	1.0	9	1.8	+0.8

June 22, 1983 Carbon Monoxide levels and calculated COHb percent in expired air samples, Wildland Fire Hand Crew Academy, Santa Barbara County, California.
Present COHb calculations based on CO p.p.m./5.
***Pre CO measurement reflects interfering substance.**

the results of this survey were based only on measurements made with the Interscan instrument.

On the average, the "pre-COHb" levels ranged from 0.8 - 2.8 percent. The average COHb was 1.3 percent. The "post-COHb" levels ranged from 0.8 - 3.4 percent, with an average of 1.7 percent. The average increase in COHb was 0.4 percent.

In essence, firefighters performing tasks associated with initial-attack-size fires absorbed some carbon monoxide during the exercises, but not at the hazardous level.

According to a report on carbon monoxide exposures by Dr. Jack Peterson and Dr. Richard Stewart[7], firefighters exposed to 35 ppm of CO for eight hours will have a COHb level of five percent. Peterson and Stewart monitored CO exposure on the Deadman and Outlaw fires in Idaho in 1974. Using the criterion of COHb$\geq$five percent, the data was analyzed.

Of the 30 firefighters tested on the Outlaw Fire, 26 had COHb levels above the five-percent level, either at the beginning of a shift, after, or both. The Stewart and Peterson study stated that no allowance was made between smokers versus non-smokers.

Similar tests on the Deadman Fire showed that 62 firefighters out of 293 sampled exceeded the COHb level of five percent. The

[7]*Firefighters Exposure to Carbon Monoxide, Smoke Inhalation Hazards, ED & T 2424, May, 1975.*

fuel types for both of these fires was grass, liter, duff, down-dead limbs (slash) and forest fuels.

In 1990 two new studies conducted by researchers at John Hopkins University and the California Department of Health Services reinforced earlier studies on the hazards of smoke and carbon monoxide while pointing out new long term health threats to wildland firefighters and the need to provide firefighters with respiratory protection. The studies were conducted in California during the 1988 and 1989 fire seasons on 100 wildland firefighters.

As previously discussed in this chapter, carbon monoxide in low levels can pose a serious problem for wildland firefighters by causing vision problems, dizziness, headache and impairment in judgment and coordination. The 1990 report further concludes that carbon monoxide could put extreme stress on the heart. Smoke also contains compounds and acids which can do long-term or permanent damage as pointed out by the studies. Depending on soil conditions, smoke contains levels of lead and sulfur. These inorganic compounds can cause neurological damage. Smoke also contains levels of aldehydes. Aldehydes are strong irritants including acrolein and formaldehyde. Many of these irritants are carcinogens. Organic acids are also found in smoke. These acids include acetic and formic which are both strong irritants. Aldehydes and acids cause firefighters eye irritations and stimulates coughing. Yet another chemical found in smoke is ozone. Ozone is formed during a fire where strong sunlight and smoke combine under a stable air mass (poor air mixing). Ozone hampers lung function and can lead to respiratory disease.

One of the most important findings released from these studies was the damage particulate matter in smoke could do to the wildland firefighters lungs. These studies showed that wildland firefighters lose as much as 10% lung capacity after one fire season. The loss of lung capacity may last for weeks after the exposure. Particulates are small (really small) grains of carbon which lodge in the lungs. These particulates can cause respiratory problems including asthma and bronchitis and they could lead to cancer.

Researcher Robert Harrison, Chief of Occupational Health for the California Department of Health pointed out that wildland firefighters often would cough up "black gunk." After a week they would think the problem was over but these new studies indicate their lungs weren't back to normal. During the 1988 fire sieges at Yellowstone National Park, 12,000 wildland firefighters sought medical assistance for respiratory problems. In addition, 600 needed additional doctors care when they arrived back home.

Incident commanders, safety officers and operation chiefs are going to have to monitor smoke exposures and closely evaluate overhaul operations during stable air masses. Divisional line assignments may need to be shortened in some situations where a stable air mass (poor air mixing) requires extended exposure to smoke or incomplete combustion. Logistical staff must also ensure that base and camp operations are located well away from potential hazards.

Since the early 1930s, over 200 wildland firefighters have lost their lives in the line of duty. Thousands more have been severely injured or burned. It seems that most injuries and fatalities occur with one or more of the following common elements:

A. Grass or sage fuel bed(s).
B. Failure to recognize changing fire behavior.
C. Taking small fire for granted.
D. Topography modified fire spread.
E. Inexperience in wildland firefighting.
F. Poor physical condition.

Fires in grass and sage fuel beds account for many fatalities, injuries and burns. The reasons may include:

A. No "anchor point" prior to starting an attack.
B. Over-aggressive attack.
C. Head attack.

Even with the smallest grass fire, no attack should be made unless an anchor point has been established. This anchor point provides security and safety during a basic flank attack. It also prevents the fire from outflanking firefighters, should conditions change.

It is very hard to resist taking equipment out into the middle of an open field to attack the small, "not-going-anywhere" grass fire. Most firefighters are taught from day one to make an aggressive attack. You can get away with making the aggressive, no-anchor-point, kamikaze attack 95 percent of the time. So, as long as the firefighter does not burn himself, the crew or vehicle, he/she continues to utilize this approach. However, this constitutes playing a game of chance, hoping the winds don't pick up, or the vehicle doesn't stall, or that the crew can handle the situation without an anchor point or safety zones.

One of the more common errors made in light fuel beds is the over-aggressive attack. This usually occurs when the first-arriving unit takes the hot flank (with the wind) and tries to make a wet line or running attack in such a hurry that spots are missed. Then visibility, heat or driver zig-zag from black to green (unburned) causes an open line to occur. When this happens, firefighters can be outflanked or trapped if winds change or shift.

Firefighters can also expend much physical effort on initial attack only to find fingers of the fire have crept through the "wet line." Many times, unless supported by additional crews, they will be too exhausted to catch the finger or spots. This is when many injuries occur.

A similar effort occurs when firefighters attempt a head or frontal attack. Using no anchor point or safety, crews take vehicles into unburned fuel to reach the head, assuming that winds or fire behavior conditions will remain constant. Even the roadside frontal attack, where you allow a grass fire to sweep through a field while you wait for it at the head, is dangerous. Both scenarios put firefighters through unnecessary heat, smoke and stress.

Grass fires are a common cause of firefighter fatalities, injuries and burns because they can creep or explode across a field. Grass requires little preheating, and even the slightest wind can increase fire intensity and behavior. Grass fires produce three-to-four-foot flame heights and 400-degree F aerial temperatures, even in short grass. These conditions exceed human ability to withstand heat and flame exposure.

All grass fires, regardless of size and intensity, should be treated with caution. Anchor your attack. Use a barrier, road, origin – or something – to keep the fire from later outflanking you or your personnel. A basic flank attack working up the flank(s) from a common anchor point is recommended.

If you only have a single resource, attack the hot flank first, working towards the head. If the fire has a large black area free from driving hazards or broken topography, you can safely drive in the black, working toward the head and even use water to take the heat out of the head. This practice does not expose your personnel or vehicle to heat, smoke or potential shift in fire spread and direction.

Never take a small fire for granted, even if it is in the mop-up stage. A number of fatalities have occurred when observers reported the fire was in the mop-up stage and looked benign.

Topography factors have also contributed to many fatalities, injuries and burns. As pointed out in Watch-Out Situation 15, the wildland firefighter must understand the effects of:

A. Slope.
B. Narrow Canyons.
C. Saddles.
D. Chimneys.
E. Narrow ridge line(s) (hog backs).
F. Broken topographic features.

A slope primarily modifies fire behavior and, especially, rate of spread. If a fire burning on level terrain burns onto a 30 percent slope, the rate of spread will double without any help from additional wind speeds or lowered relative humidity. If firefighters do not plan ahead for slope changes, they can easily be overrun.

Narrow canyons, chimney or chutes modify fire behavior. Narrow canyons and well-defined drainages increase the rate of preheating and potential for spotting and area ignition. Chutes, chimneys and saddles are paths of least resistance for a fire. These factors, along with steep slopes, change vertical flame development to horizontal, thus greatly increasing the preheating and rate of spread.

Narrow ridge lines or hog-back ridges are dangerous, because the radiate and convective heat is generally too high for firefighters to survive. Narrow ridges are not good places to make a ridge line stand for the above-stated reasons, as well as the potential for spotting on the lee side of the ridge.

A saddle is a low point between two high points or elevations. Never place personnel or equipment in or near saddles because of the tremendous heat and smoke drafting through this area.

A fire moving across broken topography features such as rock outcroppings will have a tendency to finger a lot and spread erratically, due to wind eddies. Be extremely cautious in these situations, especially when ground crews are making an indirect attack.

Any time a fire escapes initial attack size and has the potential to cover large acreage, the command team should review and plot the fire on a topographic map. These maps are available in most parts of the United States, usually at recreation stores. They also can be ordered directly from United States Geologic Survey (USGS) offices. These maps show the topography features described above so you can warn firefighters in advance of any terrain hazards or plan potential rate of spread changes.

It seems that the austere economic conditions being imposed nationwide have forced more mutual aid because fire departments are no longer being able to keep the personnel and equipment they once did. We are seeing many departments using traditional structural firefighters as wildland firefighters. In a close parallel, the growing population is pushing more and more people into the wildland/urban interface. Both of these scenarios are causing personnel inexperienced in wildland firefighting to be placed in potentially-dangerous situations.

Of course, many "leather lungs" make the contention that firefighting, regardless of the element, is hazardous, and cheating death goes with the turf, but I don't agree that you should be potentially burned, injured or stressed out to gain the training. The incident commander and operations chief should make sure that firefighters are not put in a position requiring past experience or specialized training.

An example I have witnessed was the formation of a hand crew made up entirely of municipal engine company personnel, many of whom did not have proper training in tool usage. They wore improper foot gear and turnouts and many were out of shape. Needless to say, they didn't last very long. Production rates were marginal, tempers short and many a sore muscle resulted. Luckily, no one was injured. But what would have happened if fire conditions demanded that they construct a safety zone in a hurry?

Another example was when a group of structural engines was assigned to support a firing team and hand crew during an offroad backfiring operation. Most firefighters were in full municipal turnout gear and had never worked with backfire or burnout situations. There was only a single shovel per engine as far as hand tools, and no 1-inch cotton-jacket hose. Had spot fires developed down the slope creating a need for hand tools or water, it would have been tough for those crews to pick up the spots.

Now, I am *not* advocating the banning of structural personnel and equipment on wildland fires, but I *am* promoting training in safety and basic fire-behavior and attack methods. I also think equipment should include some wildland hand tools and 1-inch cotton jacket hose. It would also be nice to have personnel outfitted in good footgear and jumpsuits of fire-resistive material. Fire shelters should also be issued to all personnel.

Watch-Out Situation 16 points out the importance of firefighter fitness. Out-of-shape firefighters jeopardize the whole crew and often become exhausted before the line assignment is completed.

Watch for personnel who take too many breaks, lean on hand tools or, even worse, drink copious amounts of water. Individuals who drink lots of water ("water buffaloes" in fire-line jargon) often get sick, limiting the crew's ability to get work done.

I believe that being in shape is paramount in wildland firefight-

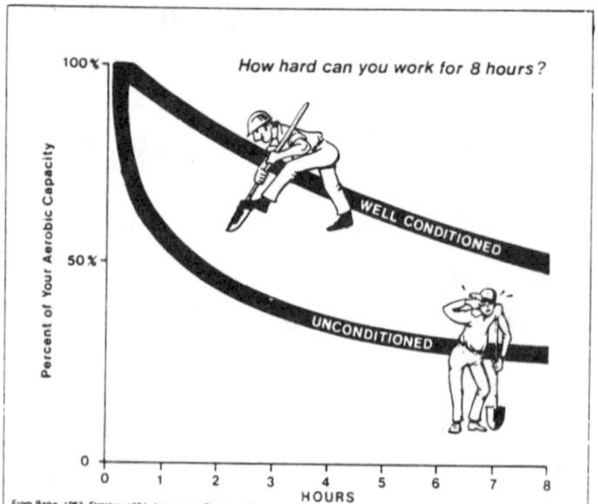

Figure 2e

ing, where heat, smoke, topography and incident duration combine to create fatigue and stress.

The wildland firefighter needs to condition his/her body towards muscular and aerobic fitness. Muscular fitness ensures the ability to use hand tools, pull hose and carry a 50-pound hose pack. Muscular fitness can be increased by doing exercises like push-ups, chin-ups and walking up a moderate slope with 50 pounds of weight on your back. Aerobic fitness, or the ability to take in, transport and utilize oxygen, is necessary for most work assignments at wildland fires. (Figure 2e.)

Typical arduous work assignments require crews to hike into the fire area with Pulaskis, McLeods or shovels and work for several hours constructing a fire line. After the line assignment, they must hike back to camp or equipment.

Walking, hiking or running are the most popular methods to increase aerobic fitness. (Figure 2f.) An important aspect of any phys-

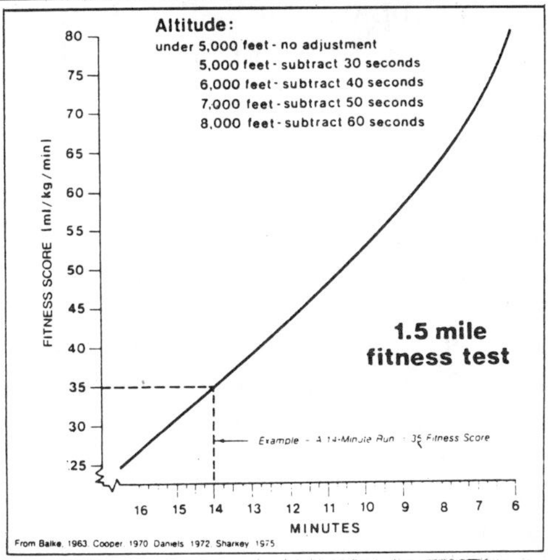

Figure 2f

ical fitness program is to start by getting a good physical from a doctor who can assist you in developing a personalized program. Start off slow, but be consistent. Exercise periods should last at least 30 minutes and be at least four times a week. They should also be balanced with good nutritional meals. Think of an exercise routine as a long-term life insurance policy (Figure 2g.)

Two very good publications relating to wildland firefighting and fitness have been written by Brian J. Sharkey, Ph.D. Dr. Sharkey is a professor and director of the Human Performance Laboratory at the University of Montana. He is a fitness consultant to the Forest Service there. The books, *Fitness and Work Capacity* and *Fitness Trail* are available at a small cost from the U.S. Government print-

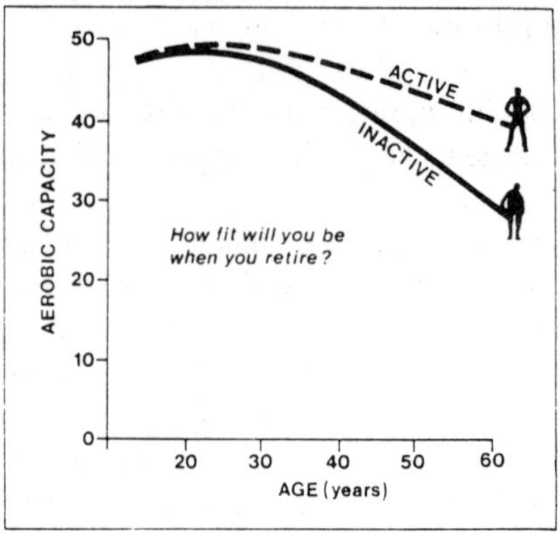

Figure 2g

ing office. Both were published in 1977.

WILDLAND FIRE SHELTERS

Designed in the early 1970s, the fire shelter is used to reduce exposure to radiant heat. It is constructed of commercial-grade aluminum foil over fiberglass cloth bonded by a non-toxic adhesive capable of withstanding temperatures to 1,400 degrees F. The shelter is shaped much like a low-profile pup tent. This design allows the firefighter to take advantage of cooler temperatures near the ground.

The shelter is held down by a combination of straps, shelter skirting and the firefighter's body weight. Straps are located at both ends of the shelter, which, when used with arms and feet, help keep the shelter taut against winds or fire effects. The shelter skirting provides extra material to help keep the shelter down with arms and feet.

The fire shelter is intended as a last-resort piece of safety gear, and, as such, must be carefully maintained and stored. Two cases protect the aluminum skin of the shelter. The first is a clear plastic envelope that allows visual inspection of the shelter, its folds and its manufacturer's label while sealing out dust and weather elements. Make sure this is sealed and free of breaks.

The sealed plastic envelope fits snugly into an outer woven-cotton case that attaches to the firefighter's belt for carrying. This case should be clean and free of cuts. Nothing should be stored inside the outer case with the shelter.

Many seasoned wildland firefighters carry a fusee or three for emergency situations (a good idea, I might add), however, the practice of stuffing shortened fusees into the fire shelter case only shortens the fire shelter's life and may hamper getting the shelter out of the case. Carry fusees in the butt pack or in fire-resistive clothing pouches.

Nothing should be carried over the fire shelter. A belt weather kit or butt pack carried over a fire shelter could jeopardize the ability to deploy the shelter.

As previously stated in this chapter, not many wildland firefighters get a chance in advance to find out their reaction to adverse fire behavior, where survival is counted in minutes or seconds. Fire shelter deployment and usage fall into this same category. Few wildland firefighters have the opportunity to deploy a shelter under realistic conditions. That's great, safety- and statistic-wise, but brings up the question of how an individual will react when it's necessary to deploy the shelter.

Fire shelter training should begin by reviewing past wildland fires in the region, or nationally, where shelters were deployed to save lives. Between 1976 and 1984, some 20 lives were saved by shelter deployment. In 1985, over 60 lives were saved by fire shelters.

Firefighters must understand that, unlike other protective equipment, the shelter is used only as a last resort. This being the case, very little pre-alert is likely – perhaps between three minutes and 30 seconds. The key is to deploy without hesitation or panic, based on training and confidence in the shelter.

The only wildland fire fatality through the 1986 fire season involving deployment of a shelter was as a result of failure to take advantage of all safety clothing. This incident involved two personnel who, confronted with an entrapment situation, deployed their fire shelters on a previously constructed helispot.

The two firefighters deployed shelters behind stores of gear, sleeping bags and chain saws on the helispot. They thought this storage might provide additional protection from radiated heat and direct flame impingement.

After deployment, the previously-mentioned combustibles caught fire and burned intensely. The firefighters felt a rapid increase in temperatures as the aluminum preheated. Eventually, temperatures outside the shelter were such that it became unbearable to remain near the burning combustible. Relocating the shelters requires coordination and, more importantly, gloves to hold down the hot aluminum skin of the shelter, however, and although both firefighters had full protective clothing on, one did not have gloves on.

The firefighter with gloves on was able to move his shelter sufficiently far enough away to withstand the entrapment. Tragically, the firefighter without gloves could not reposition his shelter and died as a result.

Shelter drills should be held under realistic conditions, during live fire training if possible. Live-fire training and hot-shelter drills (Figure 2h) allow firefighters to deploy in heat, smoke and actual ash beds.

Figure 2h
The "hot" shelter drill is a key part of annual training.

Training for hot-shelter drills should include:

A. Use full wildland protection gear (including gloves).

B. A simulated walk back to a mock safety zone (black or burned-over area).

C. Testing of individual and crew teamwork deployment.

D. Delaying deployment until crew leader gives order.

E. Allowing firefighters 25 seconds to get into shelter (on ground) once deployment order is given.

F. A minimum five-minute stay in shelter.

G. Looking for personnel who "peek," or raise up once shelter is deployed. It is very important that personnel *stay down* once a decision to deploy the shelter is made.

The key points that should be stressed during training:

A. The fire shelter is an important part of personal safety gear. It must be properly maintained and stored.

B. Daily inspection is important. Make sure shelter case(s) are clean and free from cuts and abrasions. Evaluate folds. Folds should be rounded, not flat. The primary reason folds get flattened is using the shelter as a seat on the fire line and storing other items on top of the shelter(s). A shelter's aluminum skin can easily be cracked if folds are flattened.

C. Shelters should be worn without anything stored inside the shelter case or over the top.

D. The shelter is designed to reflect radiant heat currents. It is most effective in light fuel types (grass), where thermal outputs are low and rate of spread high. The shelter's high-temperature adhesive bonding the aluminum skin to the interior fiberglass cloth may fail at temperatures of about 1400 degrees F. Most heavy fuel types and down-dead limbs are capable of exceeding this temperature over prolonged periods.

Firefighters should always consider this when evaluating possible safety zones and escape routes. Do not deploy in understory of a closed stand of pine or woodland where a good possibility of crowning exists.

E. The fire shelter is designed as a last-resort safety measure. For this reason, firefighters must understand that once a decision to deploy is made by the crew leader or supervisor, deployment must be started without question or hesitation. The firefighter may only have a few minutes – or seconds – to successfully deploy the shelter.

F. If rock outcroppings are going to be made use of, be sure rocks are stable and will not loosen. Check to see that rocks around your proposed safety zone will not roll down on you.

G. Do not plan safety zone(s) in saddle areas on ridge lines. These are paths of least resistance. Thermal outputs and turbulence are likely to exceed the firefighter's ability to survive and hold down the shelter.

H. If safety zones are planned on a ridge line, active division or burned-over area, make sure all resources and personnel likely to use these zones discuss their usage ahead of time. This is critical for a division with a hand crew or engine crew working with a dozer, as the dozer operator may need to use that zone also. Crew leaders and supervisors should discuss safety zones with dozer operators so that, if conditions are smoky, operators will be careful not to run over firefighters who may already be inside the shelters (Figure 2i).

Figure 2i
A hot shelter drill utilizing a bulldozer to share a safety zone after a firefighter has deployed his fire shelter.

I. Once the deployment order is given, firefighters must understand they are deploying as a last resort, and that means staying inside until the crew leader or supervisor gives the order to get out, and that entrapment may last over an hour (Figure 2j).

Figure 2j
A hand crew practices a "hot" shelter drill in a safety zone. Here, the crew leader evaluates the crew's performance.

J. Firefighters also need to understand that interior temperatures may exceed 150 degrees F. With full protective clothing on, this may create an uncomfortable temperature range. It is imperative that firefighters remain calm and realize that staying down and calm is their only chance of survival.

K. Training should stress a deployment goal of 25 seconds. Time should start once firefighters are in the safety zone and the outside shelter case is touched. Training should be in full protective clothing, including gloves. Initially, gloves will not give the firefighter a good feeling of being able to open up folds and precisely position the shelter. Practice, however, will create confidence.

Additionally, stress that it's most important to quickly get down inside the shelter, *then* finalize adjustments, rather than trying to push out and adjust the folds while standing. The quicker the firefighter gets down, the cleaner the air will be inside the shelter.

If possible, firefighters should deploy with feet towards the oncoming flame front, though this may be difficult to evaluate in smoky conditions. Once lying down, adjustments can help pass the time. These include making sure the corners are fully extended and the shelter ridge is pushed off the body as far as possible. Remember, the aluminum skin may get very hot, so keep it away from the body.

L. Ground hazards. During the precious seconds between arrival at a safety zone and the call to deploy the shelter, the firefighter should visually scan the ground, looking out for brush stobs, rocks and hazards. If using a burned-over (black) area, watch for white ash (hot material), burning limbs, twigs and burning stobs.

M. Hand tools/equipment. Do not attempt to take tools and equipment inside the shelter with you. Lay hand tools and equipment on the ground in a location where they will not interfere with possibly moving the shelter towards the center of the safety zone later on. A hand tool grounded too close to a shelter might cut a hole in the shelter, compromising survival chances. Do not store chain saw fuel or combustibles near deployment zone.

N. Cuts and tears in the shelter. It's possible that, in the deployment of the shelter, a cut or tear may result. This should not cause panic or undue concern. Continue to get inside the shelter, then work on minimizing the effect of the cut or tear. Although cuts or tears may allow additional smoke inside the shelter, the radiant heat will still be reflected.

O. Use water to keep hydrated and cool. A moist bandana can help, if smoke does enter the shelter. Don't drink too much, however.

P. Keep in verbal or radio communication with other members of the crew (Figure 2k). Communications will help everyone keep calm and evaluate the outside environment.

Q. Plan on several thermal pulses. Past entrapment situations indicate that it's possible to experience several thermal pulses while inside the shelter. Do not leave the shelter too early.

R. Expect outside noise. The fire may create loud noises as well as turbulence that may shake the shelter intensely. Don't panic and raise the shelter.

S. Expect the possibility of fire resources co-locating in your safety zone. You may hear a dozer's track noise or an air tanker's engine noise. Don't panic; have confidence that the dozer operator will not run over you. Do not raise your shelter.

T. If you must move your shelter, plan your move. Coordinate feet and hands to move without undue stress to the shelter. Keep low or flat if possible.

U. Once a fire shelter is deployed, do not re-use it for a fireline assignment. It *can* be used for training later on, if carefully refolded.

V. If possible, after an entrapment, firefighter(s) deploying the shelter should be allowed to return to base for medical evaluation, debriefing and rest. They should not be asked to continue the line assignment unless new shelters are issued and firefighters are not

Figure 2k
Radio communications should be clear and concise.

stressed or in need of medical assistance.

The incident safety officer should be involved any time a shelter is deployed or a fireline injury is encountered. The safety officer can also assist in securing additional shelters or making sure firefighter safety is not being compromised by allowing personnel to return to the fire front prior to medical evaluation.

W. The post-fire critique should always include discussion and review of shelter deployment.

Chapter 3

Fuel Types

Before determining an attack method or forecasting potential fire-behavior effects, it is necessary to evaluate the fuels involved. Knowledge of fuel components is necessary so the fire's thermal output and rate of spread can be projected, enabling the incident commander to select the proper attack method based on fire behavior forecast.

Basic fuel types include:

1. **Grass**
2. **Sage**
3. **Medium brush**
4. **Heavy brush**
5. **Logging slash**
6. **Timber (second growth)**
7. **Timber (mature)**

Important considerations for fuel types include: fuel loading, fuel volume, availability, size and shape, compactness, continuity, arrangement, moisture content and time-lag.

Fuel loading is a classification system whereby given fuel beds and specific fuel components are evaluated and their volume expressed in tons per acre. Using the above seven basic fuel categories, the average tons-per-acre per component breaks down as follows:

1. **Grass:** ¼ – 1 ton per acre.
2. **Sage:** 2 – 5 tons per acre.
3. **Medium Brush:** 7 – 15 tons per acre.
4. **Heavy Brush:** 20 – 50 tons per acre.
5. **Logging Slash:** 50 – 150 tons per acre.
6. **Timber (second growth):** 100 – 600 tons per acre.

7. Timber (mature): 200 – 600 tons per acre.

This chart can be used for a quick visual estimate, but accurate inventories of total fuel volume must also take into account down-dead fuels, decadent loading in sub-canopy and canopy regions and percentage of mortality in the fuel bed. Down-dead fuels (Figure 3a) –

Figure 3a
Down-dead and old-age class fuels aid preheating (thermal output). Chaparral fuel bed.

stems twigs and leaves on the ground – become an important element in the initial phases of a wildland fire by preheating the sub-canopy of heavier fuel types.

Firefighters should look at fuel beds from the availability standpoint. Ask, "What fuels will burn on the first flame-frontal passage?" In most cases, it is this first flame-front passage that exhibits the largest flame fronts and thermal output.

It is also important to point out that a wildland fire may burn over a fuel bed several different times during the course of a fire, especially if it is a wind-driven fire. A wind-driven fire may take out the light ground fuels in the first pass, then a portion of the canopy or sub-canopy during the second pass. A running crown fire in timber will take out the aerial canopy in the first pass, then follow up with a ground fire the second time around.

Availability may also play an important part in your tactical decision process. Depending on the fuel types involved, you may or may not use low availability to limit your crew's exposure to the head of a fire.

For example, if a grass or sage fire is moving into a timber mix and down-dead fuel is light, you may allow the fire to "run" into the mix, knowing once it hits the timber understory it will slow up dramatically. Conversely, if a timber fire is about to run into an area of open grassland, fire behavior can be expected to increase dramatically.

Once cured, annual grass has the highest availability, while mature healthy timber has the lowest (only its bark will burn). Chaparral that has reached 20 years and some pine species are also considered to be high availability. When evaluating availability in a fuel bed, remember that the transition of a lighter fuel (grass) to a brush species (chaparral) provides additional availability because of preheating to the canopy of the heavier fuel type.

The eucalyptus tree stands of California are noteworthy models of availability. These have high down-dead fuel loads of fine twigs and bark that provide ample preheating of the canopy and flammable resins. Once preheated, these trees explode.

Tremendous heat and flame heights are also associated with eucalyptus tree stand fires. The best approach when confronted with eucalyptus stands is to consider good fuel transition zones (Figure 3b)

Figure 3b
The fuel transition zone shown here is the grass interface with oak woodland. Keeping the fire to the lightest fuel type or first transition zone is an important strategy.

and hold the fire to the lightest fuel type to limit the preheating process.

If it were possible to eliminate all dead fuels one-half-inch or less in diameter, we could reduce wildland fires by 90 percent. It has been estimated that many fuel bed and forests add two to six percent new down-dead material annually. This one factor, alone, is an important reason for fuel management and prescribed burning of major, continuous fuel beds (over 300 acres in size).

As the age class of fuels reaches 20 years and over, the live-to-dead plant ratio in the canopy and sub-canopy changes dramatically, and the percentage of decadent stems, twigs and branches increases. This change from live to dead means less preheating is needed when a fire moves through.

Besides old-age class, another contributing reason for high percentages of decadent materials in fuel beds is ''down-dead snow kill,'' where the weight from heavy snows breaks limbs, leaving dead branches remaining in the canopy. Tree disease, beetles and moths also contribute to decadent canopies.

The easiest method of developing a fuels inventory is to pre-plan the fuel beds in your area. This pre-plan should include a fuel-bed inventory that enables you to evaluate all fuel factors on a single form. You should age class the major fuel types found in the selected fuel bed, using a tree bore, fine tooth saw or sandvik tool. From the bed's age class, you can determine past fire history as well as availability of fuel to burn.

The live-to-dead plant ratio is somewhat related to age classing, because in most brush-plant communities a major change starts to occur at 20 years. Although plant communities vary somewhat, plants with an age class from one to 10 years show good vigor, with lush growth leaders. Such a canopy will consist of 80 percent live material and very little dead or decaying material. In this case, the plant is somewhat fire-resistive, requiring so much preheating that most fires will greatly reduce their rates of spread when they burn into it. (This is an important reason for keeping fire history maps.)

On the other hand, old-age class fuel or fuels over 20 years old often have inferior new growth leaders, and a high percentage of their stems and twigs will die out. Generally, 40 to 50 percent of an old-age class canopy is decadent. This is especially true in chaparral plant communities. When the canopy and sub-canopy regions are void of young stems, twigs and leaves, a fire does not have to waste valuable thermal output preheating and driving out moisture from the fuel bed. Thus, rate of spread and fire behavior will increase (Figure 3c).

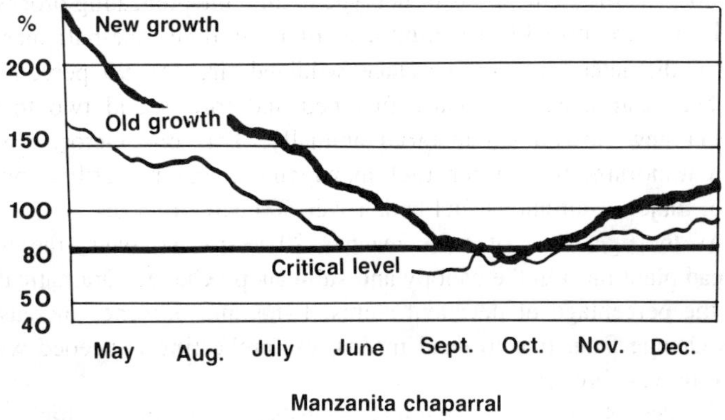

Figure 3c

When determining age classes, try to select several representative plants from each plant community and average their ages. Concentrate on eastern, southern and western aspects, as the majority of fires occur on these slopes.

You should also estimate the availability of additional down-dead and decadent fuels that could aid in a fire's spread and intensity. Although large downed logs add to the loading in timber fuel types, their availability is low. I recommend you concentrate more on down-slash or over-mature lodge poles or stands with large areas of dead canopies. These can contribute to crown fires. As mentioned earlier, the problem fuels are those one-half inch in diameter or smaller.

Continuity, compactness and **arrangement** are also key points to evaluate. **Continuity** is a term used to express the horizontal spacing or flow between fuel types. Continuity is defined as being either uniform or patchy. Uniform continuity indicates the presence of fuel-transition zones that will allow lighter fuel types to preheat heavier ones (i.e., grass to sage to chamise). Uniform continuity (Figure 3d) also indicates the likelihood that, as the fire burns through each transition zone, thermal outputs will increase, as will resistance to control.

Patchy continuity means that fuel transition zones are broken and some fuels may not have vegetation in the understory, for instance, grass next to down-dead logs next to sparse woodland areas. In a fuel bed with patchy continuity, much of the thermal output of a fire is lost in the convective column, as radiant heat has little canopy to preheat. Rate of spread and thermal outputs are generally sufficiently less than in uniform fuel beds.

Figure 3d
Annual grass displays uniform continuity and no compactness problem. Vertical arrangement allows oxygen to move freely between stocks.

Compactness is a term used to describe the extent to which fire gases or oxygen can freely move in and around fuel stocks, leaves, stems, needles and grass. A fire will burn slowly through a conifer understory, consuming primarily down needles, stems and twigs. This down-dead layer, "stacked by nature," is an example of compactness (Figure 3e). It is what we call *matted,* and fire gases and oxygen have difficulty preheating and free flowing around unburned fuel. This compactness results in slow preheating flame heights and spread.

Another example is an annual grass fuel bed with one-quarter to three-quarter ton-per-acre fuel loading. Say the average height of the fuel is eight inches, vertical spacing is excellent and there is no compactness. This is termed *fluffy*. A fire will move through this fuel bed using the fire gases and oxygen to preheat unburned fuel, increasing spread and thermal output.

The large expanses of grain in the Prairie States and the interior of California provide wildland firefighters with some of the fastest-moving fires on record. This grain can exceed one ton per acre with perfect vertical spacing. Average height is two to three feet. These grain fires can outrun the fastest brush truck or running attack operation, and will burn so hot that very little to overhaul remains once the fire burns over an area.

Arrangement is a term used to describe the relationship of ground fuels and aerial fuels. Such relationships might include:

A. Duff to standing grass
B. Grass to sub-canopy of sage
C. Sage to chamise
D. Brush to timber sub-canopy
E. Down-dead to timber sub-canopy

Arrangement, then, is the vertical relationship so important to preheating in the fuel transition zones. Often referred to as "fire ladder," it is the relative ease by which a fire moves from ground-fuel to aerial-fuel canopies.

If arrangement is good, and the fuel bed transitions from ground to aerial fuel without loss of rate of spread or thermal output, chances are fuel bed continuity is uniform. If arrangement is poor, the fuel bed may find grass transitioning into large down-dead logs or sparse woodland with no vegetation in the understory. A fire in this situation is probably burning in a fuel bed with patchy continuity. The rate of spread may be erratic, with "fingering" and thermal outputs less than in the example with good arrangement.

Wildland fuels must be preheated in order to burn. Some, like grasses, require minimal preheating, while most brush types require a lot of preheating due to the waxes, turpines and resins found in their leaves, stems and needles. Most healthy, mature timber species do not burn, because they contain too much live moisture.

Figure 3e
Fuel compactness can influence rate of spread and preheating of adjacent fuels. Here, annual grass displays a compact state.

Grasslands act as a fuse or a "primer" for medium or heavier fuel types. Grasses can basically be divided into two categories: annual and perennial. Annual grasses go through a set growth cycle then die out, becoming a part of the available fuel load. They go through three basic growing stages during this 120-to-130-day cycle: the green stage, when maximum growth and moisture occur (January-April); the purple stage, when purple veins and a fading green color appear on leaves and stock (May); and the brown, or cured, stage, when moisture level drops to three to seven percent and the plant dies.

I am sure many of you have experienced that early grass fire in May that was all smoke with little fire spread. Most early grass fires actually burn dead and matted grass from the previous year.

If the grass is still in the purple stage, moisture leaves are still such that the fire uses all of its thermal output trying to drive out the moisture so it can spread.

Perennial grasses go through a similar cycle, but, instead of experiencing total moisture loss and dying out, they store vital moisture in a root crown and survive during low moisture periods. Grasslands are a very important part of the total fuels environment, as their fine capillary-like root systems hold vital top soils, preventing erosion of the topsoil and accompanying loss of soil nutrients.

Most grasses are nearly 100 percent available to burn after curing, depending on rainfall and region. The critical months are May, June and July.

However, heavier fuel types, especially the chaparral community, are drought-resistive and store water in an extensive root and canopy foliage system. Their moisture levels are far too high to burn in May, June, and, usually, July (Figure 3f).

Time Lag and its Relationship to Moisture Levels

1-hour time lag fuel	**3 - 7%**
10-hour time lag fuel	**7 - 10%**
100-hour time lag fuel	**10 - 15%**
1,000-hour time lag fuel	**over 20%**

Figure 3f

The key here is availability to burn. In the case of the chaparral plant community, many species have live-plant moisture levels exceeding 150 percent, with lush new growth leaders in May. A fire burning from cured grass into heavy chaparral brush in May or June will most likely lose its thermal punch and spread trying to preheat moisture-laden stems and twigs.

In California, most chaparral brush species reach a high availability level sometime in August or September. The critical live-fuel moisture levels in California brush types are 60 percent in chamise and 80 percent in manzanita. Rainfall and climatic conditions will vary moisture levels, but an average moisture level drop is shown in Figure 3f.

The **time lag principle** relates the moisture in the air (surrounding the fuel) to fuel type. (See Figure 3g.) It is expressed as the

Time Lag Relationships

Alaska tussock tundra	**20 minutes**
Western States annual grass	**1 hour**
Coastal sage	**10 hours**
Pinyon-juniper	**10 hours**
Low pocosin	**10 hours**
Chaparral species	**10 hours**
Logging slash	**100 hours**
Down-dead logs - 8″	**1,000+ hours**
Mature standing timber	**1,000+ hours**

Figure 3g

rate (minutes, hours or days) at which the fuel type approaches the moisture equilibrium of its surrounding atmosphere (drying rate).

Because of all the variables associated with daily heating and cooling, relative humidity, air mass characteristics and fuel moisture levels, it is impossible to achieve total equilibrium between atmosphere and fuel type, although it is possible to reach between 60 to 70 percent of equilibrium.

The time lag principle in relationship to fuel types utilizes stock diameter as a reference. The basic categories and corresponding diameters are:

< ¼″ diameter	**1-hour time lag**
¼″ - 1″ diameter	**10-hour time lag**
1″ - 3″ diameter	**100-hour time lag**
3″ - 8″ diameter	**1,000-hour time lag**

Time lag after the fuel complex burns the first flame front passage also has an important relationship to availability. As a general rule, the shorter the time lag, the more available the fuel.

Alaska's tussock tundra (perennial bunch grass) responds quickly to changes in outside air temperatures and relative humidity. The western annual grasses are also a fuel type that rapidly changes fuel moisture as the outside temperature and relative humidity change. Both Alaska tussock tundra and western annual grasslands are nearly 100 percent available when cured.

Depending on age class, chaparral (chamise, manzanita and sage species) is considered 50-to-70-percent available. In its old-age class (over 20 years), it may exceed 70 percent availability. The pinyon-juniper fuels found in the Great Basin states will also be in the 50-to-70-percent availability range. As a comparison: healthy, mature standing timber may be less than 20 percent available (bark burn only).

An important part of the fuel-inventory pre-plan is locating fuel transition zones, where grasslands interface medium or heavy fuel types. Most personnel and resources will be much more effective on a grass fire than a brush fire. The heavier the fuel type, the more heat, smoke and fatigue problems.

The canopy foliage and needles of heavy fuel types are largely oils, turpines and waxes that must be raised to their ignition temperatures before they will sustain burning. Ever wonder why we have so many old-age-class fuel beds that never burn? Many times it is because these fuel beds are void of grass or light fuel types to preheat the heavy brush canopies.

This condition also occurs in the chaparral plant community as a natural survival feature. Chaparral plants give off a plant toxin in an "alleopathic" process. The plants' phyto-toxins kill off competition like grasses, forbs and flowers in the understory where the seed bed is established, so there is limited competition for soil nutrients and moisture.

Usually found in age classes over 10 years, this process allows the chaparral to deposit seeds on the ground that lie in wait for a fire to germinate the next generation of chaparral.

In Southern California since 1985 several species of chaparral (ceanothus, arctostaphylos) have been experiencing what is termed "chaparral dieback." Primarily found in fuel beds with south facing slopes below 2,500′ elevation this dieback is creating large blocks of standing dead brush which will be readily available to burn (for decades) until a fire(s) eliminates the problem. The fungi attacks upper leaves, twigs and cambial tissues. The primary fungi identified as being responsible is *Botryosphaeria ribis*. The taxonomy is unclear but it appears the fungi attacks chaparral weakened by drought stress and air pollution.

The extended drought (1986-1990) experienced in the Western States has allowed fuel and fire managers to more clearly understand and appreciate the Palmer Drought Severity Index (P.D.I.) much like a live fuel moisture chart. This graphic generally has a range from +7 (wet years) to −7 (very dry years). The graphs horizontal lines (see Figure 3h) represent normal, severe drought and extreme drought levels. Since the majority of the Western States have been in either severe or extreme drought during fire season it has been a

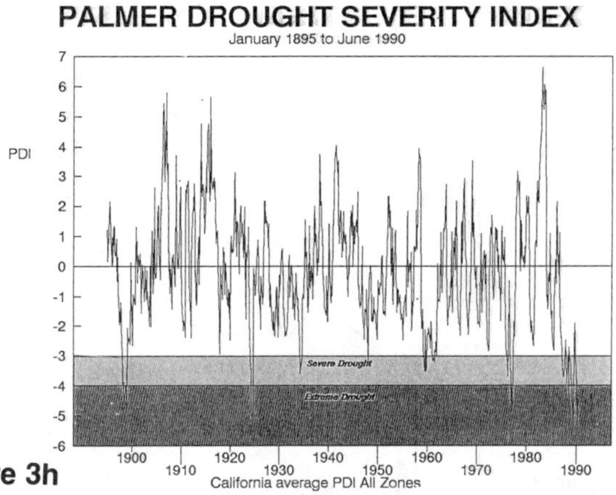

Figure 3h

valuable tool in assisting fire managers in developing staffing patterns and resource deployment augmentation based on regions where vegetation was being critically stressed due to lack of rainfall. It's interesting to note that Santa Barbara County, California and the Los Padres National Forest were at a −7 on the P.D.I. at the time when the Paint conflagration occurred on June 27, 1990. The −7 is a record low since the P.D.I. was established around 1900. When vegetation is stressed to this level it's easy to visualize why the high rates of spread (208 chains per hour) occurred on the Paint conflagration.

NATIONAL FUEL TYPES AND ASSOCIATED PROBLEMS

Pacific Northwest States Washington, Oregon, Northern California, Northern Nevada and Western Idaho)

Principal fuel types in this region include Douglas fir, hemlock, spruce, cedar and hardwood mixes. The Pacific Northwest has the highest live-fuel loading in tons per acre in the nation. The threat of a major wildland fire is most intense in areas with large acreages of logging slash. In addition, timber stand improvement (TSI) can also create a problem.

The northwestern states have a high percentage of east-west drainages. The Northwest, especially west of the Cascade range, depends on cool Pacific Ocean breezes to keep relative humidity high and air temperatures cool during fire season.

Rainfall also plays an important role in relationship to fuels. The coastal spruce forests of Oregon, Washington and Northern California average 64 to 128 inches of rain annually. The Douglas fir ranges of Oregon, Washington and Northern California average 32 to 64 inches. Cedar forests in Oregon and Washington average 32 to 64 inches. The pine forests of interior Oregon, Washington and Idaho average 16 to 32. The pinyon-juniper ranges of Nevada average less than eight inches of rain.

Approximately 75 percent of wildland fire activity is associated

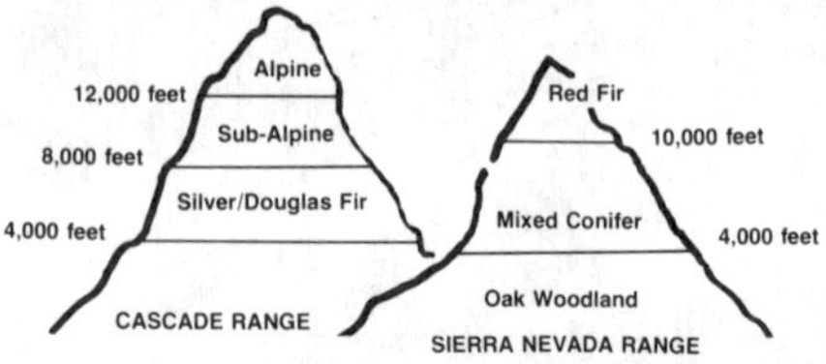

with the "Pacific High." A Pacific High breaks the land-breeze and sea-breeze cycle. It features wind speeds of 20 to 30 mph with a resulting high-pressure subsidence that preheats aerial fuel canopies to a critical level.

If large expanses of down-dead forest fuels are present, surface fires will reach aerial canopies. Then crown fires become a problem. The critical months for this are September and October.

The tremendous down-dead fuel loading in many fuel beds means that, even with high humidities and mild air temperatures, thermal outputs associated with a wildland fire are tremendous – posing a severe problem for wildland firefighters.

Under adverse fire weather, high live-fuel loading (tons per acre) and down-dead fuel problems make for a high resistance to control. Lightning is the leading cause of forest fires in the Pacific Northwest. During these fires, tremendous fuel loading created superheated convective columns that extend over 20,000 feet into the atmosphere and can create long-range spotting up to seven miles.

The diverse topography and variation in elevation (sea level to 12,000 feet) increase smoke inversion. This can create problems with firefighter safety, deployment of aircraft and locating of spot fires.

Diverse fuel types (primarily timber) make using fixed-wing air tankers very difficult. Pinpointing a target and penetrating the dense canopies becomes even more difficult.

The Pacific Northwest has some of the highest resource values in the nation. This requires that firefighters, when possible, make an aggressive initial attack. Dense Douglas fir and ponderosa pine forest fuels and steep topography often limit the use of engines and bulldozers. Aircraft and hand crews must be designated as primary initial-attack resources.

Great Basin States (Nevada, Utah, Idaho and Eastern Oregon)

The Great Basin states comprise approximately 90 million acres

Photo by Wayne Eddy

Poor timber harvesting or logging practices often leave 50-100 tons-per-acre of down-dead fuels. This can add tremendous thermal output to carry a surface fire to aerial canopies.

of diverse fuel types. The Great Basin encompasses Nevada, Utah, Idaho and eastern Oregon. The basin is formed between the Sierra Nevada (west) and Wasatch Front Mountain ranges (east). At the south end of the basin is Salt Lake City; the north end is Baker, Oregon.

Much like the Pacific Northwest, the Great Basin has very diverse fuel types and topography. There are six primary fuel types located between the 2,000- and 8,000-foot elevations. In the 3,000-to-4,000-foot elevations, we find the northern desert shrub. The desert shrub consists of sage and bitterbrush. These fuel types are explosive, primarily due to oils and resins found in the canopy foliage. Most fuel beds in the 3,000-to-4,000-foot elevations display good continuity and arrangement.

The 4,000-to-6,000-foot elevations average six to 10 inches of rainfall and a 120-to-160-day growing season. Wildland fires spread rapidly during daylight hours, while good relative humidity recovery slows fire spread at night. Fires of 5,000-10,000-acres are common in the Great Basin.

The next-most-severe wildland fire problem stems from pinyon-juniper fuel types. Pinyon-juniper species are located in the 6,000-to-8,000-foot elevations, where the average rainfall is eight to 10 inches. Pinyon-juniper woodlands provide a transition between desert sagebrush and fir, spruce and mountain mahogany forests.

The pinyon-juniper woodlands have an explosive understory of sage and grass. In addition, pinyon-juniper species have explosive oils in the canopy foliage. Old-age class pinyon-juniper is decadent in the understory and loses its continuity.

Based on the above variables, fire behavior in pinyon-juniper wildlands can be diverse. Spotting can occur under some wind models, but is generally confined to a short range – under one-quarter mile.

Fire-season air temperatures in the 2,000-to-8,000-foot elevations range from 78 degrees to 90 degrees F. Good relative humidity recovery can be expected during the night. The majority of wildland fires burn only during a one-burn period in this elevation zone.

The northern desert shrub area is dominated by sage and bitterbrush with a grass understory. Black sage is the common species, often reaching six feet in height. Good continuity and arrangement are characteristic of these fuel beds. Fire behavior can vary, and firefighters trying to use the weather to their advantage should know that, normally, a fast-moving sage fire will slow up and die during the nighttime. A 5,000-acre wildland fire is common in this fuel type.

The 2,000-to-4,000-foot elevations contain the lower-desert salt shrubs. These species include greasewood, sage, salt brush, rabbit brush and grass. This zone is arid, averaging under five inches of rainfall. The weather can be very diverse and unpredictable. Hot summer days and cold winters are common, as is a very short growing season.

The lack of rainfall in this elevation zone helps reduce the wildland fire problem. Continuity, arrangement and fuel loading are such that the potential for a major fire is low. It is possible, following a wet winter, to have abundant grass growth on the lower desert floor, producing a fire with erratic, fast spread, but low thermal outputs.

Many areas within the Great Basin have elevations over 8,000 feet. Generally termed "true forest" or "alpine," they are primarily the home for aspen, spruce, fir, pine and mountain mahogany. The understory vegetation consists of fragile grasses, forbs and wild flowers.

The rainfall here exceeds 15 inches annually and the growing season averages 100 days. High temperature for an average fire-season day will be 68 degrees F. The 8,000-plus elevation traditionally has a minimal wildland fire problem and frequency. Lightning is the primary cause of wildland fires in all elevation zones of the Great Basin.

Rocky Mountain Region (Eastern Oregon, Western Montana,

Idaho, Western Wyoming, Utah and Southern Colorado)

The Rocky Mountain Region runs from the Canadian border on the north to Utah and Colorado's southern border. Idaho and Western Wyoming comprise the middle area. The region also includes eastern Oregon and western Montana.

The Rocky Mountains, like the Pacific Northwest, have quite diverse elevation ranges (2,000-to-8,000 feet) and fuel types. The principle fuel types found at higher elevations include ponderosa pine, lodgepole pine, white pine, red cedar, grand fir, spruce and western hemlock. The lower elevation fuel types include pinyon, juniper, oak brush, mountain mahogany, big sage and grass.

Active timber operations in this region may have tremendous down-dead slash buildups. This down-dead slash is an important concern to firefighters, as it often is responsible for carrying a ground fire to the aerial fuel canopies, creating a running crown fire. It is not uncommon for these down-dead slash areas to exceed 100-tons-per-acre fuel loading.

Environmental concerns have also created problems in the major fuel types. For instance, millions of acres of lodge pole pine have been damaged or destroyed by mountain pine beetles. The areas hardest hit by pine beetles include Umatilla, Whitman, Gallatin and Targhee national forests. These forests are very susceptible to a major timber fire, due to a tremendous amount of decadent material standing dead or damaged.

The spruce forests of Wenatchee and Lolo are being damaged or destroyed by a spruce-bud worm infestation. Douglas fir stands on the Umatilla, Wallowa and Whitman national forests are being damaged or destroyed by tussock moths.

The above environmental damage will annually increase the probability of a major timber conflagration over the next decade.

Another problem is urban interface. The Rocky Mountain region has several areas where the wildland/urban interface population is encroaching on previously-forested and other wildland open-space areas. This encroachment into environmentally-damaged forest areas could increase not only the probability of a major forest fire but also that of a wildland/urban interface fire with all its accompanying structural and human-life loss.

The Colorado front country between Fort Collins and Colorado Springs is one critical area. The area around Boise, Idaho is another with a rapidly-developing wildland/urban interface. In western Montana, the areas surrounding Kalispell, Butte, Bozeman and Helena are developing wildland/urban interfaces. The ponderosa pine and mixed conifer forests of Coeur D'Alene and Sandpoint,

Idaho and Spokane, Washington are also developing wildland/ urban interfaces at a fast pace.

Southwest Region (West Texas, New Mexico, Arizona and Southern California)

Elevations in the Southwest region run from sea level to 11,000 feet. Primary fuel types include grasses, both annual and perennial. Annual grasses are found at elevations below 1,200 feet, while perennials are found on steeper slopes, to 4,000 feet.

Another major fuel type is the pinyon pine. Mixed among the pinyon pine are juniper woodlands. The pinyon-juniper species have a very high resin-oil content and are explosive during fire season. The pinyon-juniper species are found at the 3,000-to-4,000-foot elevations.

New Mexico is home to the largest pure stand of ponderosa pine (yellow pine) in the United States. The ponderosa pine is found between the 3,000-foot and 7,000-foot elevations.

Many parts of New Mexico and Arizona have pinyon-juniper stands with an understory with little or no grass. In these stands, the opportunity for a wildland fire to spread or escape initial attack is minimal. However, firefighters should be very alert to pinyon-juniper stands that have abundant down-dead and grass understories, as this understory will provide sufficient thermal outputs to preheat resins, oils and turpines in canopy foliage. A pinyon-juniper fire in this situation can create tremendous heat valves and erratic rates of spread.

The Colorado Plateau (Mogollion Rim) supports the largest

Photo by Bureau of Land Management, NM

The light and medium fuels' complex (annual grass, sage) transition into woodland areas found in drainages.

Photo by Bureau of Land Management, NM

Sage is the primary transition fuel between grasslands and woodland areas of New Mexico. Here, a two-three ton-per-acre fuel loading in sage.

Photo by Bureau of Land Management, NM

The jet stream often takes a southern route over New Mexico and the southwestern United States. This high speed band of air can create adverse wind models which can create erratic fire behavior in light fuel types or broken fuel beds.

ponderosa (yellow pine) stand in the world. The ponderosa pine can be found between 6,000- and 8,000-foot elevations. Timber operations to actively thin these stands are creating major areas of slash, which pose two problems for firefighters – first, tremendous thermal outputs and, second, a transition (fire ladder) from ground fuels to aerial canopies. The elevations between 8,000 and 10,000 feet are home to mixed conifer forests.

The chaparral plant community is one most often associated with major wildland fires and wildland/urban interface fires. Originally found in Southern California, chaparral now extends throughout the southwest, including Texas, Arizona and New Mexico.

In Arizona and New Mexico, the chaparral belt is found between the desert scrub and ponderosa pine. In the transition zone of chaparral and ponderosa pine, you often find sufficient fuels to provide a good transition from ground to aerial canopies. This combination contributes to high thermal outputs and large flame heights.

The Southwest regions also have some rapidly-developing wildland/urban interfaces. Flagstaff, Prescott and Walnut Creek are key development areas in Arizona. In New Mexico, Los Alamos, Taos, Chama and Ruidosa are rapidly developing. In west Texas, the grassland and grass-sage interfaces of the Davis Mountains are developing a number of subdivisions.

Southeast Region (Texas, Florida, Georgia, Virginia, Louisiana, Tennessee, Kentucky and North Carolina)

The southeastern states represent over 400 million acres of forest lands. This region has some of the largest tree farming businesses in the nation. The southeast region is also extremely diverse in topography and climate. This area has three geographical regions:

1. **Appalachian Mountains**
2. **Piedmont**
3. **Coastal Plains**

The Appalachian Mountains cover nearly 100 million acres of wildland and forests. The topography is inconsistent in this

Photo by George Cooper, FL State Div. of Forestry

Annual grass and herbaceous fuels provide ample heating to carry subcanopy and canopy of Florida's sash pine.

Photo by George Cooper, FL State Div. of Forestry

Hard-wood leaf litter and grasses provide a fluffy surface compaction and arrangement ideal for a surface fire in Florida.

mountain range, varying from 500 feet to nearly 6,700 feet at Mt. Mitchell, North Carolina. The Appalachian range can best be described as steep and rocky with large outcroppings of granite, sandstone or shale. A high percentage of the wildland forest is inaccessible except by foot traffic.

Fuel types include hardwoods, pines, mountain laurel and hardwood litter. Fuel loading is 10 to 20 tons per acre.

During the winter, if snowfall is light, the hardwood leaves do not compact. Because they remain loose and fluffy, they can carry a moderate rate of fire spread.

Part of the Appalachian mountains is considered deciduous forest. The Appalachian highlands and surrounding interior plains are home to nearly 50 major tree species and many more minor tree species. The great variation in elevation, rainfall and soil series makes for a diversity in plant communities and growth. A few of the major tree species include sugar maple, birch species, hemlock, aspen, oak species, ash and hickory.

The vast Appalachian oak forests consist of black oak, white oak and northern red oak. A moderate rate of spread in hardwood litter can also occur under a high wind model.

The Piedmont Plateau covers approximately 100 million acres. Seventy-five percent of the Piedmont is heavy forest. Topography consists of rolling terrain with clay soil series. The Piedmont has many streams and creeks.

Primary fuel types in the Piedmont are hardwoods, pine species,

Photo by George Cooper, FL State Div. of Forestry

Palmetto and brush provide firefighters with a very hot fire. Shown here in understory of Southern Pine.

surface leaf litter and riparian vegetation. As mentioned earlier, the Southeast also has tree farming and pine plantations, and fuel loading can average 15 to 25 tons per acre.

Unlike the Appalachian range, fuel continuity in the Piedmont is often broken up by urban encroachment and agri-business. As aforementioned, the tree farm industry is a major one. There are southern pine, sash pine and loblolly pine plantations in various growth states including seedling, pole and sawlog sizes.

The wide variety of tree farms and age classes makes availability and fire effect difficult to predict. The younger plantations (under 10 years) have large amounts of ground litter, hardwood debris and grasses to carry a fire into the aerial pine canopy. Sapling-size plantations can carry a crown fire. The density of the tree plantations often presents an access problem for firefighters.

The Coastal Plains cover approximately 200-million acres. Topography is basically flat. The Coastal Plains have some of the larger-acreage fires occurring in the southeast region.

Two bottomland forests are found along the coast plains. A major one extends north from New Orleans along the Louisiana/ Mississippi border up to Tennessee and Missouri. The second bottomland forest runs north along the coastal plains and includes the states of Georgia, South Carolina, North Carolina and Virginia. These forests are riparian wetlands. They contain some 70 species of hardwoods (oak, gum, and cypress forests). The bottomland forests comprise 33 million acres.

The swamp forests of northern Florida and Georgia and dismal swamp of Virginia and North Carolina have experienced some of the largest fires in the coastal plains. Swamps are capable of carrying a high-intensity fire after a drought condition. The fire seasons of 1844, 1860, 1910, 1931, 1954, 1955, 1985 and 1986 produced major swamp fires of between 10,000 and 150,000 acres in size. On "Black Friday," May 19, 1985, 29 counties in Florida exploded when a large lightning storm caused hundreds of wildland fires, burning 600 homes in one day.

In addition to hardwoods, bottomland forests and swamps, the coastal plains are home to the pocosin brush species. The word pocosin means "upland swamp." These upland swamps can be 300 feet above sea level. Pocosin is classified as either "low" or "high." The pocosin is an evergreen brush species found mixed in hardwood forests. Its leaves have a high oil content and are very flammable during fire season.

High pocosin can have a fuel loading of 40 tons per acre, but 30 is average. These plants can reach 20 feet in height. There are often substantial volumes of shrubs, vines, leaves and miscellaneous litter on the ground, which assist in preheating the aerial canopies.

The low pocosin has a much lighter fuel loading, averaging 10 tons per acre. Brush height is under six feet. Like the high pocosin, the brush interfaces with hardwoods, and shrub pond pine species.

Northeast Region (Connecticut, Delaware, Illinois, Indiana, Iowa, Maine, Maryland, Massachusetts, Michigan, Minnesota, Missouri, New Hampshire, New Jersey, New York, Ohio, Pennsylvania, Rhode Island, Vermont, West Virginia and Wisconsin)

The nation's most famous and destructive wildland/urban interface fire ever occurred in this region. In October of 1871, the 16 communities surrounding Peshtigo, Wisconsin burned, killing more than 1,500 people and consuming more than 1.2 million acres of forest. Additionally, in 1894, the Hinkley Forest fire, also in this region, killed over 400 people and burned several hundred thousand acres of forest.

The Northeast Region has 11 major fuel types, including large forests of oak, hickory and pine. Topography is varied from flat to steep and broken. Elevations range from sea level to over 6,500 feet (New Hampshire).

Photo by Dept. of Natural Resources, MI

The Lake States (Michigan) experienced some of the most destructive wildland fire in this nation's history. The dense Jack Pine (dog hair) shown is a prime carrier fuel in most major fires.

Photo by Joe Hughes, New Jersey Forestry

New Jersey Pine Barren

Oak woodland and hickory hardwoods are found in all 21 northeastern states. Nineteen of these states have ash/elm/cottonwood hardwoods. Seventeen states have oak-pine forests. Fifteen have extensive white-, red- and jack-pine forests. Thirteen states have spruce fir forests. Over 90 percent of the nation's spruce-fir ecosystem is located in the northeast region.

One of the more-critical fire areas in the northeast is the New Jersey pine barrens, over 1.2 million acres of highly-flammable pitch and short-needle pines. The pine barrens experience 2,000 wildland fires annually. This is one of the nation's fastest-growing wildland/urban interfaces – all within 35 miles of New York City and Philadelphia. This area is ripe for a major wildland fire and large loss of structures built in the pine-barren fuel beds.

Another key problem exists in Pennsylvania. The state has over eight million acres of oak/hickory forests. Over a million acres have suffered mortality from the oak leaf roller. In addition, the gypsy moth has severely damaged many thousand additional acres. Pennsylvania has some of the steepest and most-rugged topography in the northeast. The Myles Standish State Forest and surrounding Cape Cod area in Massachusetts are also rapidly developing.

The northeast lake states – Michigan, Minnesota and Wisconsin – comprise another critical region. These three states have 70 million acres of wildland. The wildland fires there are greatly influenced by the Great Lakes (Superior, Michigan and Huron).

As mentioned before, the Lake States have had some of the largest and most-destructive wildland fires in this nation's history. Between 1871 and 1918, the Lake States burned over one million acres, resulting in over 2,500 deaths.[1] Most of these destructive fires involved jack or red pine.

Like the southeast states, the lake states have vast areas of pine tree plantations. The density and continuity of these plantations present firefighters with fire-behavior and access problems.

The aerial fuels of the Lake States are complemented by ground fuel depths of up to 18 inches. This ground fuel is a combination of live and slash fuel, including perennial grass, leaves, ferns and blueberry vines.

Perennial grass is noteworthy for most readers from the western states who deal with annual grass that grows through three stages, dies, then becomes part of the dead-fuel loading. The perennial species do not brown out; they stay green and will burn readily during fire season. Blueberry thickets will burn during fire season with a flame that burns hot, spreads rapidly and will create spotting.

Unique surface and sub-surface peat fires can be found in the Lake States and Wisconsin. Peat is raw, and accumulates partially-decomposed plant matter under very-moist conditions. Peat soils contain high percentages of woody and herbaceous materials. Peat fires can burn well past the end of fire season and, if permitted, will burn in snow.

Peat bogs are associated with spruce, grass meadows, tamarack

---

[1]*The Mack Lake Fire, United States Forest Service Technical report NC-83, St. Paul, MN, Sept., 1983.*

swamps and aspen-scrub oak areas. The Lake States experience their fire season in April, May and June.

Alaska

Alaska's fire zone runs from sea level to the 3,500-foot elevation. Above 3,500 feet, the terrain is dominated by alpine tundra and does not present a fire problem.

The north slopes are usually covered by black spruce and high tundra tussocks. South-facing slopes are covered with hardwoods. Riparian zones are covered with white spruce.

Seventy-five percent of the wildland fires in Alaska involve black spruce. Black spruce is found on poorly-drained sites underlain with permafrost. The black spruce range is generally found in rolling hills or valleys. It seldom exceeds 30 feet in height or a trunk diameter of eight inches.

Wildland fires in the black spruce are hot and intense. The black spruce has a year-round low live-fuel moisture level. A fire in black spruce will generally consume needles, stems and branches, killing all trees involved.

The Alaska black spruce is a crown-fire-prone fuel type. The low live-fuel moisture and lichens (feather moss) commonly found on lower branches of the black spruce make it very easy for a ground fire to reach the aerial canopies.

The south slopes are home to the hardwoods, primarily birch and aspen. They are an indicator of well-drained soils and less permafrost. The hardwoods, unlike black spruce, do not pose a crown-fire threat. A ground fire, namely down-dead leaves, litter and limbs, is the most common threat. A ground fire is usually slow-moving, but compounded by extensive root systems and peat moss.

The Alaska tussock tundra is a perennial bunch grass, much like prairie bunch grass. Tussock tundra is found primarily in western Alaska on level or gentle, rolling slopes. It can burn intensely, much like annual grass, under dry summer conditions (under 30 percent relative humidity).

FUEL CLASSIFICATION SYSTEMS

NATIONAL FOREST FIRE LAB FUEL MODELS

Fuel Model

1. **Short Grass, 12 inches or less in height**
2. **Timber with grass understory**
3. **Tall grass, 28 inches in height**
4. **Chaparral, 6 feet in height**
5. **Brush species, 2 feet in height**
6. **Brush, slash**
7. **Southern rough**

8. Timber litter
9. Hardwood litter
10. Timber (litter and understory)

UNITED STATES FOREST SERVICE FUEL CLASSIFICATION SYSTEM

Type 1 Grass
Type 2 Grass/sage mix
Type 3 Mature timber
Type 4 Bear clover
Type 5 Manzanita/brush mix
Type 6 Medium growth timber
Type 7 Light to medium chamise
Type 8 Brush mix with sage
Type 9 Mixed brush in timber
Type 10 Mixed Douglas fir and brush
Type 11 Medium brush-oak woodland
Type 12 Heavy, pure manzanita or chamise
Type 13 Heavy mixed brush
Type 14 Heaviest mixed brush
Type 15 Second growth — timber
Type 16 Logging slash
Type 17 Woodland

NATIONAL FIRE DANGER RATING SYSTEM — 1972, FOREST SERVICE

Fuel Model Key — NFDRS 1972

I. The area is not timbered; less than one-third of the area is occupied by trees. (Stunted tree species and conifer reproduction are grouped with shrubs and called brush. Slash is not considered brush.)

A. Grass and other herbaceous plants or mosses and lichens are the predominant fuel. Brush, slash and trees together occupy less than one-third of the area.

1. Fuel depth 1 ft., short grass typically .... Model A
2. Tall grass (2.5 ft.) thick-stemmed, nonwoody, cover dead only .... Model L

B. Grass and other herbaceous plants are not the predominant fuel.

1. Brush or tree reproduction make up the predominant plant cover; occupies one-third or more of the area.
   a. The foliage of the predominantly woody cover species burns readily.
      (1) The predominant cover occupies two-thirds or more of the area.
         (a) One-third or more of the woody portion of plants is dead; much of it is 2 inches in diameter or larger, or there is a duff/litter layer at least 3 inches deep. Cover must average 6 feet or more in height Model B
         (b) The cover contains little dead, woody fuel larger than 2 inches in diameter and the duff/litter layer is less than 3 inches deep .... Model D
      (2) The predominant cover occupies one-third, but less than two-thirds of the area .... Model C
   b. The foliage of the predominant cover species does not burn easily .... Model F
2. Slash is the predominant fuel.
   a. The foliage is still attached to the slash.
      (1) Coniferous slash
         (a) Light (40 tons/acre) .... Model K

(b) Medium (120 tons/acre) .... Model I
(c) Heavy (200 tons/acre) .... Model J
(2) Hardwood slash .... Model M
b. The foliage is no longer attached to the slash; settling is evident.
(1) Herbaceous plants have invaded the area .... Model C
(2) Brush has invaded the area — both live foliage and dead fuel burn readily .... Model D
(3) Cover is dormant or live foliage does not burn readily .... Model M

II. The area is timbered. One-third or more of the area is occupied by trees.
A. The area has been thinned or partially cut, leaving slash as the major fuel component.
1. Coniferous slash with needles attached .... Model B
2. All hardwood slash or coniferous slash with needles no longer attached .... Model G
B. The area has not been thinned or partially cut.
1. Grass and other herbaceous plants are a common ground fuel; the canopy of the overstory is commonly "open." .... Model C
2. Duff/litter, branch wood, are the primary ground fuel; the canopy of the overstory is "closed" though openings may be common in the stand.
a. Two-thirds or more of the overstory consists of deciduous species.
(1) The overstory is dormant; leaves have fallen and leaf litter is not compact .... Model E
(2) The overstory is not dormant; or leaf litter has been compacted by rain or snow .... Model H
b. One-third or more of the overstory consists of evergreen species.
(1) The overstory is mature or over-mature and is often decadent. There is an exceptionally-heavy accumulation of branch wood, downed trees and duff/litter on the forest floor. .... Model G
(2) The overstory is immature or mature. There is only a nominal accumulation of debris on the forest floor.
(a) Brush or reproduction occupies less than one-third of the area.
(i) The ground fuel is primarily needles 2 inches or more long (most pines) .... Model E
(ii) The ground fuel is primarily needles less than 2 inches long .. Model H
(b) Brush or reproduction occupies one-third or more of the area.
(i) The foliage of the understory burns readily or needle drape is prevalent .... Model D
(ii) The foliage of the understory does not burn readily and there is little or no needle drape .... Model F

Chapter 4

Topography

Topography, as it relates to wildland fires, refers to the configuration of the earth's surface, including relief and the position of natural features – "lay of the land," if you will. Topography can give a wildland firefighter many clues as to potential fire behavior. Topography can modify wind speeds and direction and create wind eddies.

Important factors associated with topography include:

A. Aspect.
B. Elevation
C. Thermal belt
D. Steep slopes
E. Narrow canyons
F. Narrow ridge lines (hog back)
G. Box canyons
H. Saddles
I. Orographic lifting

Aspect is the direction the slope faces – its exposure in relation to the sun. Fire conditions will vary dramatically according to aspect. Solar exposure, or lack of it, is the chief reason for this.

We know that southern exposures receive maximum solar and wind influences, while the northern slopes receive the least. Generally, eastern aspects receive early heating from the sun and early slope winds, while western aspects receive late heating and transitional wind flows (Figure 4a). Wildland fire starts and fires that continue to burn after initial-attack efforts can be graphed by aspect as illustrated in Figure 4b.

Elevation is also important. Two factors to consider are (1) elevation above sea level and (2) elevation changes in relation to

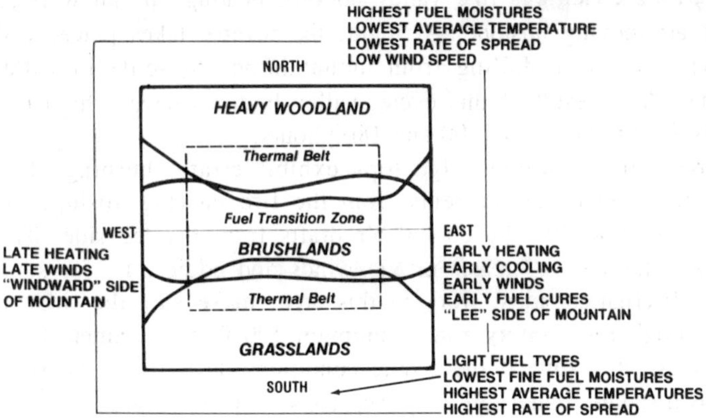

Figure 4a

surrounding topography features. In mountainous country, a variety of climatic zones exist between valley bottoms and mountaintops. Fire behavior between these zones can vary greatly. For instance, valley floors will exhibit warm temperatures, low humidities, lower wind speed, early snow melts, early grass cures and longer fire seasons. The mountain-ridge-line climatic zone will display lower temperatures, higher gusty wind speed, later grass cure, late snow melt and a shorter fire season. Elevations above 9,000 feet are generally characterized by few cured fuels and a very short, if any, fire season.

Valley bottoms and mountain ridges may display different burning conditions at various times during a 24-hour period. Stable

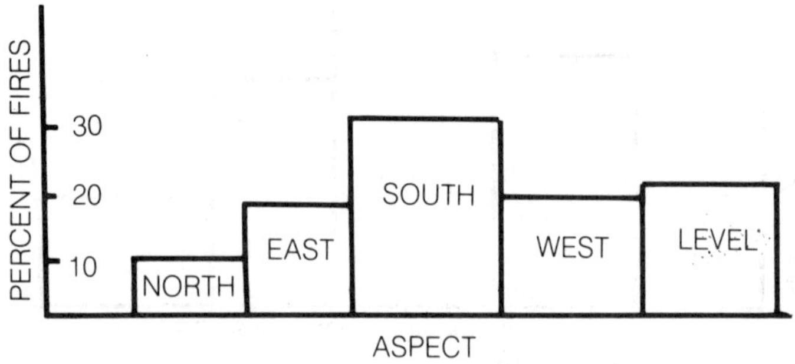

Figure 4b

summertime conditions find valley bottoms heating up and warmer, lighter air moving upslope. At night, the reverse takes place, with heavier, cooled air falling from mountaintops to settle in valley bottoms. As a result of this cycle, valley bottoms have a high propensity for fire between 1000 and 1800 hours.

Fires burning along ridge tops exhibit erratic burning characteristics. Heated air currents from the fire moving upslope are met at the ridge line by cooled air drafts from the lee side. This clash and turbulence creates erratic winds and eddies. If, for some reason, firefighters must work in this area, make sure the ridge is wide enough for a safety zone (minimum 100 feet in diameter) and plan to use this zone if the erratic conditions develop. If the ridge line has a saddle, make sure you keep crews out of this area.

Between valley bottoms, as mentioned above, **thermal belts** have neither the high temperatures of valley bottoms or the low temperatures of mountaintops. However, because of heating and cooling exchanges between mountaintops and valley bottoms on a 24-hour cycle, the thermal belt is a windy region. Over a 24-hour cycle, thermal belts have higher average temperatures and lower relative humidities than any other location. Thermal belts can be very active fire zones at night, and firefighters working in mountainous areas should be alert to this fact.

Besides elevation and aspect, fire behavior can be modified by topographic features (e.g., rock outcroppings and **steep slopes**), as well as fuel volume available on the slope. Statistics have shown that

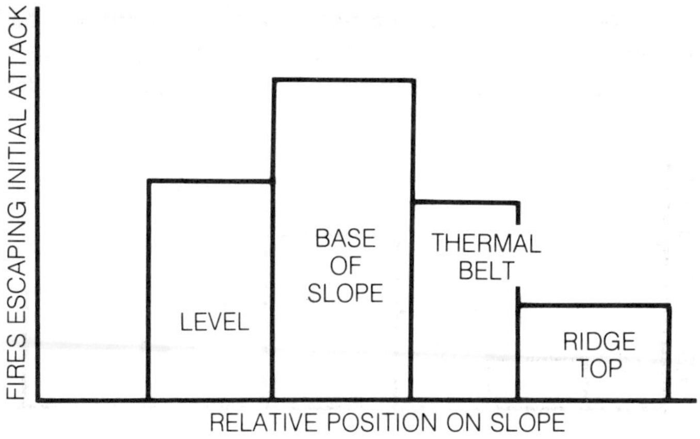

Figure 4c

a wildland fire starting at the base of a slope has a greater chance to escape initial attack than one on any other position on the slope (Figure 4c).

The primary reasons for this phenomenon are draft and preheating of fuels ahead of the fire. A slope will provide the fire with enough angle to change a vertical flame model to a horizontal flame model, thus increasing radiant and convection ranges and enabling more fuels to be preheated. The less thermal output loss by the fire, the greater the fire spread and resistance to control.

In regards to slope and rate of speed, a basic rule of thumb says, "For every 20 percent increase in slope, the rate of spread will double."

All factors being equal, a fire will burn upslope faster than on level ground. As mentioned earlier, draft and preheating are the primary reasons for this. Also, a fire burning on level ground will have a vertical flame model (low wind speeds); thus radiated and convective heat will affect only a limited area of the surrounding fuels. If the fire is on a slope, it will maximize the radiated and convective heat that pre-conditions fuels in advance of the fire.

Studies compiled by the Forest Service on 21,000 fires on National Forest lands[1] show that 62 percent of the fires occurred on slopes steeper than 20 percent. Only 16 percent involved level ground. This same study pointed out that 18 percent of the fires that occurred on slopes greater than 20 percent escaped initial attack efforts.

Fires burning up steep slopes generally have a wedge shape with a narrow head. Many times, flames on the flanks will be drawn inward. Heated air rapidly rises in a building convective column and cooler drafts are drawn inward.

Narrow canyons and the steep slopes associated with them often allow both slopes in the canyon to be preheated to the point of spotting and area ignition. Because these narrow canyons create their own microclimatic conditions, a fire moving into a narrow canyon raises temperatures and lowers humidity and fine-fuel moisture to a point where fire spread is dramatically increased and firefighting is often too hazardous to risk. The associated wind patterns, unlike those in wind canyons, are well defined and conform to the canyon shape.

Many narrow canyons have only one way in and one way out. These are called **box canyons.** Box canyons act like chimneys, providing avenues for intense updrafts and a potential for a blow-

---

[1]*United States Forest Service, Research Paper 29, J.S. Barrows Northern Rocky Mountain Forest Fire Laboratory, Aug., 1972.*

up. If the fire is slow-building, and smoke creates an inversion over the canyon, the same process can occur, but over a longer period. Poor canyon ventilation and smoke inversion can create a carbon-monoxide buildup. It is very important to post a lookout with a clear vantage point to observe the developing fire and watch out for spot fires across the canyon. If spot fires develop, make sure you are in a safe position or can reach a safety zone in a short time, since a blow-up or area ignition may be imminent. If the narrow canyon has side canyons at its head, this area will be critical for wind eddies and erratic wind patterns. This is especially true in rocky, broken topography.

Wide canyons have steady prevailing wind patterns and a low potential for spotting. Box canyons are very much like narrow canyons as far as fire behavior, except there are no side drainages or ways out of the canyon head.

Saddles are the low topography between two high points. Saddles are points of least resistance for winds and eddies. Many fatalities have occurred on ridge lines when firefighters in a saddle area could not withstand intense heat and smoke as the fire moved upslope towards them (Figure 4d). Saddle areas should *not* be used as safety zones.

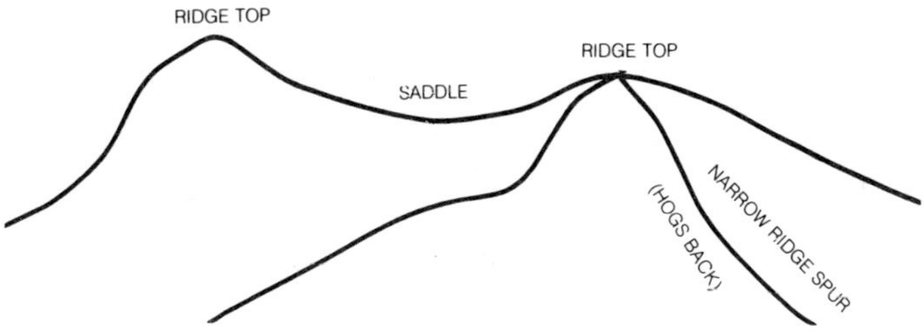

Figure 4d

Prior to starting a line assignment in mountainous topography, utilize a topographic or orthographic map to locate narrow canyons, ridges and saddles in the fire area. Discuss them with your personnel before starting the line assignment. This data should be included in the incident action plan.

Fuel breaks on ridge lines should be constructed so that safety zones are located on ridge tops and high points. This is especially important during nighttime fire operations, when topography and fuel types are not visible. **Narrow ridge lines** or ridge spurs, called

"hog backs," can also be hazardous for much the same reason. Heat, smoke and flame heights are usually severe enough that hand crews or bulldozer operators cannot survive.

If you must implement a control line along a narrow ridge or hog back, safety zones should be constructed every 10 chains of line. Safety zones should be a minimum 100 feet in diameter. If this cannot be done, then the command team should re-evaluate the incident action plan and select a safer ridge to work down.

Orographic lifting takes place in mountainous areas where warm, rising air is forced aloft by the barrier created by the mountains. This lifting action forces the warm air aloft, where it cools and forms a cumulus cloud(s). In the summer months, these clouds are a visible indicator to firefighters of gusty winds along ridge lines and strong down drafts. Erratic fire behavior can result from fires located beneath these clouds.

MAP READING AND SYMBOLOGY

Incident action plans use a detailed map to illustrate access, key facilities (i.e., ICP, base, staging), ridges and canyons. This map is

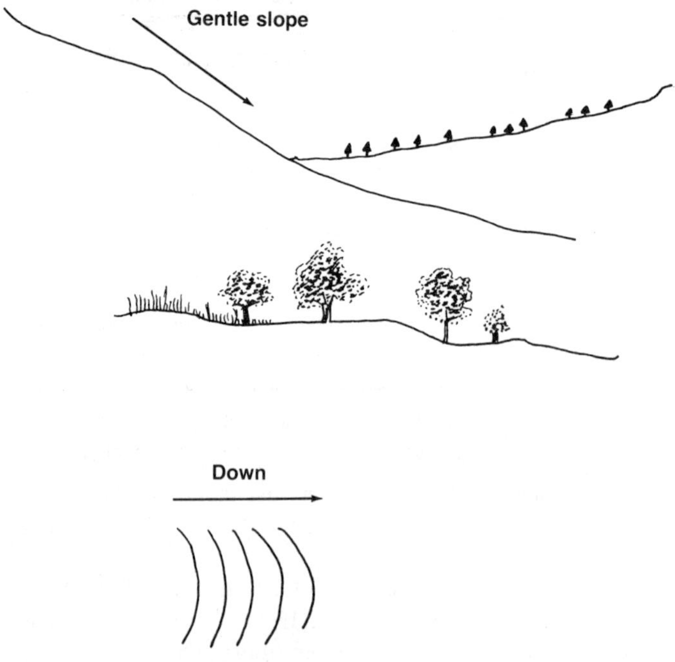

Uniform gentle contours

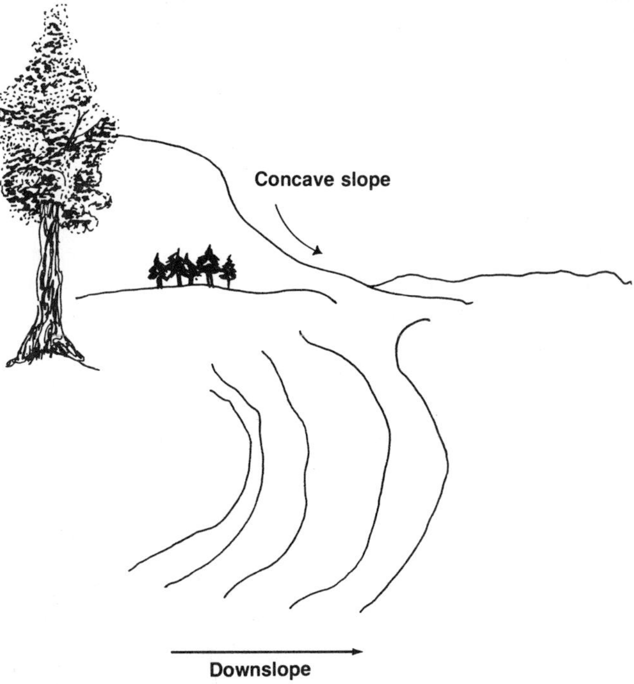
Concave slope
Downslope

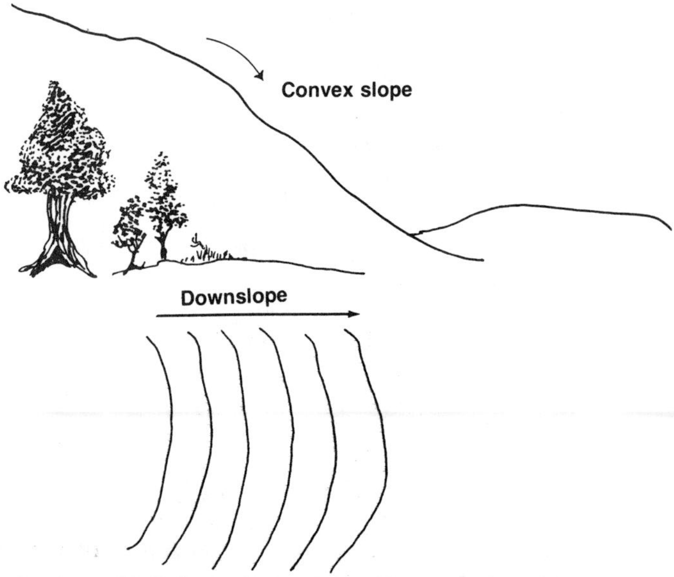
Convex slope
Downslope

also important in plotting projected control lines and identifying areas of resource limitations (dozers and engines).

Three basic map systems, **topographic, township and FIRE-SCOPE** are used on wildland incidents.

The **topographic** map system utilizes graphic delineation to show geographic features. Cartographers employ a series of lines, shapes and angles to show land features such as canyons, ridges, valleys, roads, trails and waterways. The topography map most commonly used by the fire service is a 22-by-27-inch map called a quadrangle (quad). The quad will vary in size, but generally covers 60 to 90 square miles. The quad will also reference and display township map sections (solid and broken red lines). The quad map is referenced by the name of a landmark or feature common to that quad such as, "San Marcos Pass, California."

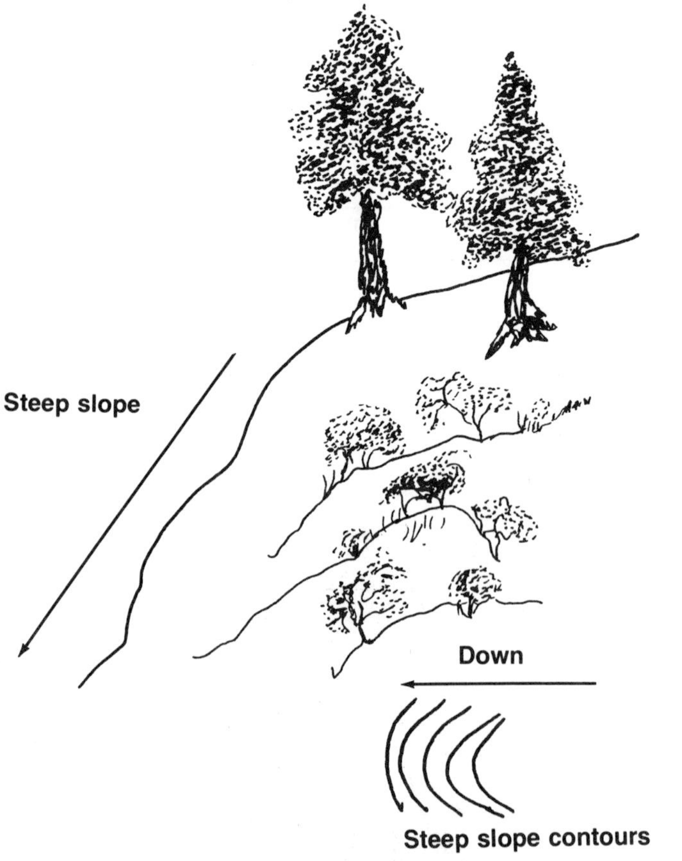

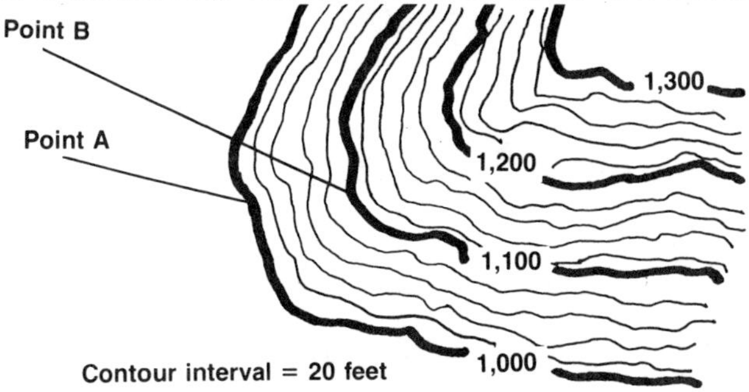

Contour interval = 20 feet

Map scale: 1:24,000, or 1 inch = 2,000 feet

Reading slopes: Every fifth line (contour) will be darker, to indicate a reference elevation, which will assist you in determining the contour interval and slope percentage.

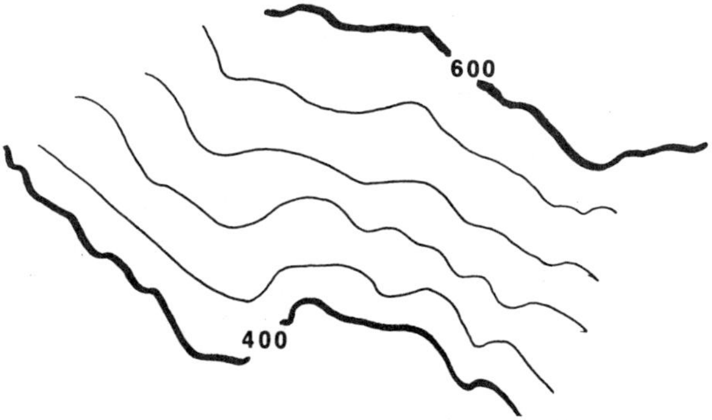

In this example, the contour interval is 40 feet. slope is gentle.

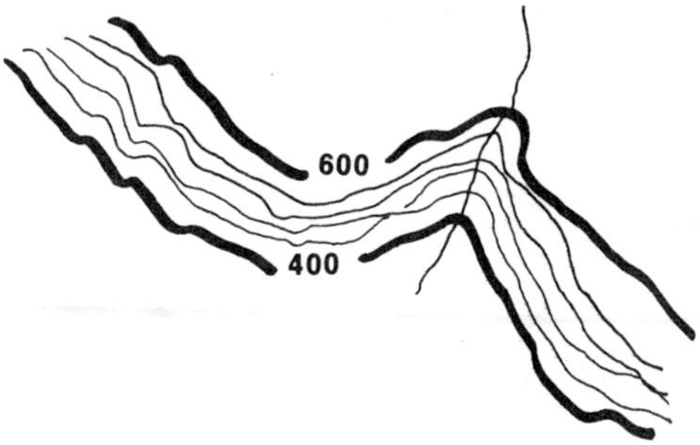

This example shows a steep slope and well-defined drainage.

Contour interval is again 40 feet.

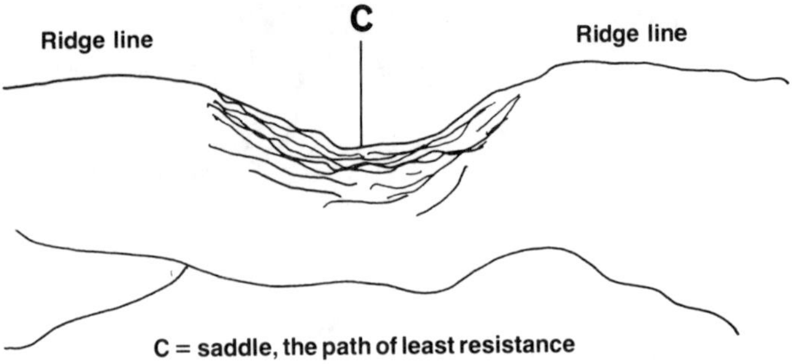

C = saddle, the path of least resistance

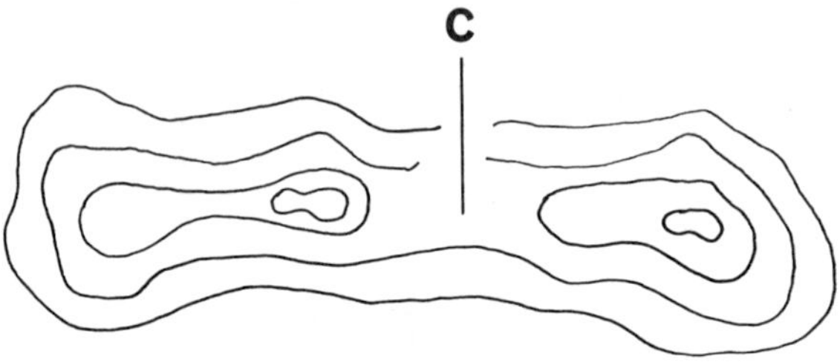

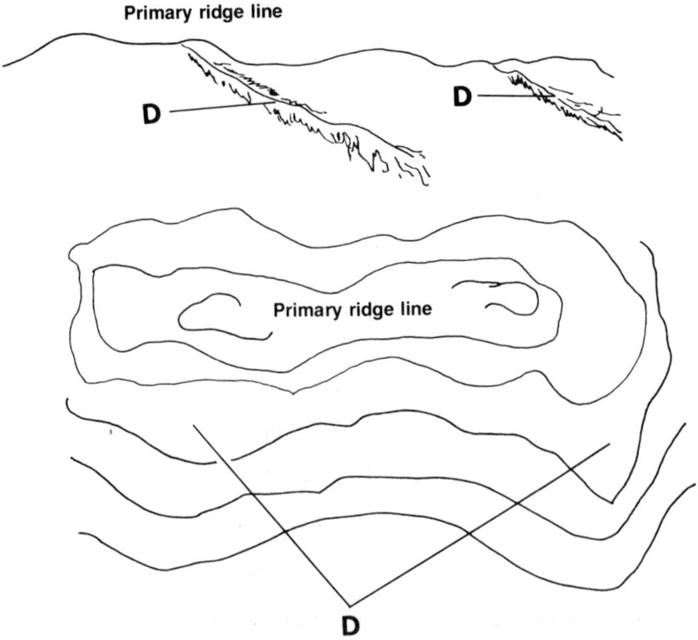

D = spur ridges

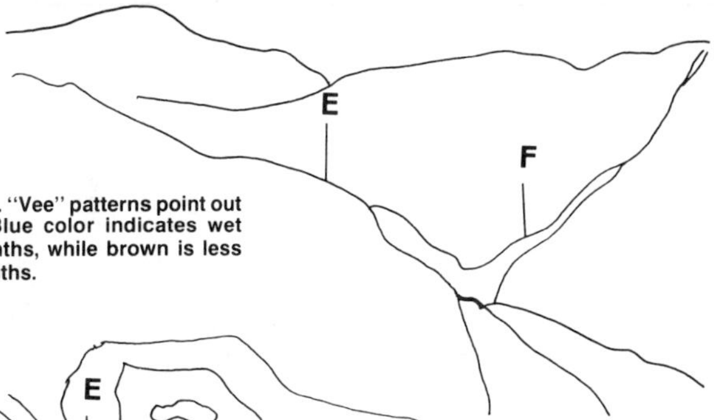

E = drainage. "Vee" patterns point out drainages. Blue color indicates wet over six months, while brown is less than six months.

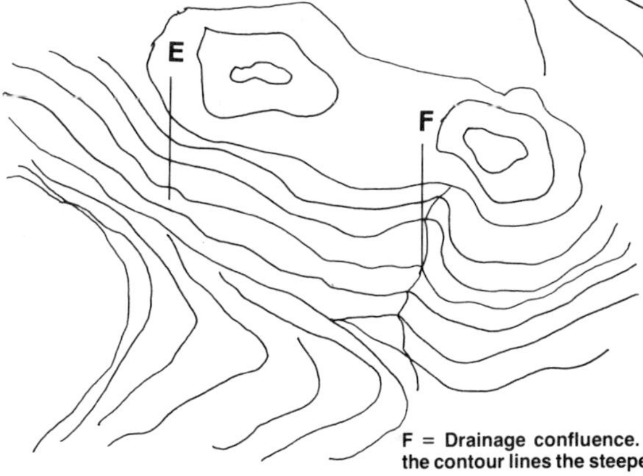

F = Drainage confluence. The closer the contour lines the steeper the drainage.

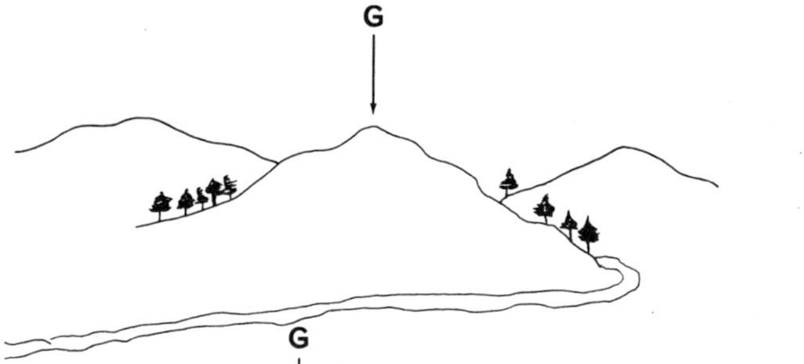

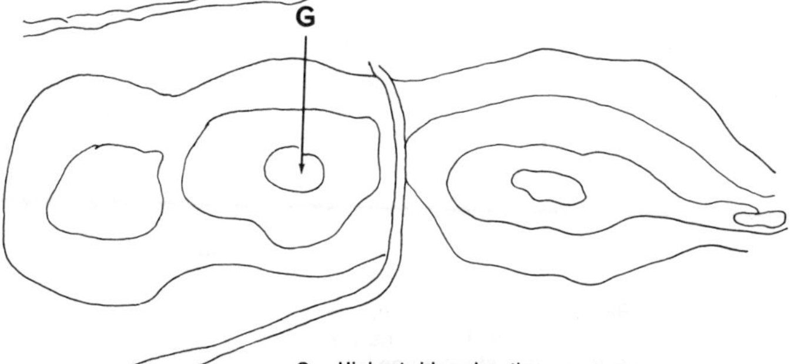

G = Highest ridge elevation

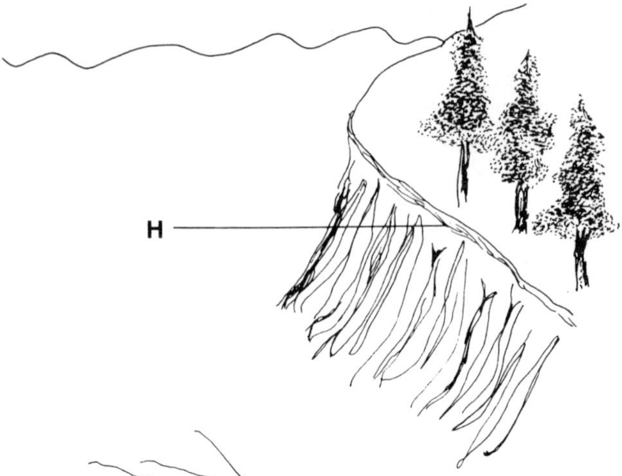

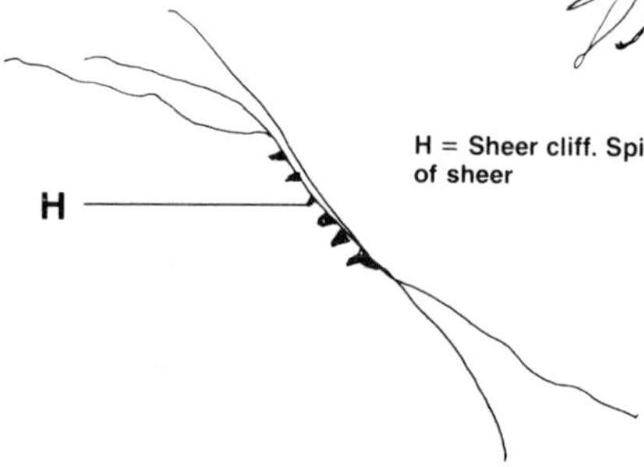

H = Sheer cliff. Spikes point direction of sheer

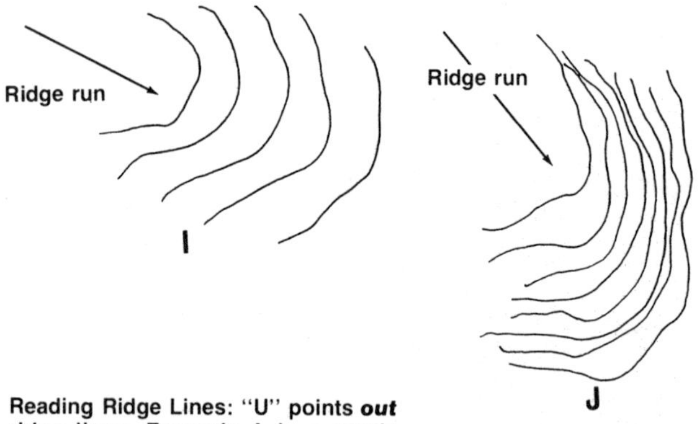

Reading Ridge Lines: "U" points ***out*** ridge lines. Example I is a gentle slope. Example J is a steep ridge line.

Reading Drainages: Drainages can be wet or dry (blue or brown), reflect wide or narrow canyons, and point to saddle areas near ridge line. "V" points out drainages.

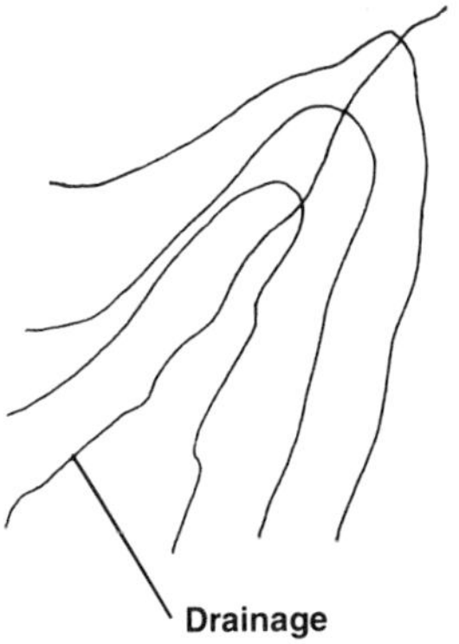

Gentle slope, wide canyon

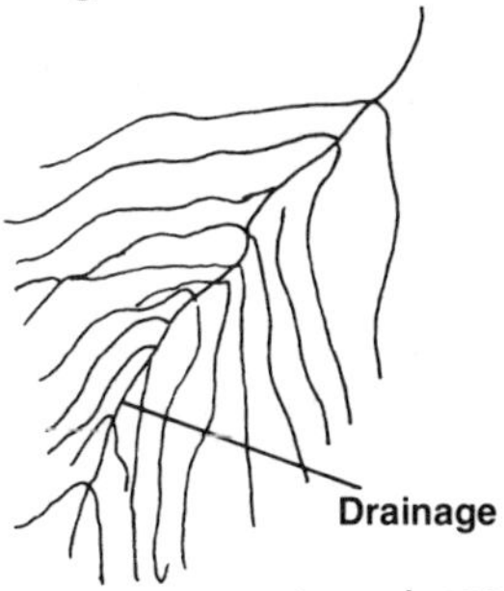

Narrow canyon, steep slopes

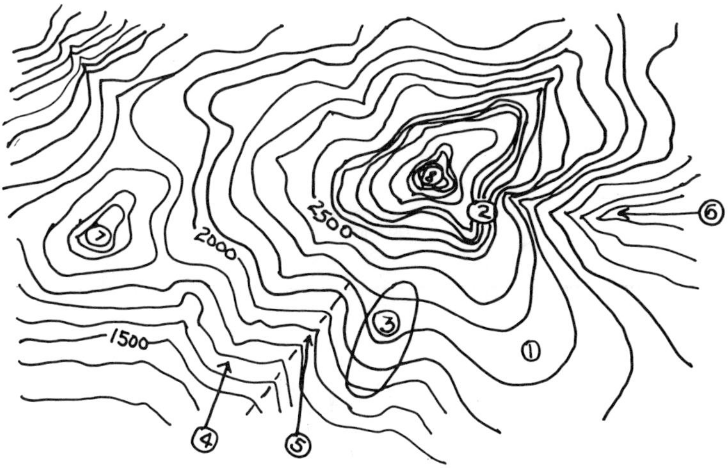

1. GENTLE SLOPE
2. STEEP SLOPE
3. BROAD RIDGE TOP, LINES POINT DOWNHILL
4. POINTED RIDGE TOP
5. WIDE VALLEY, DRAINAGE--LINES POINT UPHILL
6. NARROW CANYON
7. PLATEAU
8. PEAK

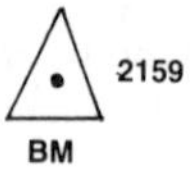

Ridge top bench marker indicating highest point on the ridge is 2,159 feet above sea level. Bench marks can be at any elevation point.

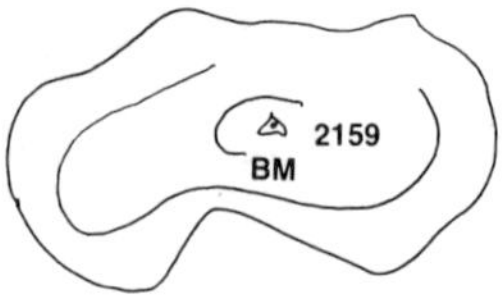

X

X indicates a reference elevation point above sea level.

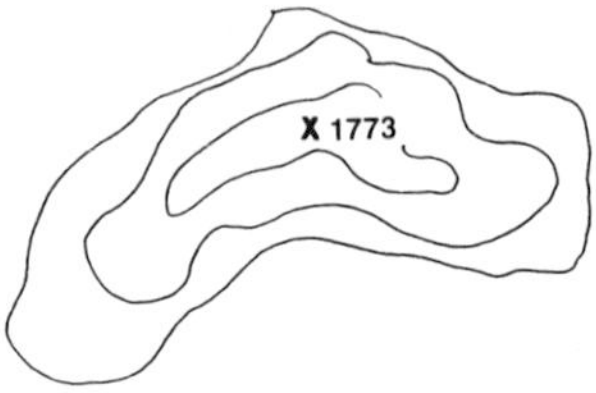

Roadways

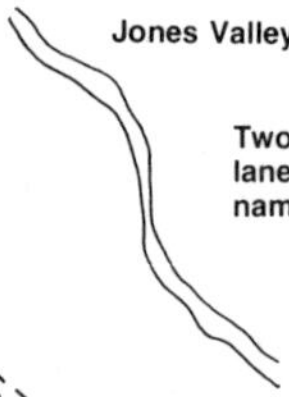

Jones Valley Rd.

Two parallel solid lines indicate a two-lane, all-weather surface road — road name is attached.

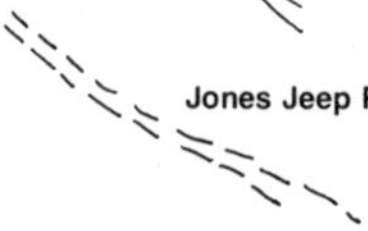

Jones Jeep Road

Two parallel broken lines indicate any unmaintained road.

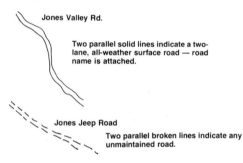

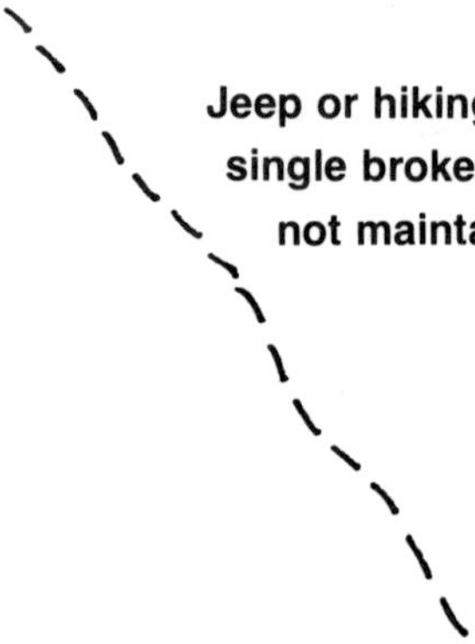

Jeep or hiking trail single broken line not maintained

Spring

A blue colored circle indicates wet drainage. Depending on map age, may be accurate or not

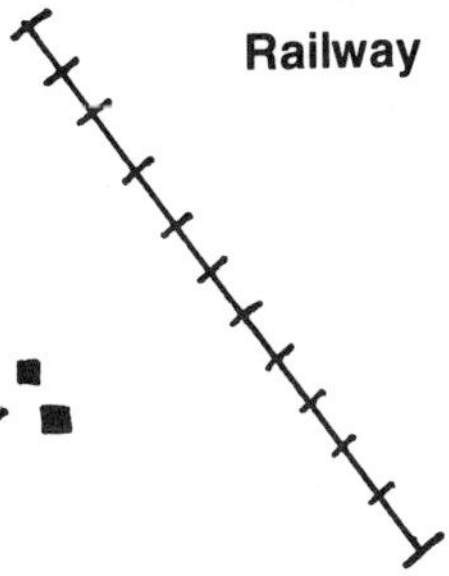

Railway

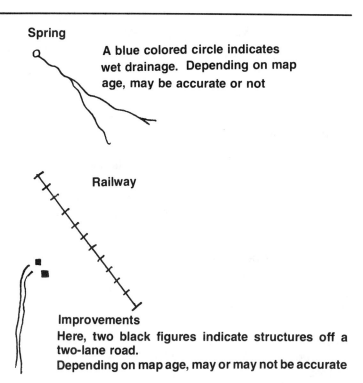

Improvements

Here, two black figures indicate structures off a two-lane road.
Depending on map age, may or may not be accurate

SIMPLE POINTS TO REMEMBER WHEN READING A TOPOGRAPHIC MAP

1. Contour — A line of constant elevation denotes geographical feature(s).
2. Contour Interval — Spacing, in feet, between contour lines. Common intervals used are 20, 30, 40, 50 and 100.
3. Colors — NOTE: the age of the map will determine the accuracy of the vegetation density or color.
    - Green = vegetation density
        - light green — light fuels
        - dark green — dense vegetation
    - Brown = lack of ground cover
        - desert lands
        - agriculture lands
        - in drainage: lack of year-round water in stream or creek
    - Blue = presence of water
        - lake or stream

MAP INTERPRETATION DATA

1. Lower right-hand corner (USGS maps) has the map's quadrangle name and date.
2. Lower middle map scale:
1:253,400 map scale = 1/4-inch to one mile land scale
1:126,720 map scale = 1/2-inch to one mile land scale
1:63,360 map scale = 1-inch to the mile land scale
1:31,680 = 2 inches to one mile land scale
1:24,000* = 2.63 inches to one mile land scale.
***Most common map scale (USGS quads)**
Contour interval is located under the map scale.
Lower left-hand corner has the aerial photograph and north reference data.
TN = True North
GN = Grid North
MN = Magnetic North
True North = actual direction of the North Pole
Grid North = Direction all vertical lines on map point to. Compensates for the curve in the earth's surface.
Magnetic North = Direction the compass needle points to. The magnetic pole is located near Hudson Bay and is 16 degrees of true north.

The **township** map is used extensively in land surveys. It breaks down an area into one-square-mile blocks called "sections." A township is made up of 36 sections. The land is described in terms of range (north-south reference), townships (east-west reference) and a section number from one to 36 (i.e., R28W, T6N, section 27).

From this legal description, a 640-acre section can be further broken down by compass point description, i.e., "NW one-fourth of section 27 (160 acres)." Fire lookouts are able to pinpoint lightning strikes and small smokes a good distance away down to a five-acre area using this system and an Osborne Fire Finder.

The newest mapping technique is the **FIRESCOPE** system being developed in California. This system blends standardized symbology, planographic scale maps and an orographic map. The symbology is identical to FIRESCOPE incident-command system symbology used in the development of an incident action plan. The planographic maps come in three scales: One map unit may equal 6,000, 12,000 or 24,000 land units.

READING A TOWNSHIP MAP

Land is divided by cardinal lines running north, south, east and west. Each square designates a township of approximately six square miles. Each square is then divided into 36 sections of approximately one square mile. Each section is 640 acres. An acre is 43,560 square feet, and is the standard wildland fire reference in regards to area burned.

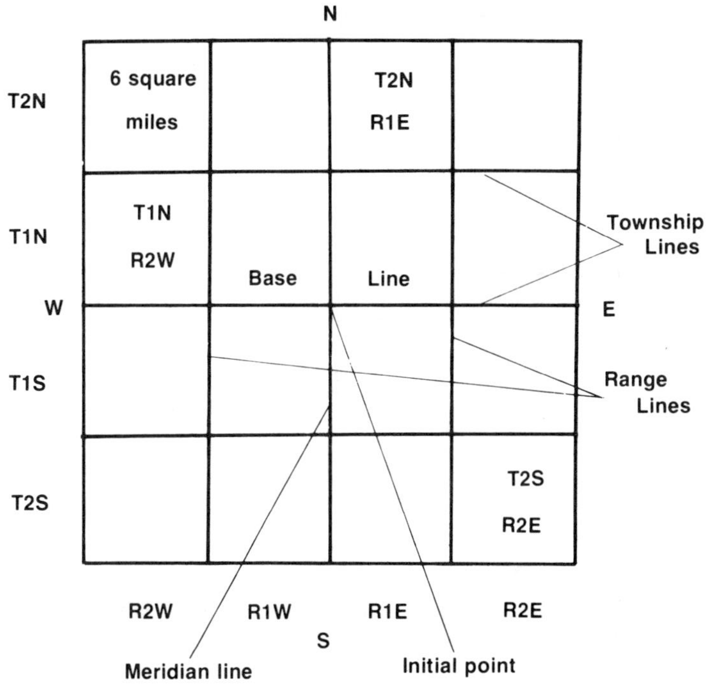

NUMBERING THE SECTIONS WITH THE TOWNSHIP

six miles

6	5	4	3	2	1
7	8	9	10	11	12
18	17	16	15	14	13
19	20	21	22	23	24
30	29	28	27	26	25
31	32	33	34	35	36

six miles

SECTION 35

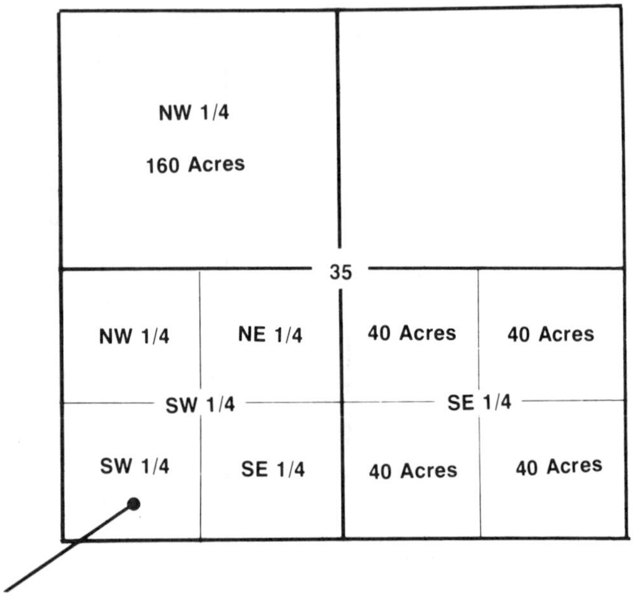

This dot is at the SW 1/4 of the SW 1/4 section 35. This area is approximately 40 acres.

The square-mile sections can now be divided into four subdivisions of 160 acres each. Further subdivision can be done either using acreage or compass descriptors.

INCIDENT COMMAND SYSTEM MAP SYMBOLOGY

The following are the key symbols used in the incident map portion of the incident action plan:

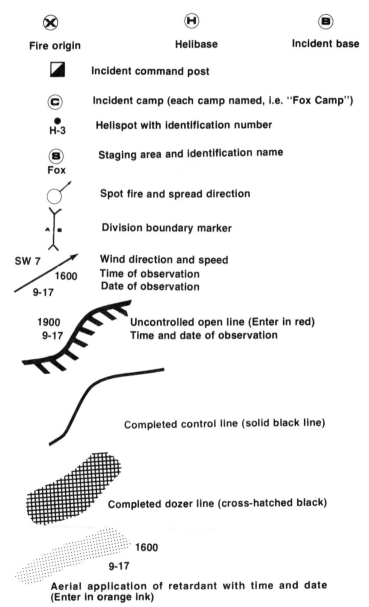

Fire origin

Helibase

Incident base

Incident command post

Incident camp (each camp named, i.e. "Fox Camp")

Helispot with identification number

Staging area and identification name

Spot fire and spread direction

Division boundary marker

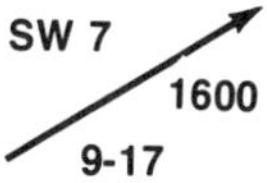

Wind direction and speed
Time of observation
Date of observation

Uncontrolled open line (Enter in red)
Time and date of observation

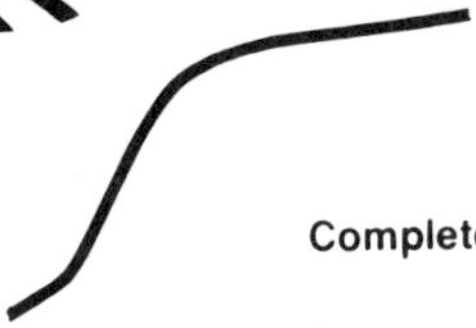

Completed control line (solid black line)

Completed dozer line (cross-hatched black)

Aerial application of retardant with time and date (Enter in orange ink)

CALCULATING SLOPE FROM A TOPOGRAPHY MAP
To calculate the slope, find the vertical rise in elevation. Then calculate the horizontal distance (run). Divide vertical rise by horizontal run and multiply by 100.

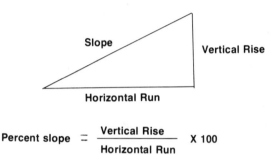

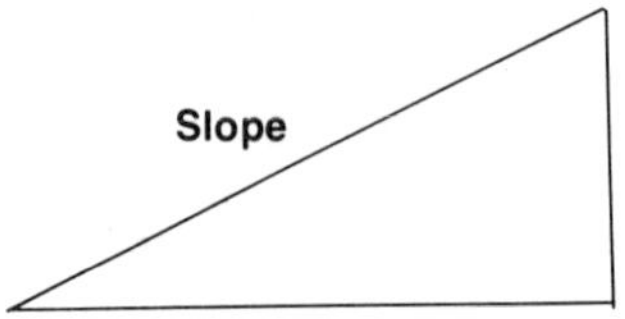

$$\text{Percent slope} = \frac{\text{Vertical Rise}}{\text{Horizontal Run}} \times 100$$

Chapter 5

Weather

Weather is the most critical element of fire behavior. Weather is also the most unpredictable element for the firefighter.

Many books, papers and theories have been written on the laws of weather, motion and atmospheric conditions as they pertain to fire. This chapter will review aspects of weather important to the wildland firefighter. In this author's opinion, these elements include:

A. **Weather Regions**
B. **Air Masses**
C. **Atmospheric Stability**
D. **Lifting**
E. **Winds and Wind Patterns**
F. **Air Temperature**
G. **Atmospheric Moisture**
H. **Clouds**
I. **Barometric Pressures**
J. **Weather Maps**
K. **Regional Weather Influences**

WEATHER REGIONS

The firefighter must be familiar with three weather zones:

1. **Synoptic**
2. **Regional**
3. **Microclimatic**

The **synoptic zone** encompasses both the polar and equator regions of the earth. This zone exhibits hemispheric movement of fronts and air masses.

The polar regions are heavily influenced by snow packs and cooler

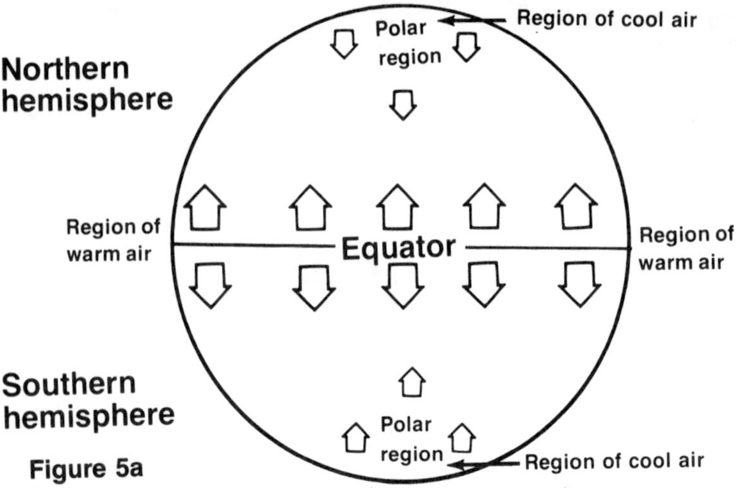

Figure 5a
Synoptic zone of weather non-rotating Earth

air temperatures. Cool air from the polar regions moving toward the warmer equator region is typical (Figure 5a).

Warm moist tropical air rises aloft from the equator. This rising air becomes less dense, creating a lower barometric pressure at the equator. As the air flows from high pressure to low pressure, it goes from cold to warm.

The earth's rotation influences the movement of air, deflecting it to the east (northern hemisphere, Figure 5b). The majority of the United States is influenced by the Prevailing Westerlies (30-degree to 50-degree latitude band) shown in Figure 5c.

The weather service uses synoptic weather charts to track air mass

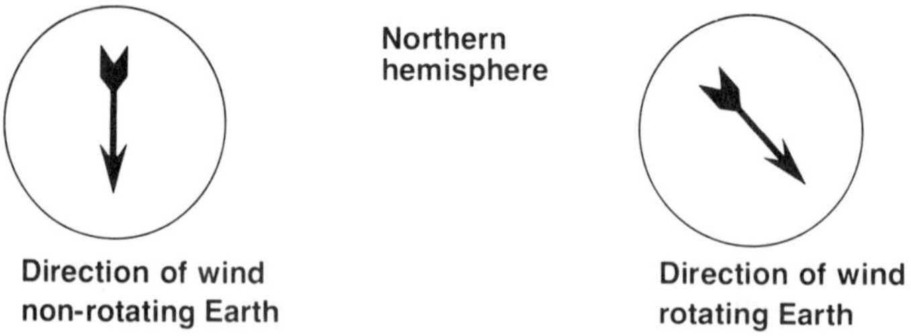

The Earth is approximately 25,000 miles around at the equator. The Earth makes one complete rotation every 24 hours, hence, the speed of the rotation at the equator is 1,000 mph. The rotation speed across the United States is approximately 800 mph.

Figure 5b
Effects of wind from Earth's rotation

and wind movement. The most common synoptic weather charts are 500 millibar (18,000+ feet above sea level) and 300 millibar (30,000 feet above sea level). The 500 millibar chart is more widely used because it describes the "zone of weather." In this zone, we find the vertical cloud series and frontal activity and most wind activity (Figure 5d). The 300-millibar chart can be very useful in tracking the jet stream and its influences.

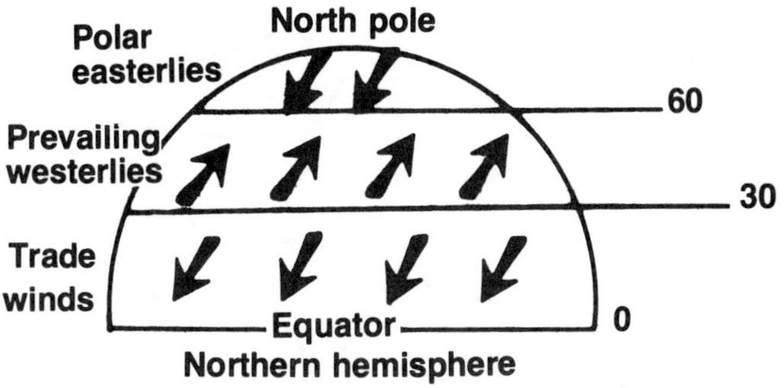

The United States lies between 30 and 60 degrees latitude with a general wind direction to the west.

Figure 5c
Prevailing wind directions with the Earth's rotation

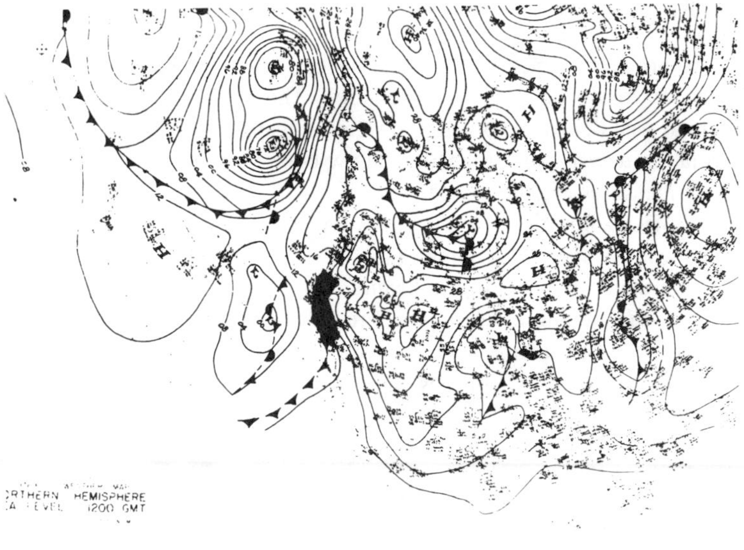

Figure 5d
500 millibar weather map

Each geographical **region** is influenced by some form of frontal activity. The diurnal cycle – heating and cooling differences between land and water – influences wind patterns. As previously mentioned, *the general wind direction in the United States is westerly.* The jet stream (Figure 5e) typically moves from west to east. The jet

Figure 5e
Jet stream tracks over the United States generally 30,000 to 40,000 feet above sea level

stream can block or modify air-mass movement. This is important during fire season when the jet stream may block moisture from a region.

As previously mentioned, most severe fire weather is influenced by an air mass (mostly high-pressure). The firefighter can monitor regional weather by following the weather maps in some of the larger-circulation newspapers. Maps that show both weather fronts and barometric pressures are the most useful.

Microclimatic. Once a fire starts, it will, to a degree, influence local weather. The larger the fire and the longer it burns, the more influence it has. *Microclimatic condition* (Figure 5f) refers to the area surrounding a developing fire. It may be one or two canyons to either side of the fire, or it may be a mile from the fire's burning edge. Microclimatic conditions impact local air temperature, relative humidity and local winds. Firefighters use a belt weather kit to monitor microclimatic conditions.

AIR MASSES

An air mass, by definition, is a large parcel of air that may cover hundreds of thousands of square miles. This parcel of air has a consistent air temperature and relative humidity.

For the purposes of this text, we will look at summertime air

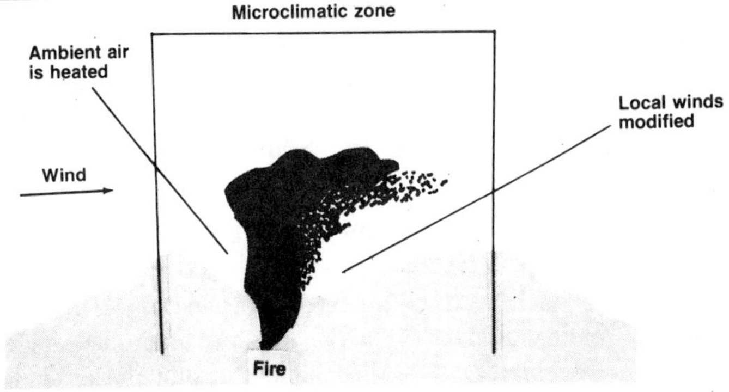

Figure 5f
Microclimatic conditions

masses and source regions important to the wildland firefighter. Air masses are classified by their relative warmth or cold and by relative moisture content. Air masses that form over the polar regions consist of cold, dry air. In the summer months, these are regions of high pressure.

The tropical region (equator) is a region of warm, moist air. Low-

CHARACTERISTICS OF AIR MASSES

Source Region	Atmospheric Pressure	Degree Stability	Surface Turbulence	Surface Visibility	Cloud Series
Polar	high pressure	unstable	high	good	vertical
Tropical	low pressure	stable	low	poor	horizontal

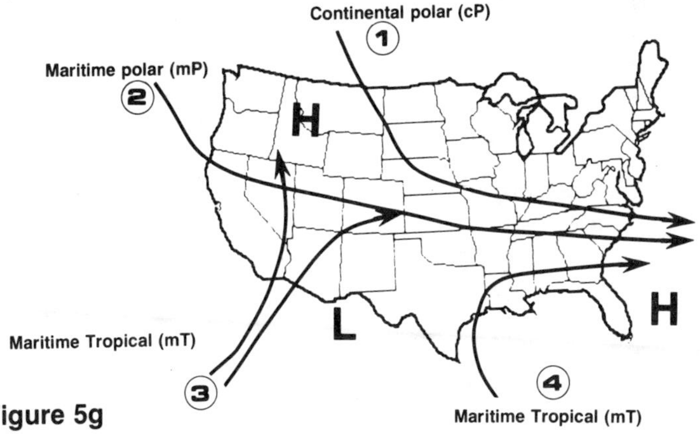

Figure 5g
Air mass tracks and source regions over the United States in the summertime

pressure air masses form in the tropical region in the summertime.

Air masses are also further classified by whether they form over land or water (Figure 5g). Air masses that form over land are called **continental.** Those formed over water are termed **maritime.** Continental or maritime air masses are identified by a lower-case **c** or **m.** This is followed by an upper case **T** or **P** to indicate source region.

Summer Air Mass Characteristics (Figure 5h)

1. Continental Polar (cP). The summertime continental polar air mass is a lofty air mass of mild temperatures and unstable air. Unlike the winter continental polar air mass, which is bitter cold and associated with severe winter storms, the summer months in Canada and the Yukon territories are somewhat warm, so there is less temperature difference between the source region and the United States. Some frontal fair-weather cumulus clouds may form, but, generally, this air mass is associated with clear, fair weather. It is often called the **Great Basin High** because it regularly becomes stationary over these states. The Continental Polar edges into the Great Basin states, then flows eastward with general wind flows.

2. The Maritime Polar (mP) is a region of moist, cool air flowing over cold ocean currents. The Maritime Polar air mass produces marine influences (fog) along the Pacific Coast and a stable air mass. As the air mass moves inward (eastward), it dries out and relative humidities drop.

3. Maritime Tropical (mT). Both the Gulf of Mexico and the

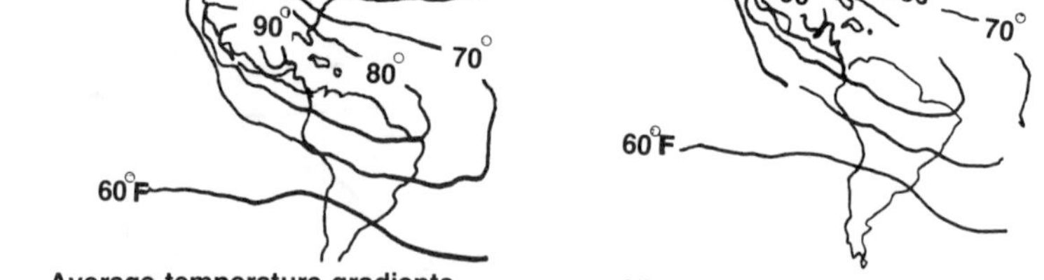

Average temperature gradients July, Northern Hemisphere

High-pressure source regions July, Northern Hemisphere

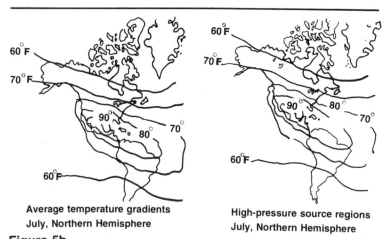

Figure 5h
Northern hemisphere temperature gradients and air mass source regions in July

Pacific Ocean have summertime air masses that are moist, hot and humid. The Pacific Maritime Tropical is often associated with low-pressure instability, bringing in tropical thunderstorms and high humidity into California, Arizona and New Mexico. This air mass is often called the **Pacific High.** The maritime tropical that forms in the Caribbean brings heat and high humidity to the southeast and northeastern states. This air mass is called the **Bermuda High.**

Air masses do have a tendency to change identities as they go from water to land and vice versa. A cold air mass that moves into a warmer region will slowly warm as the air mixes. In summer, the United States is dominated by regional zones of high pressure. Often, these high-pressure air masses warm and become stable, remaining stationary for days or weeks. This **high-pressure subsidence** results in a uniform heating pattern from the surface level on up to several thousand feet into the atmosphere. This condition causes high temperatures, low relative humidities, low wind speeds and low fuel-moisture levels. Severe fire conditions will occur when high-pressure subsidence forms in peak fire season periods (Figure 5i).

As mentioned earlier, air masses are always seeking equilibrium with land and air temperatures as they move from their source regions and change characteristics. The greatest weather activity associated with an air mass is the **front.** A front is the leading edge of an air mass, the first part of it to change as it mixes with another air mass (Figure 5j). The word *front* is generally preceded by either the term *warm* or *cold.* A warm front is a warm air mass riding over a colder

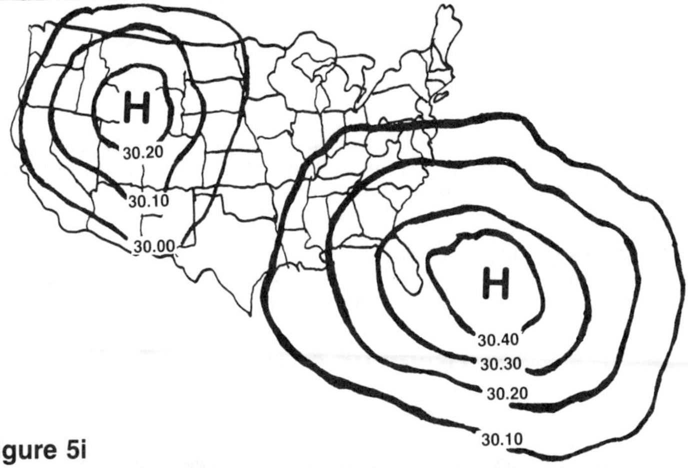

Figure 5i

Regional high pressure subsidence. Stable air flows and general warming trend.

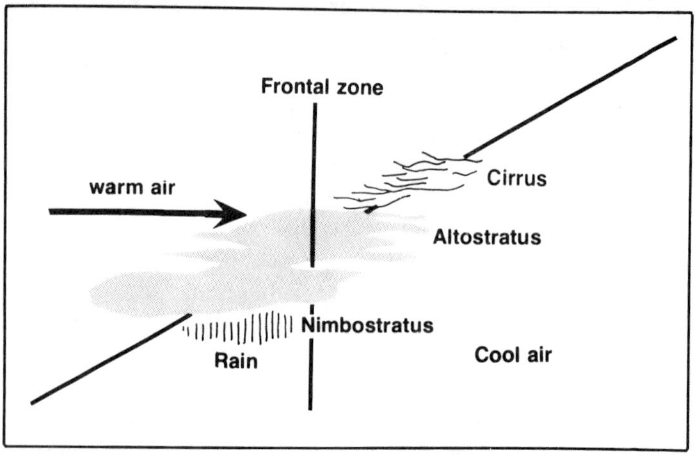

Warm stable air rides slope of cold air. Cirrus cloud series is followed by stratus series. Heavy rains likely behind frontal zone (nimbostratus).

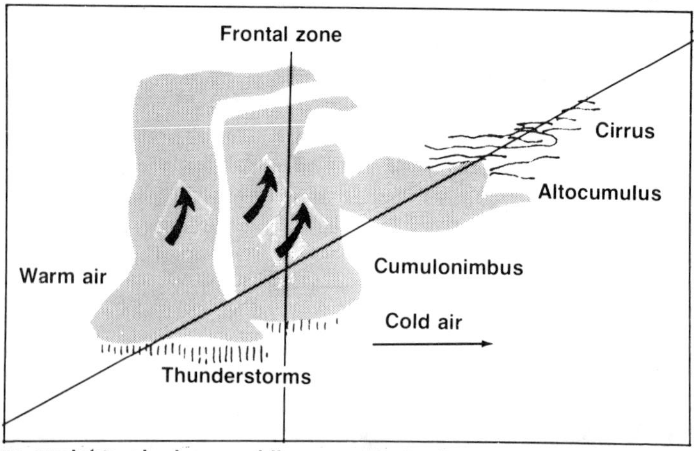

Warm unstable air rises rapidly on cold air slope, developing cumulus cloud series (cumulusnimbus). Thunderstorms are likely.

Figure 5j
Warm fronts (cross sections)

air mass. A cold front is a cold air mass wedging under warmer air (Figure 5k).

ATMOSPHERIC STABILITY

Atmospheric stability is the tendency of the atmosphere to resist vertical motion. The adiabatic process is used to measure atmospheric stability. We will discuss the **dry** adiabatic process here because it is more relevant to wildland firefighting. The word "dry" means there is little or no condensation or evaporation of water.

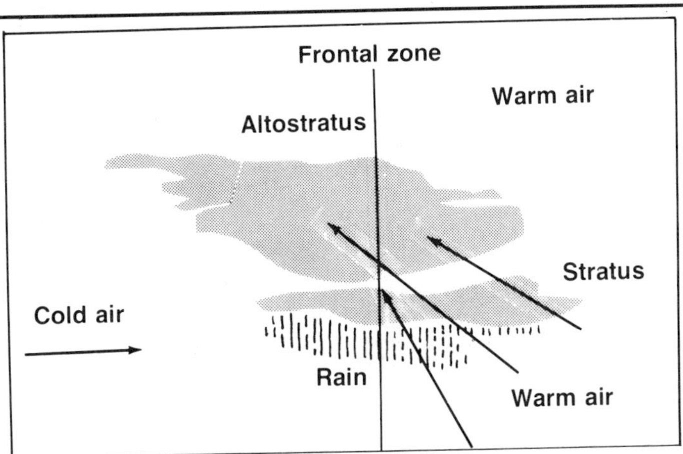

A cold, stable air mass is displacing warmer air. Stratus cloud series. Heavy rains behind frontal zone.

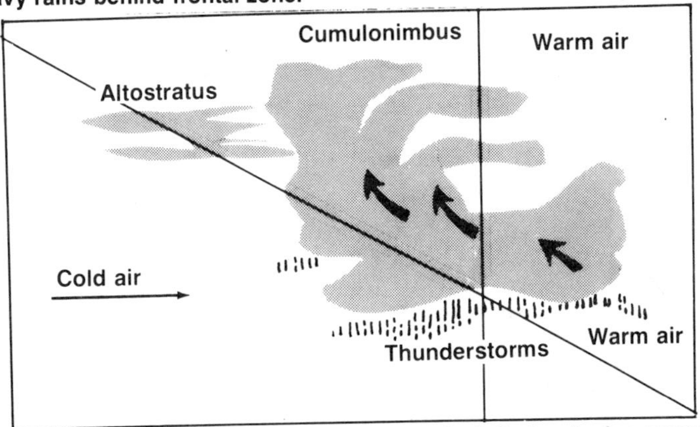

A fast moving wedge of cold air forces warm air aloft, developing cumulus clouds (unstable air).

Figure 5k
Cold fronts (cross sections)

The adiabatic process is when a large parcel of air cools with vertical motion and warms with downward motion (Figure 5l). The temperature change occurs because of changes in atmospheric pressure (Figure 5k). There is no gain or loss of heat. In a dry adiabatic process, air cools with vertical motion and warms with downward motion at a rate of 5.5 degrees F per 1,000 feet.

The relative stability of a large parcel of air can be determined by plotting the temperature of the air at various elevations (Figure 5m). The degree of stability or instability can be visually determined by a smoke column or cloud formation.

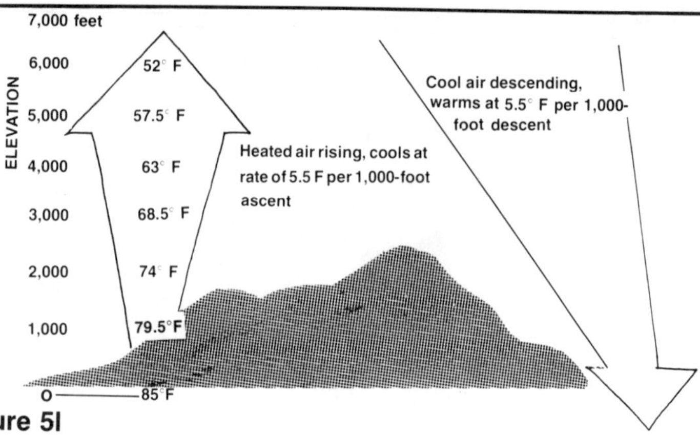

Figure 5l
The adiabatic process

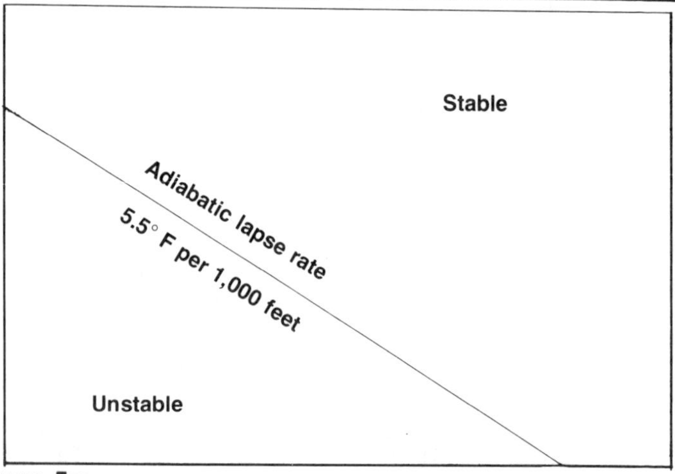

Figure 5m
The relative stability of a parcel of air can be determined by plotting the temperature at various elevations.

Recognizing that the lapse rate may change in each elevation layer, from stable to unstable or vice versa, we can use the following smoke column formations as basic visual indicators of stability or instability (Figure 5n). For instance, if the temperature aloft actually increases, this is called an inversion layer. If the smoke column layers out at the point of temperature increase, there is stable air.

A developing wildland fire burning in a continuous fuel bed under high temperatures with little surface winds may exhibit this profile. Here, the temperature actually remains constant for several layers

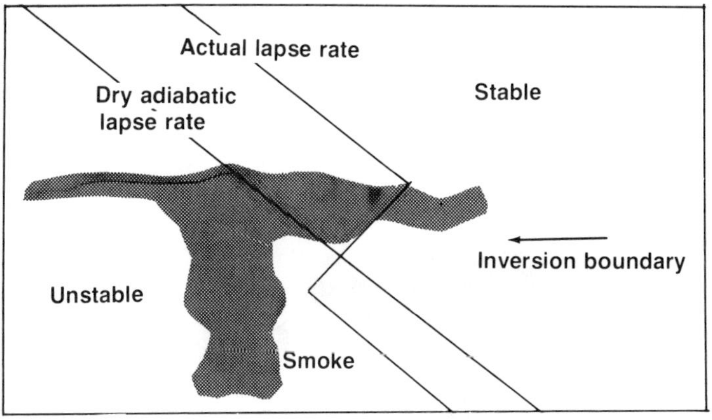

Figure 5n

An inversion layer is when the air temperature aloft actually increases. The smoke column will form stratus layers at the point of temperature increase, which makes the air mass stable.

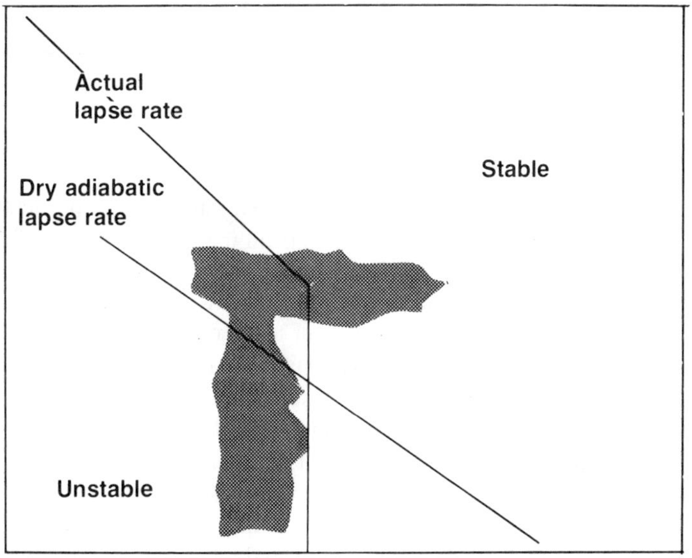

Figure 5o

When the temperature remains constant for several thousand feet, it is called an isothermal column. This smoke profile is common to a developing wildland fire and adverse fire behavior and is also associated with long-range spotting. This is an example of an unstable air mass.

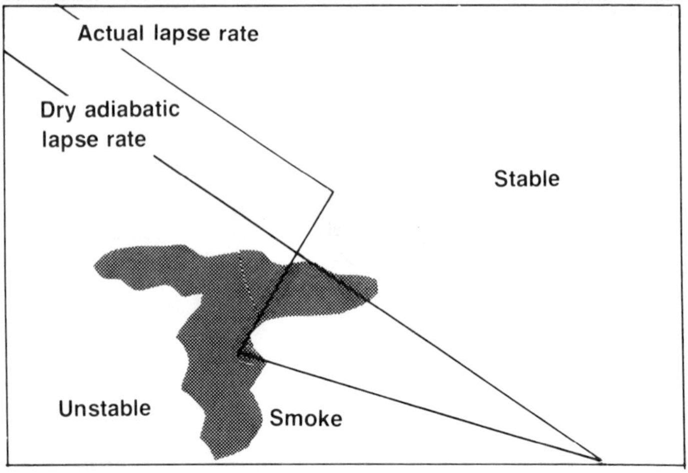

Figure 5p

Characteristics of the above situation are extreme lapse rate, intense surface heating, unstable air on surface and stable air aloft. Depending on winds aloft this smoke can cause short range spotting (under ¼ mile).

known as **isothermal unstable air** (Figure 5o). This smoke profile is often associated with a developing wildland fire and adverse fire behavior. It may also go hand-in-hand with long-range spotting (over 1/4 mile) depending on winds aloft.

If there is an extreme lapse rate due to intense daytime heating of the surface, there may be unstable air on the surface, with stability aloft (Figure 5p). Depending on wind speeds aloft, a developing wildland fire with this profile may create short-range spotting (under 1/4 mile). Here we have an increase of temperature from the surface, continuing for several layers. This is called a surface inversion. (Figure 5q). This smoke profile is often associated with a stable air mass and early-morning or late-evening wildland fires and relative humidity recovery. It is also associated with marine inversion layers.

Clouds can be useful indicators of atmospheric stability. Since moisture is present in the atmosphere a majority of the time, they make reliable visual indicators and should be used. Clouds form once air temperature has been cooled to a point where condensation takes place (100 percent relative humidity). This is called **dew point** temperature (Figure 5r).

LIFTING PROCESSES

Vertical clouds are developed by four principles:

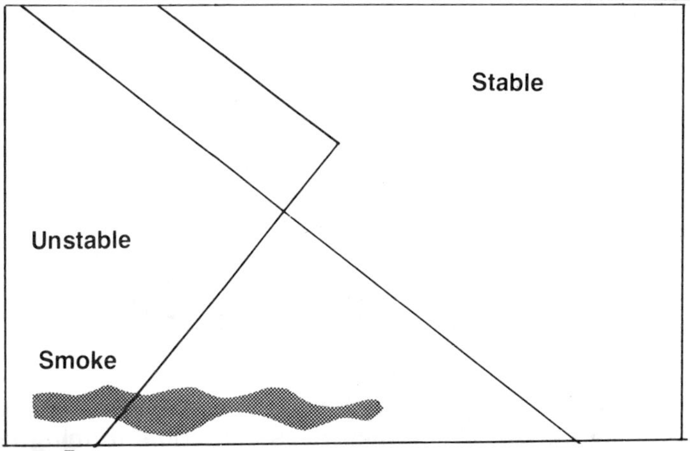

Figure 5q
Shown is an example of a surface inversion, which is when the temperature increases with elevation. Stable air mass is present also. Early morning and late evening wildland fires often exhibit this profile.

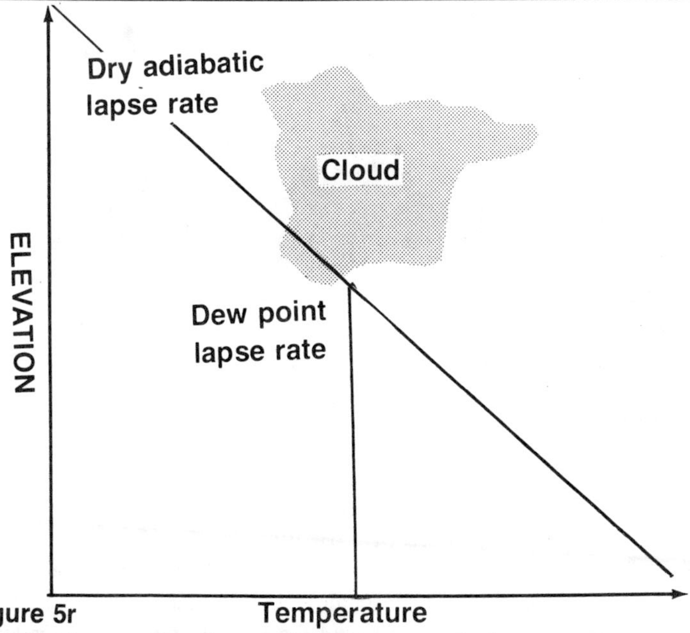

Figure 5r
Clouds form once the air has been cooled to a point where condensation takes place (100 percent relative humidity), termed the dew point temperature.

1. **Thermal**
2. **Orographic**
3. **Frontal — Cold (fast moving)**
4. **Frontal — Warm (slow moving)**

Thermal (Figure 5s). Intense surface heating causes air to rise by convection and cool air to be drafted into areas of low pres-

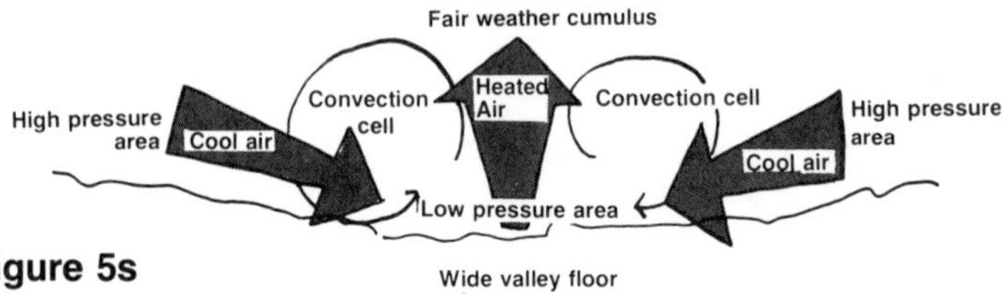

Figure 5s

Thermal lifting is when intense surface heating over a large area heats the air, which then rises and cools forming fair weather cumulus clouds.

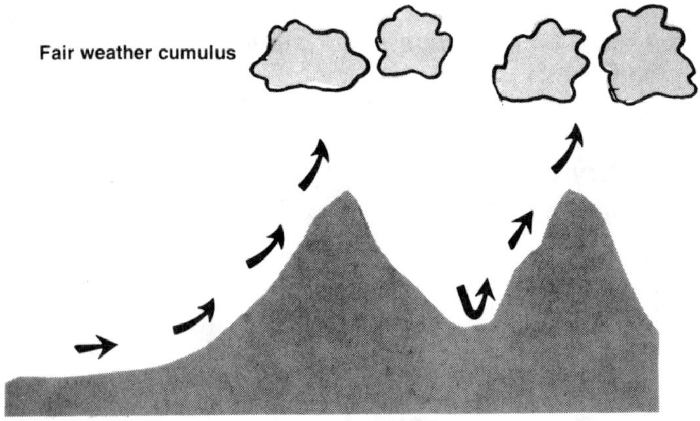

Figure 5t

Heated air moving across a valley or canyon is forced aloft by the barrier created by topography. Fair weather cumulus form once the heated air cools.

sure. Arid areas of the southwest have daily thermal activity. Winds associated with thermal lifting can be gusty and erratic.

Orographic (Figure 5t). Heating the land's surface causes connective currents to flow upslope during the day. Mountains form a barrier, forcing this heated air aloft until cooler air drafts from the lee side and temperatures aloft cool the air sufficiently for condensation to occur.

Frontal — cold (fast moving) (Figure 5u). Cold, dense air

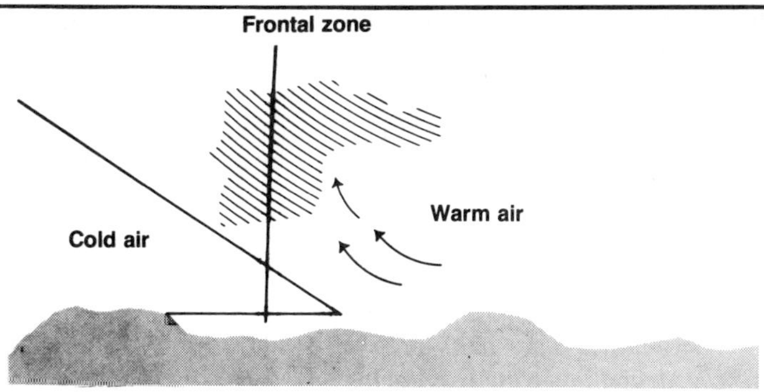

Figure 5u

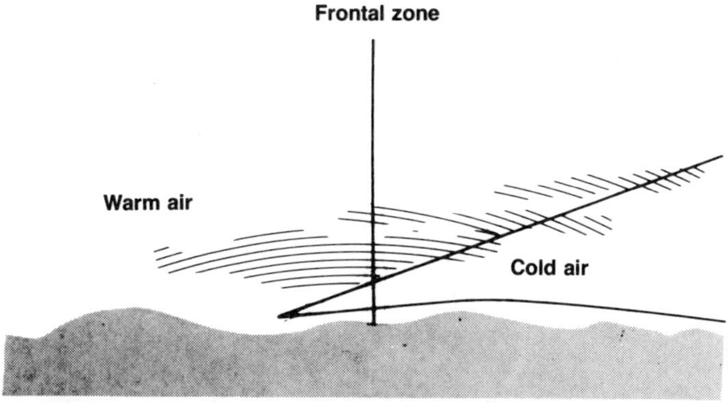

Figure 5v
Frontal lifting is when there is either a fast moving cold front or slow moving warm front.

rides close to the frictional layer. The cold air overtakes the warm air, which, because of its warm-temperature buoyancy, allows the cold air to wedge underneath. The fast-moving wedge forces the warm air aloft. Erratic down drafts in the frontal zone can reach 50 mph, and wind shifts of from 90 to 180 degrees can be anticipated as the front passes. Wind shifts in the northern hemisphere are clockwise.

The lifting process can also influence horizontal cloud development. Unlike vertical clouds, horizontal clouds are not normally associated with adverse wind speeds or wind shifts.

Frontal — warm (slow moving) (Figure 5v). Warm air is less buoyant than the cold air, so a warm front will overtake cold, dense air. Because of the stable, higher-barometric pressures associated with a warm front (clockwise, subsiding air), horizontal clouds are formed. Warm fronts are generally associated with lower wind speeds, gradual wind shifts and a rising relative humidity.

WINDS AND WIND PATTERNS

For the purposes of this text, winds will be classified into three categories:

1. **Local**
2. **Gradient**
3. **Frontal**

Local winds are a by-product of the diurnal cycle – daily heating and cooling patterns. Land masses and water masses heat and cool differently. Dark soils absorb more heat than light soil. Bare soil absorbs more heat than grass. Land masses heat more rapidly than water during daylight hours, but land cools more rapidly than water at night.

Local winds start as the solar influence preheats the eastern aspects (Figure 5w). After the land is heated, the heated air rises, producing a **slope wind.** The slope wind is quite localized early in

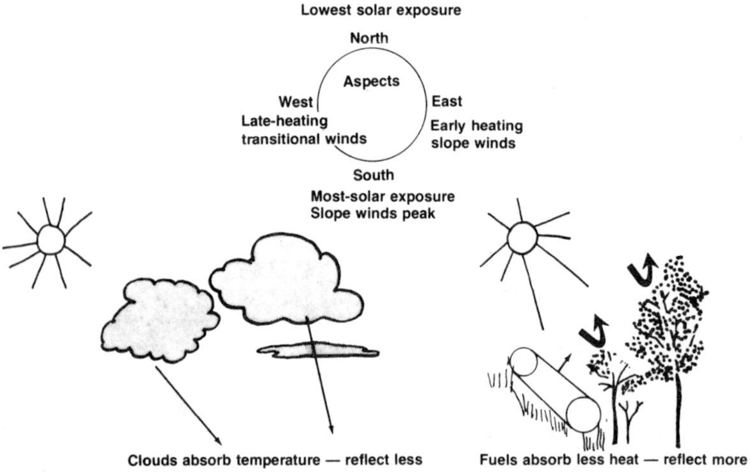

Figure 5w
The solar influence

the morning and may average three-to-five-mph velocity.

As the solar cycle continues, the slope wind influences a greater area. By midday, the sun is directly overhead. The south aspect will influence a large area, including east and west aspect. Upslope wind is now termed **up-canyon** or **valley wind** (Figure 5x).

An up-canyon or valley wind may reach seven to 10 mph. Late-afternoon heating on the west aspect causes a transition to downslope winds and relative humidity recovery. Eastern and southern aspects will be in shadow (Figure 5x). The ridge line cools first, then air falls down the slope. After sunset, the downslope winds intensify, flowing into canyons or valleys. Downslope canyon or valley winds average five to seven mph.

Local winds are very important in mountainous regions where thermal belts actively burn during the night (Figure 5x). After sunrise, slope heating makes convective currents start to rise. The pool of cool air in the canyon or valley fills the void left by rising convective currents and, by midday, the pool of cool air is virtually warmed by the convective cell (Figure 5x).

After sunset, the process reverses itself as cool ridge-line air travels downslope, settling in the canyon bottom. This pool of cool air builds until sometime after 2300 hours, when downslope winds

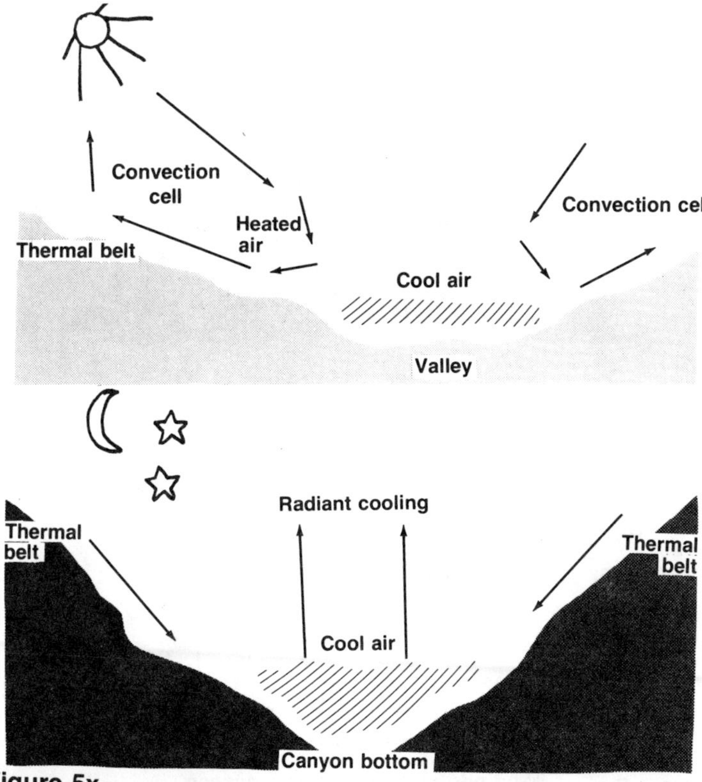

Figure 5x
The diurnal cycle

slow. During both cycles, the thermal belt region (middle one-third) remains active with wind.

Gradient and local winds can be influenced by barriers like topography features and dense fuel types. These influences may create wind eddies and turbulent flows over a fire area or lessen surface winds (Figure 5y). As local surface winds are modified by gradient flows aloft, a smoke column rising above the highest topography feature will fracture in the direction of gradient wind flow.

Dense fuel types may also impact local winds. Barriers such as mountains or broken topography create wind eddies on the lee side of barriers (Figure 5z).

Air flowing on the windward side of a mountain is forced aloft (orographic lifting). Winds aloft increase wind speed on a ridge line.

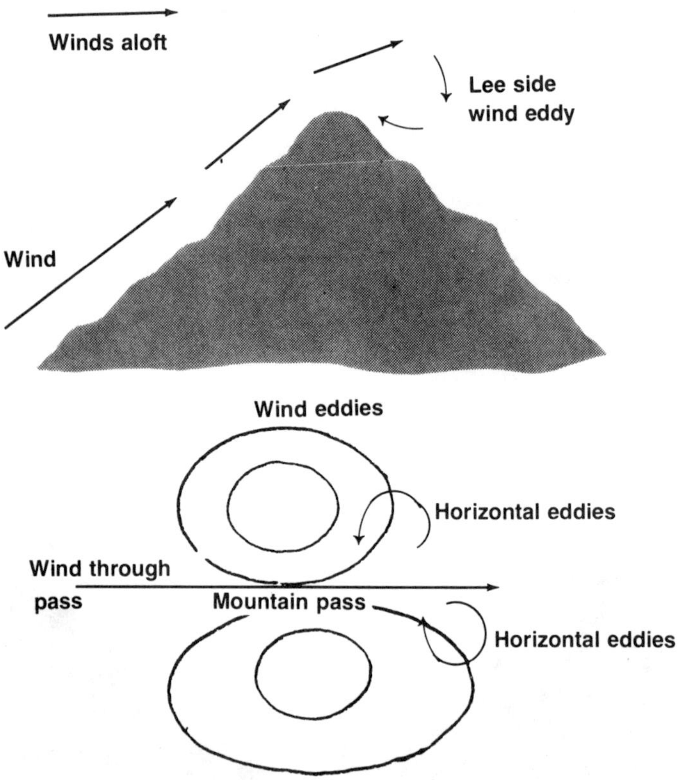

Figure 5y Wind eddies and mountain passes
Wind eddies form on the lee side of barriers.

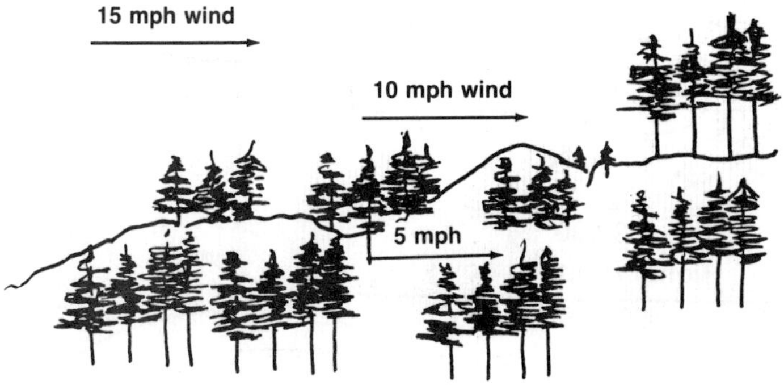

Figure 5z
Barriers and local winds

As air moves over the ridge line, a void is created, and cool air from the lee side flows into the void. Areas affected by wind eddies are microclimatically unstable and gusty.

Remember, air flows from high pressure towards low pressure. Wind speed increases as barometric pressure **gradients** increase. The spacing of isobars on a weather map will give a general idea of gradient wind speeds and stability (Figure 5aa). Gradient winds will modify local winds. Gradient wind speeds can average 15 to 25 mph.

As previously mentioned, a **front** is the leading edge of an air mass. This is also the zone of activity for the air mass. As the front approaches, local wind patterns will change. The approaching cold front is a most important consideration for the wildland firefighter, as wind shifts of from 90 to 180 degrees occur as the front crosses the fire area (Figure 5bb). As the cold front approaches the fire area (Point A), the wind will shift clockwise until the front passes (Point D). This shift may be rapid, depending on the speed of the front. Accompanying wind speed will be gusty and erratic.

In this example, attacking the fire on the right side of Point A will be very risky as the front passes, as this will likely become the head of the fire.

Warm fronts are associated with gradual wind shifts and a slower moving front. Warmer temperatures and lower wind speeds create less of an impact on a fire area. Using Figure 5bb, we can visualize a 45-degree wind shift. Although gusty winds may impact the fire as the front passes over, they will not influence the fire behavior as a cold front does.

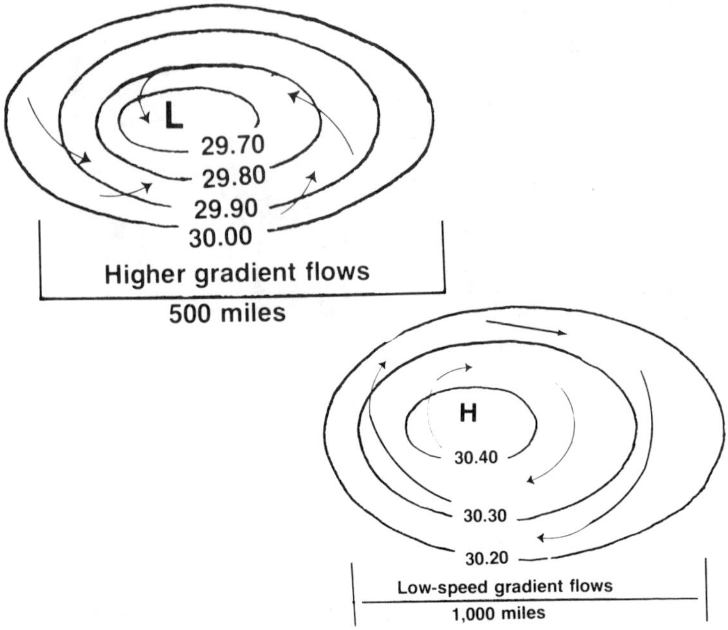

Gradient flow can modify local surface winds.

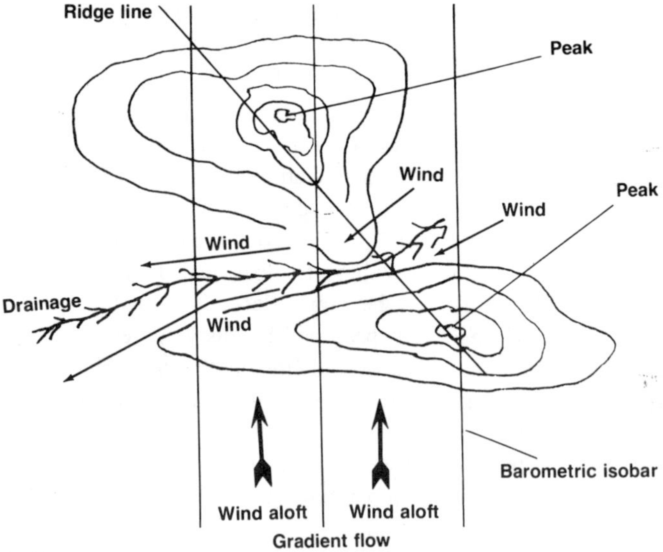

Figure 5aa
Gradient wind flows can average 15-25 mph.

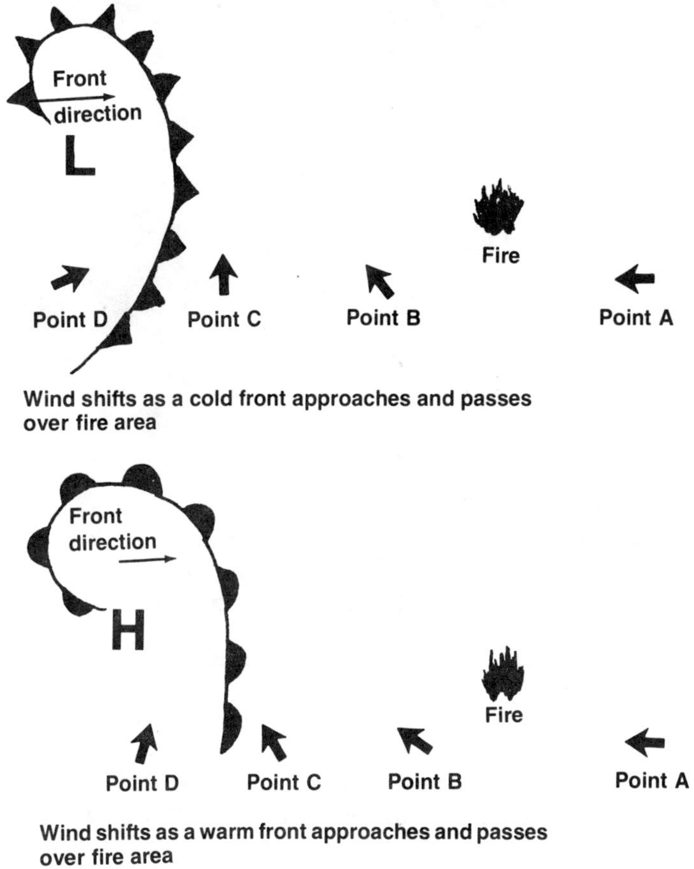

Figure 5bb

Fronts and wind shifts over a fire area.

AIR TEMPERATURE

Air temperature can be defined as the degree of hotness or coldness in the free air. Temperature is expressed in degrees fahrenheit or celsius. Temperature, for the wildland firefighter, is most accurately measured four feet off the ground with the aid of a belt weather kit (Photo 5cc).

Air temperature affects fire behavior both directly and indirectly. The solar influence, which dries both surface and aerial fuels has a direct effect. Local wind movement and mixing of air temperature influence relative humidity – and indirectly influence fire behavior. Solar influences transmit short-wave radiation to the earth, influencing

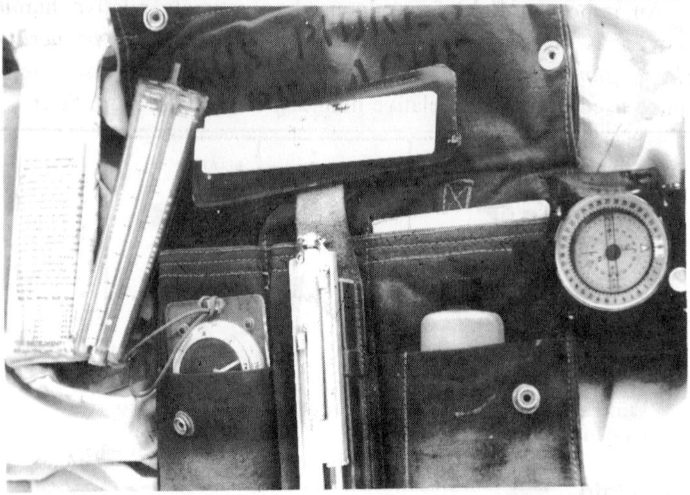

Figure 5cc
The belt weather kit consists of a hand-held wind meter, compass and a wet & dry bulb thermometer set called a sling psychrometer for measuring air temperature and relative humidity.

the air temperature's effect on aspect, fuels and clouds (Figure 5w).

Summertime diurnal changes are also important in regards to air temperature. Dry, arid regions like the Southwest will experience a 40-degree F diurnal change. In turn, the Southeast region experiences a 30-degree F change and the West Coast a 30-degree F change.

The diurnal change is important in relationship to **relative humidity recovery.** Relative humidity recovery is important in most national regions, because it impacts late-afternoon and evening fire behavior and spread. The fuels of the Southeast may burn at a higher relative humidity than most others, but, generally, relative

TEMPERATURE	RELATIVE HUMIDITY
60°F	80%
80°F	40%
100°F	20%

TEMPERATURE	RELATIVE HUMIDITY			
	40%	30%	20%	
80°F	7.5	6.0	4.3	Fuel Stick %
90°F	7.0	5.5	4.3	
100°F	6.5	5.5	4.0	

humidity to 50 percent greatly impacts fire spread.

An important **field formula** used to estimate relative humidity recovery is that *for every 20-degree F increase in air temperature, relative humidity decreases 50 percent*. The inverse is also true, and can be used to estimate relative humidity recovery (Figure 5dd).

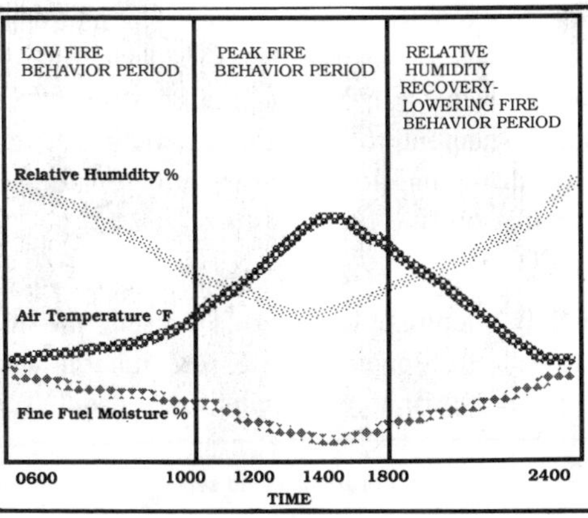

Figure 5dd

ATMOSPHERIC MOISTURE

Seventy-one percent of the earth is covered by water. Moisture in the atmosphere varies by source region (continental, maritime) but is continually changing its physical state – condensing into liquid, freezing into ice, melting into liquid and evaporating into gas.

As the diurnal cycle occurs, the **energy-release process** takes place in the form of evaporation and condensation. Evaporation is a process that changes moisture from liquid to vapor. As oceans, streams and lakes heat up during the day, moisture molecules rise off the water body and are carried aloft by winds and convective currents. These molecules carry with them energy in the form of heat, which cools as they rise above the water's surface. Some molecules, however, will fall back into the water body in the condensation process, once again becoming liquid.

Atmospheric moisture levels are very important to the firefighter. It is vital to monitor relative humidity in the lower atmosphere to determine moisture levels.

Relative humidity is the ratio of moisture, in volume of air, to the amount that volume could hold at a given temperature and air pressure. Relative humidity is expressed in percent (0 to 100). One-hundred percent is total saturation (dew point). The belt weather kit is used to estimate relative humidity in the field.

In regards to fire behavior, 50 percent relative humidity is about the percentage where most fine fuels stop spreading under normal conditions. Thirty percent relative humidity is considered favorable for fire spread. Ten percent relative humidity is considered *critical*.

Relative humidity also influences fine fuel moisture. Figure 5dd illustrates this relationship. During the initial attack stages of a wildland fire, a fire behavior technical specialist using a belt weather kit may notice few microclimatic changes in temperature and relative humidity. However, as the fire's duration increases, ambient air will influence relative humidity and local winds. It's important on a developing incident to monitor microclimatic conditions at a variety of elevations and locations to fully evaluate potential fire behavior influences on fine-fuel moisture.

CLOUDS

As previously mentioned, water is present the majority of the time in the lower atmosphere. Clouds are reliable visual indicators of moisture in the atmosphere (minute water droplets, tiny ice crys-

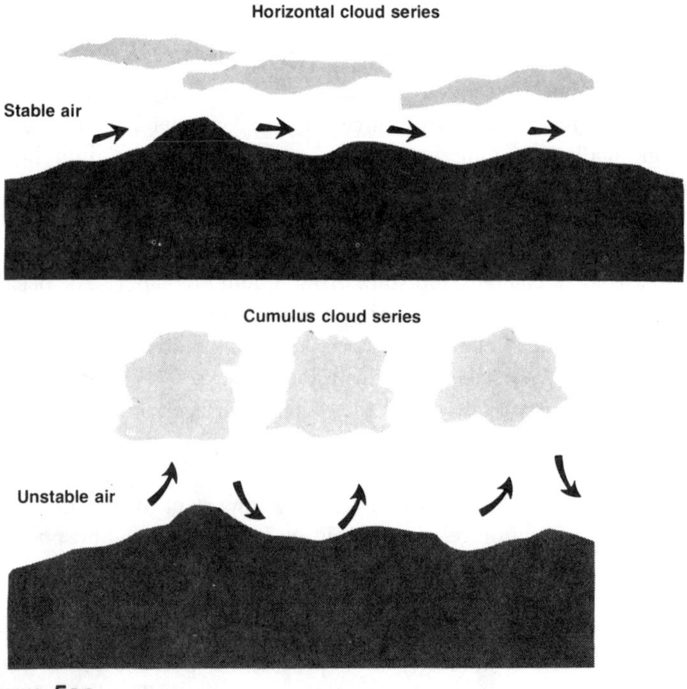

Figure 5ee
Visual indicators of atmospheric stability.

tals, or both). Clouds can also be used with a high degree of reliability to determine stability in the lower atmosphere. Clouds are primarily one of two forms: vertical or horizontal (Figure 5ee).

Vertical clouds are formed by either convection or instability in the atmosphere. The firefighter is most interested in vertical cloud development because it is often associated with down drafts, erratic wind shifts, gustiness, fronts and thunderstorms, all of which influence fire behavior.

The diurnal cycle is responsible for the convective cloud that forms as a result of intense heating of the land's surface in arid regions. The cumulus cloud series shown in Figure 5ff illustrates the development cycle of a vertical cloud. In stage one (fair weather) and stage two, developing vertical clouds are growing as a result of indrafts of warm expanding air. These two stages may not directly influence fire behavior and are hard to visualize on the surface. The third stage is critical, however, and can be visually evaluated.

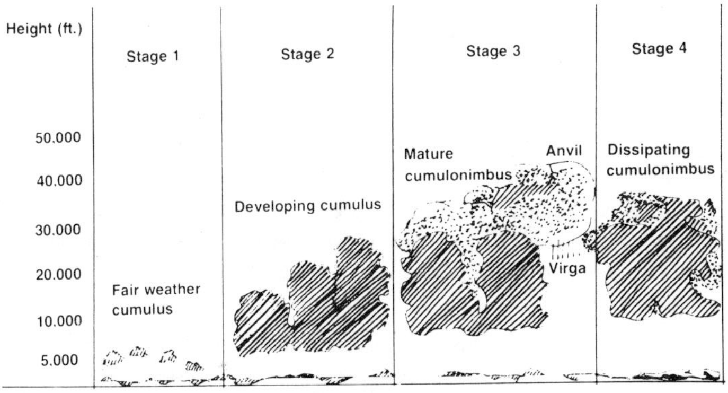

Figure 5ff
Cumulus cloud profiles in stages

Stages One and Two were developed by indrafts of expanding warm air. A clear, well-defined cloud indicates that the freezing level had not been reached. That's an important point to remember when evaluating cloud forms. Also, the clear, well-defined cloud indicates water droplets are present (above 32 degrees F). Clouds displaying this form are still in the developing vertical stage and dominated by indrafts.

A mature cumulus (cumulonimbus, stage three) will grow to a vertical height often exceeding 40,000 feet. This is above the freezing level. A cloud that extends above the freezing level will lose clear definition and outline. Once the freezing level is reached, the cold air plummets as it downdrafts. Downdrafts can often exceed 50 mph, and are usually gusty and erratic. Stage four in a cumulus life cycle is the dissipation stage when the anvil feathers out.

As a general rule of thumb:

1. Fair weather cumulus forenoon, expect thunderstorms, instability and downdrafts by early afternoon.

2. Vertical clouds present over the fire area, plan for gusty, erratic, clockwise wind shifts (northern hemisphere).

Convection Clouds

Convection clouds are formed as a result of intense surface heating over a large area. Heated air rises, expands and cools. Cooler drafts rush to fill the void left by heated rising air (Figure 5s).. Over an arid region like the Southwest, the convection cloud can trigger micro-climatic instability daily during the summer.

A horizontal cloud form is an indicator of stability in the atmosphere. Where the vertical cloud series was formed by convection, a horizontal cloud results from the distribution of air and heat by *advection*.

Horizontal cloud forms are known as stratus (Figure 5gg). One of the more common fire season stratus series is fog. Fog is formed when air becomes saturated and condensation occurs, producing water droplets. These droplets become suspended in the air when air-temperature and dew-point temperature coincide. Ground fog can also occur with high-pressure subsidence – clear hot days and cool nights. The air cools by radiant heat transfer and the ground cools by conduction, causing the dew point to be reached close to

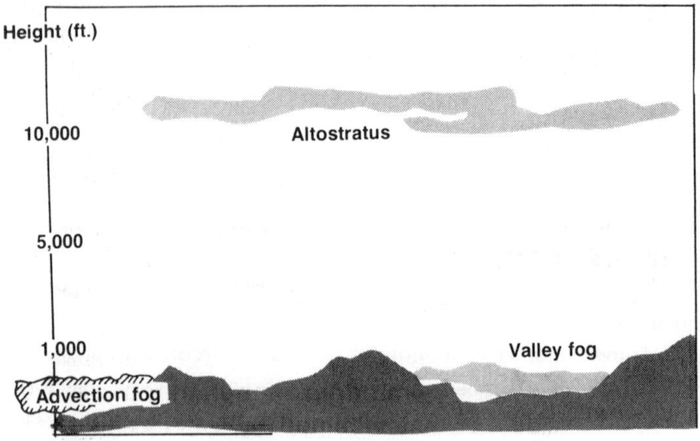

Figure 5gg
Stratus cloud profiles

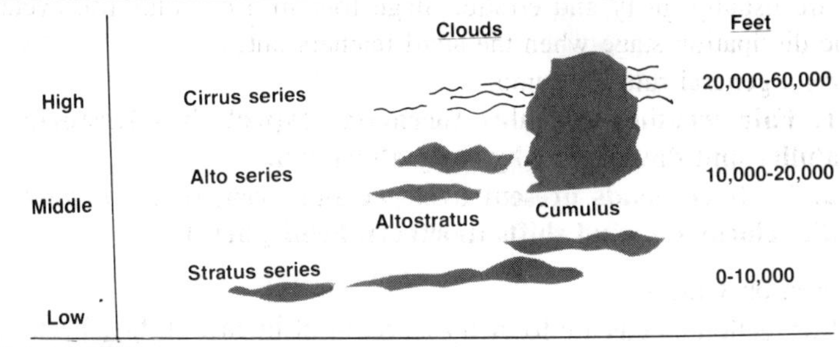

Figure 5hh
Cloud classes

the surface.

Clouds are also advance indicators of changing weather. Three basic cloud classes are found between sea level and 60,000 feet. They include the cirrus, alto and stratus series (Figure 5hh).

CIRRUS. Thin, white, and fibrous. If over 50 percent sky cover, expect a possibility of rain in 24 hours. A paucity of cirrus means fair weather ahead (Figure 5ii).

CIRROSTRATUS. A white or fibrous grey haze or veil. If covering over 50 percent of the sky, rain is likely.

ALTOCUMULUS. Globular masses, small and flattened. Usually in waves or lines. Indicate gusty winds, unsettled weather.

CUMULUS (Fair weather). These develop in mid-morning, dissipate at night. Cumulonimbus can develop in early afternoon. Could mean dry lightning storm, gusty erratic downdrafts.

CUMULONIMBUS. Heavy grey base, ice crystal anvil top. Great vertical height – to 40,000 feet. Thunderstorm, dry lightning a possibility, as are downdrafts to 50 mph and erratic wind shifts.

ALTOCUMULUS LINTICULARIS. Elongated clouds gener-

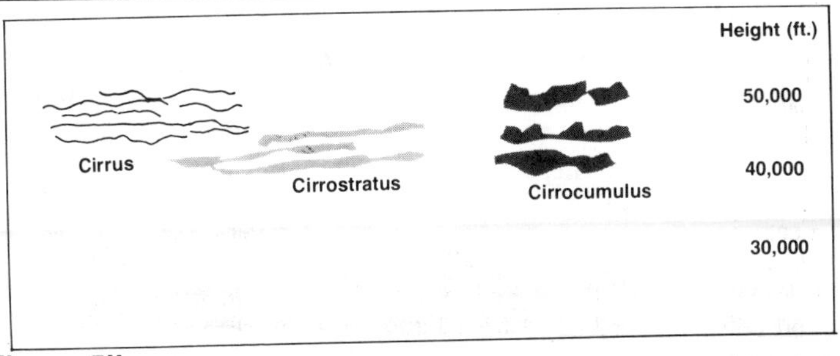

Figure 5ii
Cirrus cloud profiles

ally found over mountains. Associated with jet stream and fronts. Indicate high speed winds aloft. These winds could affect a ridgeline fire and fire behavior.

THUNDERSTORMS AND LIGHTNING. An unstable atmosphere (see adiabatic lapse rate) must be present for towering cumulonimbus to form. As with other vertical clouds, convection is responsible for the lifting up and beyond the freezing level. Heated air rises, expands and cools to the point of condensation, forming a cloud. Condensation, by itself, is a process that releases heat, thus triggering additional expansion of air and vertical lift. Both the initial indrafts and the condensation process promote accelerating indrafts. With continued vertical-cloud development, more water vapor is drawn into the cloud. The level of lifting is important, because for electrical discharge lightning to occur, the freezing level must be reached.

As previously discussed, the development of a cumulus cell has three basic stages prior to dissipation. The mature stage (stage three) is critical for thunderstorm/lightning activity. A thunderstorm can be described as an area of unstable air where one or more mature cumulus cells have developed. Each cumulus cell will have a different life cycle, lasting from 10 to 30 minutes prior to dissipating. It is this short-lived "burst of energy" that makes the thunderstorm so violent and unpredictable.

The Aviation Weather Handbook[1] estimates that *over 40,000 thunderstorms occur over the earth every 24 hours*. Thunderstorms can measure five to 30 miles in diameter. This is important to the firefighter, because the downdrafts associated with the thunderstorm can influence a large geographic area and produce erratic wind speeds up to 50 mph and wind shifts of 90 to 180 degrees. The direction of a thunderstorm's travel can be tracked by following the direction of the anvil on a mature cell.

Lightning occurs in a cumulus cell or thunderstorm when cloud development rises above the freezing level. The process of rapidly infusing air into the cell cap coupled with the condensation process creates a positive electrical charge (Figure 5jj). The cloud base becomes a region of negative charge. The negative charge in the cloud base will induce the positive charge in the ground. When resistance in surrounding air is overcome, a lightning discharge takes place. Virga visible in a cloud is a key visual indicator of a charged cell – and a potential for lightning discharge.

Cloud-to-cloud lightning occurs in the base region of the cloud,

---

[1]*Aviation Weather Handbook, Dept. of Commerce, Washington, DC, 1965.*

induced by the positive ground charge. The majority of lightning discharges are the cloud-to-cloud variety.

The lightning strike has two phases, the **leader** and the **flash stroke.** The leader starts in the positive-charged anvil and works down

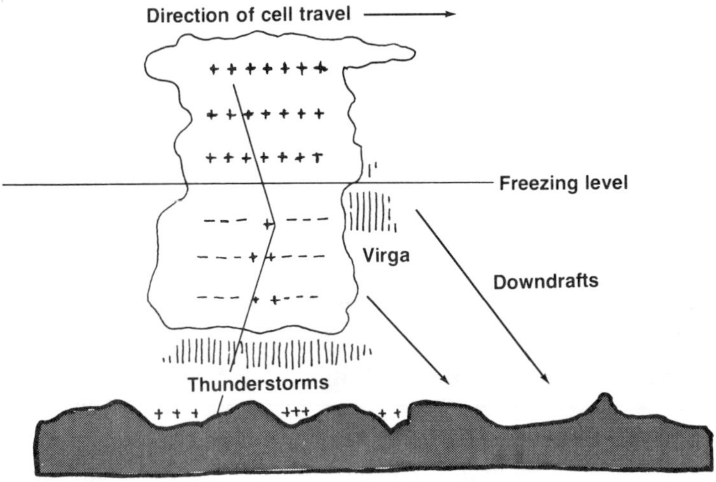

Figure 5jj
Lightning from a cumulus cell

to the ground, ionizing the air and reducing the path of resistance. The flash stroke is a rapid, explosive charge that travels along the path of resistance. The noise associated with the flash stroke (thunder) is an explosion of heated air along the leader's path. It is often termed a *compression wave.* Thunder travels at the speed of sound (one mile in five seconds).

The Southwest and Southeast regions are especially prone to summertime thunderstorm activity as a result of moist, tropical air flows and the Bermuda High pressure system.

BAROMETRIC PRESSURE

The word **barometer** means weight meter. Gravity is always exerting pressure on the earth's surface. If we were to place a one-inch-wide column of air from the top of the atmosphere to sea level, that column would weigh 14.7 pounds. Mercury is used in barometers because it is a heavy liquid at normal temperatures. Using the example just mentioned, the earth's gravity exerts 14.7 pounds pressure at sea level, which is approximately equal to a 30-inch column (29.92 inches) of mercury.

With elevation, as a general rule, you lose one inch of barometric pressure up to 7,000 feet for every 1,000 feet elevation increase of 34 millibars (Figure 5kk).

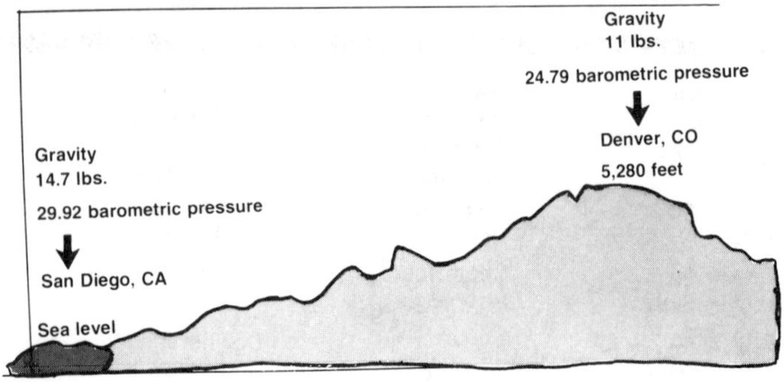

Figure 5kk
Barometric pressure and elevation

The millibar is used as a common unit of measurement for pressure. A sea-level barometric pressure of 29.92 inches of mercury is equal to 1013.25 millibars (mb).

Air masses having varying temperature and moisture characteristics influence the atmospheric pressure. A low-pressure air mass may have a center reading of 990 millibars, or 29.30 inches of mercury. A high-pressure air mass may have a center of 1033 millibars, or 30.50 inches of mercury.

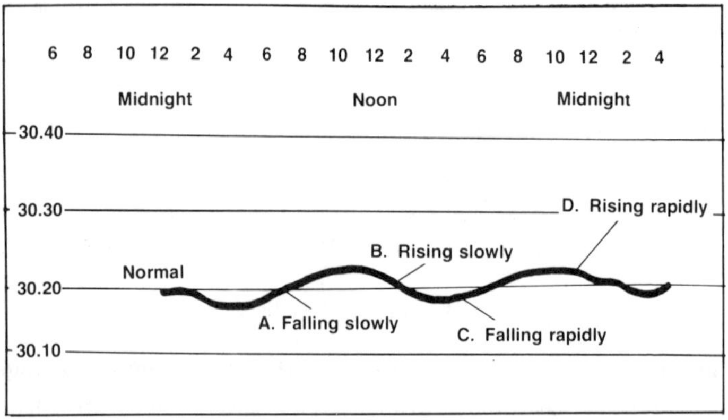

Figure 5ll
Barometric chart of diurnal variation

It is normal for the barometer to rise slightly between 0400 and 1000 hours and again from 1600 to 2200 hours. It is also normal for a barometer to fall slightly between 1000 and 1600 hours and 2200 and 0400 (Figure 5ll).

BAROMETRIC PRESSURES AND GENERAL WEATHER FORECASTING

Barometric Pressure	Wind Direction	General Forecast
Above 30.20 Steady	Southwest to Northwest	Fair next 48 hours
30.10 to 30.20 Steady	Southwest to Northwest	Fair next 48 hours
30.10 to 30.20 Rising rapidly	Southwest to Northwest	Fair, Warmer next 24 hours
30.10 to 30.20 Falling slowly	South	Rain within 24 hours
30.10 to 30.20 Falling rapidly	South to Southeast	Rain within 12 hours, gusty winds
30.00 to 29.90 Falling slowly	Southeast to Northeast	Continuing rain next 24 hours
30.00 to 29.90 Falling rapidly	Southeast to Northeast	Rain with heavy winds
30.20 or above Falling slowly	East to Northeast	Fair, warm, light winds
30.20 or above Falling rapidly	East to Northeast	Thunderstorms probably in 24 hours
30.00 to 29.90 Rising slowly	South to Southeast	Clearing then fair weather
29.80 or below Falling rapidly	South to East	Severe thunderstorms within a few hours
29.80 or below Falling rapidly	East to North	Severe storm, gale force winds
29.80 or below Rising rapidly	West	End of storm, clearing

A rapid rise or fall in barometric pressure in a three-hour period indicates a weather change is occurring. A rapid rise or fall is deemed to be .05 to .09 inches or more in three hours .

WEATHER MAPS

During the fire season, it's a good practice to review regional weather on a daily basis. Most major news services provide good weather programming. Several newspapers also have excellent weather data.

Some basic keys to reading a weather map include:

H and L
HIGH PRESSURE = Good
LOW PRESSURE = Bad

A region dominated by high pressure is generally marked by clear, dry and fair weather and some daily cumulus from daytime heating. Barometric pressures will range from 29.96 to 30.50, winds from five to 15 mph, with gradual shifts. High-pressure areas may be associated with warm fronts and horizontal cloud series.

Low pressure over a region during fire season can create problems in the form of unstable weather and gusty, erratic winds. This condition is associated with lowered barometric pressures (29.50 to 29.96) and vertical cloud series, and gusty, shifting winds 15 to 35 mph veering 90 to 180 degrees. Cold fronts moving across a fire area have been responsible for many fireline injuries and fatalities.

Barometric pressures and winds.

A steady or rising barometer coupled with westerly winds means fair weather. A steadily-falling barometer coupled with southerly winds means rain is likely.

Frontal activity

The zone of weather associated with an air mass is called a front (Figures 5mm and 5nn). In the United States, air masses generally track from west to east. (See Air Masses.) You should review the tracks for your region as a reference (Figure 5oo).

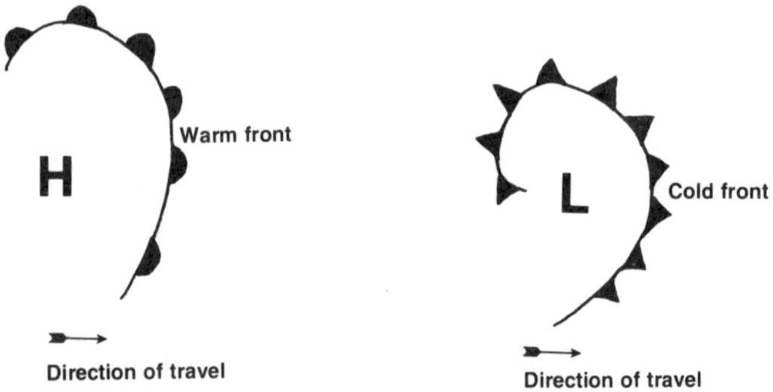

Figure 5mm
Frontal activity

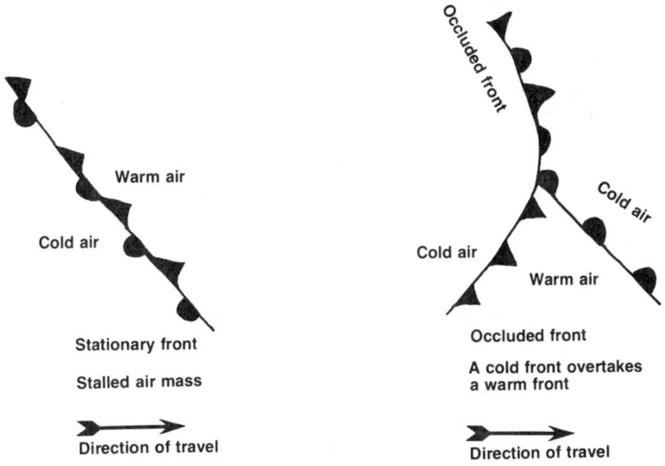

Figure 5nn

Less frequently occurring fronts

Isobar spacing.

Gradient wind flows and wind speeds can be estimated by reading an isobar chart (Figure 5pp). Ridges are a line of high pressure. Barometric pressure is higher along the ridge line than to either side.

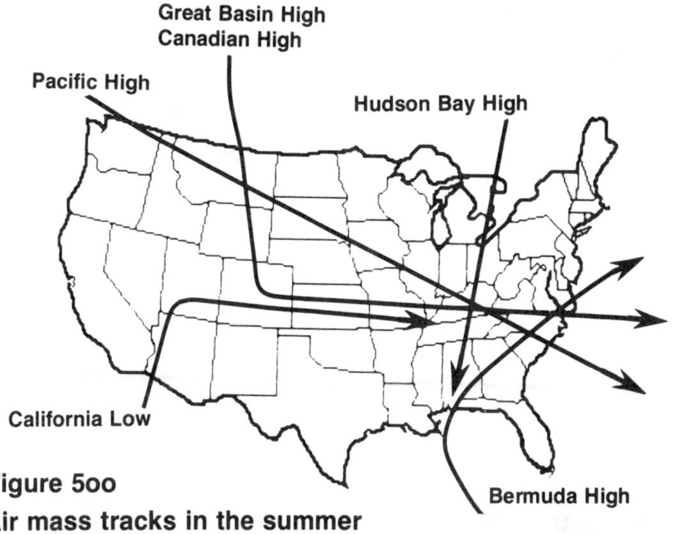

Figure 5oo
Air mass tracks in the summer

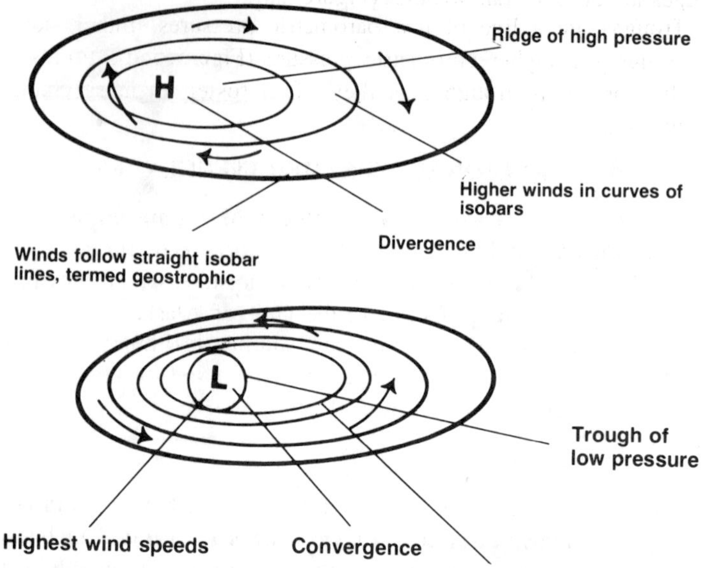

Figure 5pp
Isobar spacing and air masses

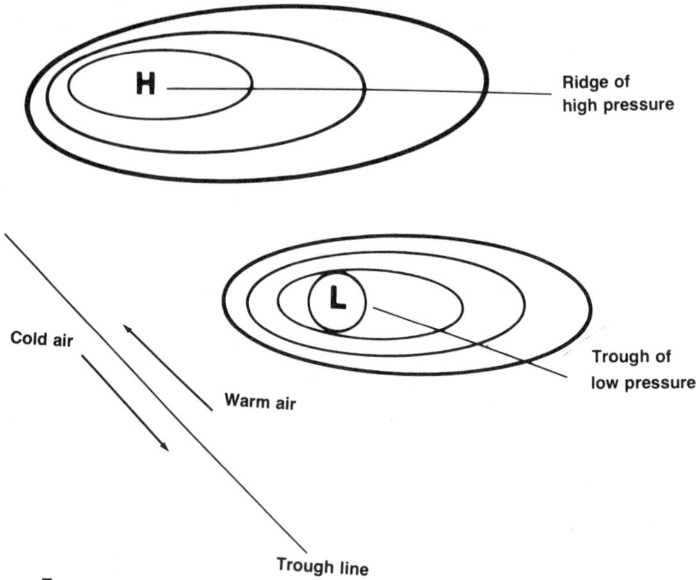

Figure 5qq
Ridges and troughs

Ridges are areas of fair weather (Figure 5qq).

Troughs are a line of low barometric pressures. Either side of the trough has higher barometric pressure (Figure 5qq). Fronts are usually formed in troughs, as they often foster air-mass changes (Figure 5qq).

REGIONAL WEATHER INFLUENCES

Northwest Great Basin and Rocky Mountain States.

The **Pacific High** is a key influence for severe fire weather in this region. This condition occurs when moist, eastward-moving air formed over the Pacific Ocean in the Gulf of Alaska travels across the Pacific Northwest and into the southeast (Figure 5oo). The Pacific High dries out as it moves inland, taking on characteristics of the land mass it moves over. Such an air mass may influence over 1,000 square miles.

Another high-pressure condition in this region is the **Canadian, or Great Basin, High.** Unlike the Pacific High, the Great Basin High is formed over land in northwest Canada (Figure 5oo). The Pacific and Great Basin highs are responsible for approximately 75 percent of this region's severe fire weather in July, August and September. This severe weather occurs as a result of north, northeast or east wind flows associated with both high-pressure systems.

Depending on the barometric pressure differences between the 500 Mb 18,000+ feet and the surface-high temperatures over 100-degrees F, low relative humidities of 10 percent or less and moderate

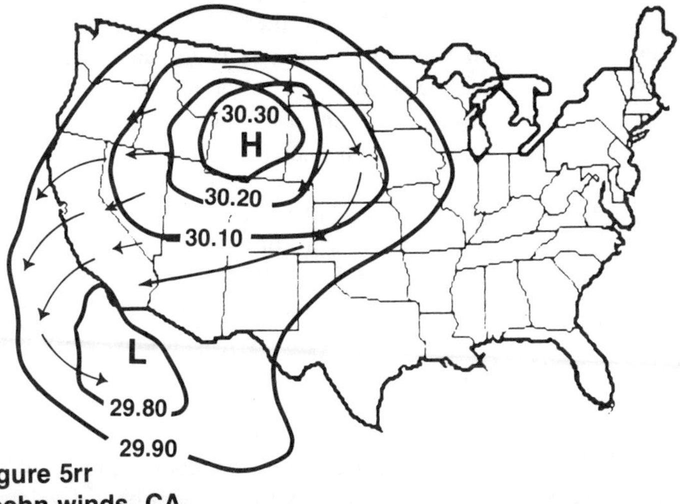

Figure 5rr
Foehn winds, CA

winds of 20 to 30 mph may result.

A severe regional drying of fuels may result if either high pressure system becomes stationary over the Great Basin. This condition is termed **high-pressure subsidence.** The lack of air mixing and intense heating over a large area preheats aerial canopies in forest areas and dries out 100- and 1,000-hour fuels to a critical state. This condition can last from seven to 10 days prior to breaking down.

Foehn Winds (Figure 5rr)

The north, northeast and east winds are triggered by the positioning of the low-pressure system. Air flow around high pressure is clockwise (divergence), flowing towards low-pressure in a counterclockwise direction (convergence). Depending on the snow pack over the region and the time of year, the foehn condition can produce strong, cold air flows or hot, dry winds. Foehn winds are very erratic in intensity and direction. Wind speeds may change from 0 to 70 mph in minutes and directions vary from north to east.

Southeastern States

Two fire seasons impact the southeastern states. The spring fire season is influenced by Hudson Bay High pressures (Figure 5oo) when cold, dry air from Canada and the lake states moves south and east into the region. The spring fire season is associated with gusty, erratic winds.

The coastal plains are also impacted by the diurnal cycle. Land heats during the day and sea breezes move inland and intensify the convective heating process.

The Bermuda High (Figure 5oo) may influence the southeast by limiting the flow of moist air from the Gulf of Mexico. Like the Pacific or Great Basin highs, the Bermuda High can produce high-pressure subsidence and a general drying of the region.

Cold fronts may also create problems in the southeast, as a result of sub-tropical high pressure over the southwest and a well-established low-pressure system in the northeast. This is characteristic of not only the spring fire season, but also the fall fire season.

Northeastern States

The Hudson Bay High (Figure 5oo), introduces severe fire weather to this region. This system produces temperatures in the 60-degree F range with low relative humidities (10 to 20 percent) and gusty winds 12 to 25 mph, these winds produce shifts from southwest, west, northwest and northeast. The northeast shifts produce the most critical burning conditions.

The weather in the northeast region changes rapidly. A fire weather forecaster is a must for any command team on a developing incident.

Southwestern States

This region (including Southern California) has the longest fire season (10 months in some years) and some of the most severe burning conditions anywhere. Most notable weather-related factors:

1. Foehn winds over Southern California (Santa Ana Wind, Figure 5oo).

2. Lightning fires over New Mexico and Arizona.

3. High temperatures, low humidities, low rainfall.

4. Windy conditions over West Texas in spring.

5. Sundowner winds of Santa Barbara and Ventura counties, California.

1. Foehn winds occur as a result of high-pressure subsidence over the Great Basin states and low pressure off of Baja, California. Strong surface-pressure gradients produce winds 15 to 70 mph out of the north and northeast.

Although the Foehn wind is responsible for a general drying influence on fuels and high rate of fire spread, the real hazard for firefighters is associated with the day of transition. The day of transition is the first day when offshore flows subside and cool, moist onshore flows begin gradually returning.

The Foehn wind pattern may persist for three to five days, with peak north/northeast winds on the third day. The fourth or fifth day may be the transition day, when westerly flows reestablish themselves. The transition day is very important to firefighter safety and tactical deployment, as this is when fire spread changes from downslope to upslope.

The return of a westerly flow means downslope fire spread will return to upslope spread. This change of fire spread can impact the ability of an incident command team to aggressively attack a major fire, as the change could come at any time.

2. Warm, moist tropical air flowing north out of the Gulf of Mexico is responsible for producing dry lightning storms over Arizona and New Mexico. Moist warm air flowing over hot, dry desert lands triggers thunderstorms, towing cumulus cells. Arizona and New Mexico have the highest incidence of lightning fires in the nation. May and June produce the highest number of lightning fires.

3. May through November can produce daytime temperatures of 90-degrees to 100-degrees F and average 20 to 30 percent relative humidity. In October and November, under a Foehn influence, it is not uncommon to have 90-degree F temperature and 15-percent relative humidity. This, coupled with critical live-fuel moisture levels, produces peak burning conditions.

4. The jet stream (Figure 5e) influences the spring fire season

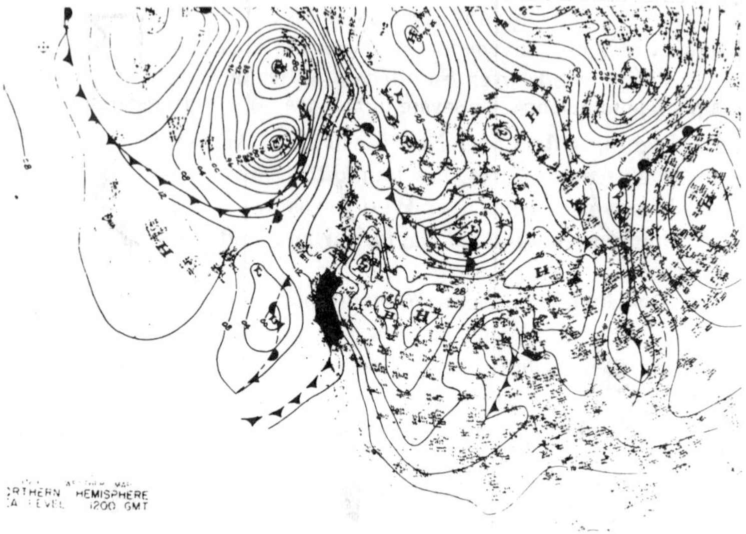

US Weather Bureau, 1981

The hemispheric satellite photo allows weather forecasters to monitor polar and tropical air masses.

in West Texas, producing south/southwest wind flows. One- and 10-hour fuels are very responsive to these gusty, erratic winds.

5. The Sundowner wind, as its name implies, is a wind that intensifies at sunset, greatly influencing nighttime fire behavior. It is indigenous to Santa Barbara and Ventura counties in California. Usually the Sundowner's influence will stop by 2400 hours, but on the 1971 Romero Canyon fire, it lasted until 0500 the next morning. This wind is most often associated with Foehn conditions. A high percentage of north and south drainages will intensify this strong, downslope mountain wind (often referred to as a SDMW).

The Sundowner wind can occur without a Foehn influence as a north wind. This condition, like the Foehn, occurs primarily in late September, October, November and December. A surfacing Sundowner can produce winds 50 mph, with peak gusts slightly higher as dry air reduces relative humidities and fine-fuel moistures.

Although much research and study of this wind has been conducted, the exact reason for its appearance is still not known. However, some research shows a relationship between barometric pressure differences in the triangle area between Tonopah, NV, Los Angeles

INTERNATIONAL WEATHER MAP SYMBOLOGY

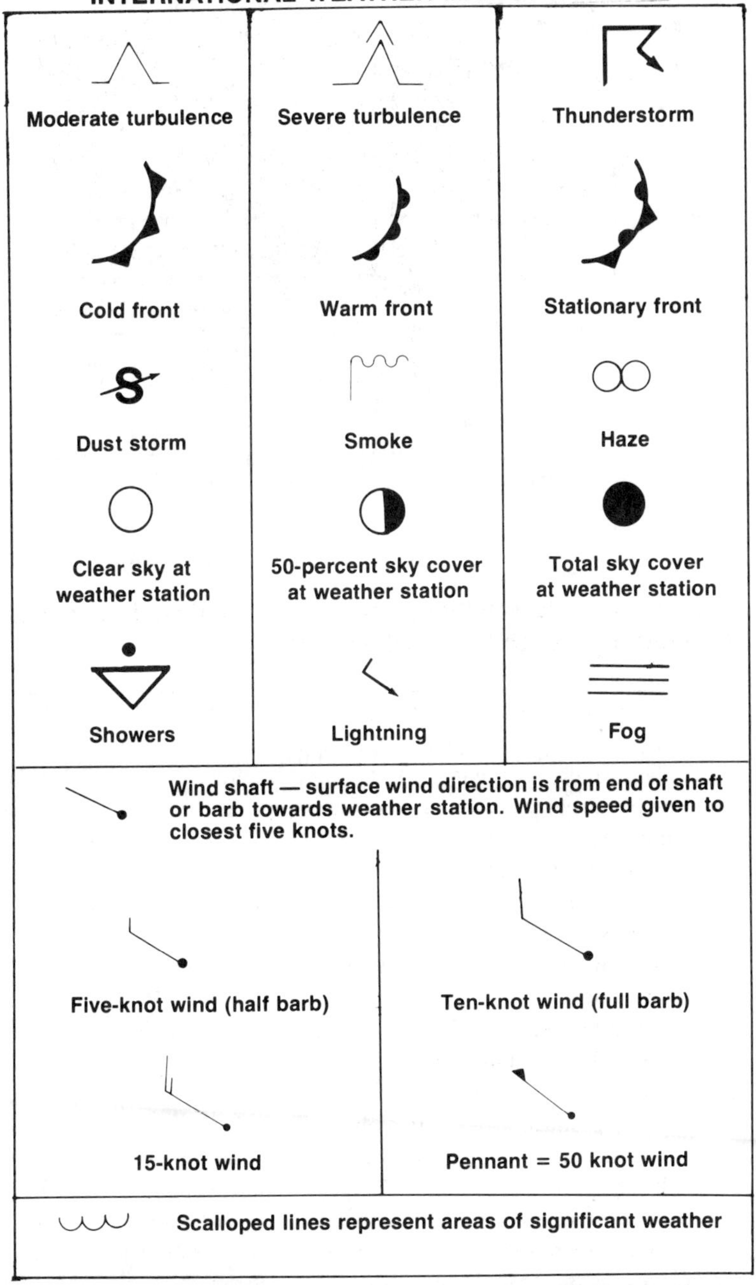

Moderate turbulence
Severe turbulence
Thunderstorm
Cold front
Warm front
Stationary front
Dust storm
Smoke
Haze
Clear sky at weather station
50-percent sky cover at weather station
Total sky cover at weather station
Showers
Lightning
Fog
Wind shaft — surface wind direction is from end of shaft or barb towards weather station. Wind speed given to closest five knots.
Five-knot wind (half barb)
Ten-knot wind (full barb)
15-knot wind
Pennant = 50 knot wind
Scalloped lines represent areas of significant weather

Fire Danger in Relation to Position of Fire on Slope

Time	Factors	Position On Slope		
		Valley	Thermal belt	Ridge Line
Day	Temperature	Highest	Moderate	Lowest
	Relative Humidity	Lowest	Moderate	Highest
	Fire Danger	Highest	Moderate	Lowest
Night	Temperature	Lowest	Highest	Moderate
	Relative Humidity	Highest	Lowest	Moderate
	Fire Danger	Lowest	Highest	Moderate
24-hour Average	Temperature	Moderate	Highest	Lowest
	Relative Humidity	Moderate	Lowest	Highest
	Fire Danger	Moderate	Highest	Lowest

and San Francisco.

If barometric pressures were 11 millibars or greater between the cities, a Sundowner condition could result in Santa Barbara or Ventura Counties.

Alaska

Here the months of June and July are marked by nearly 24 hours a day of sunlight. This reduces the impact of nighttime relative humidity recovery. While, during daytime, conditions may be 80 degrees F with 25 percent relative humidity, at night the temperature may drop to 75 degrees and the humidity rise to 30 percent. Most Alaska fuels burn readily at 30 percent.

Lightning-caused blazes account for 70 percent of Alaska's wildland fires. Thunderstorms are a daily occurrence in May, June, July and August.

The Pacific High (Figure 5oo) can dry Alaska's interior, while cool, moist Arctic air can create erratic wind.

Chapter 6

Fire Behavior

Fire behavior is defined as the **ignition process, flame development** and **fire spread** of a wildland fire. The fire service has adopted the fire triangle to simply illustrate fire behavior (Figure 6a). For a wildland fire to exist, it must have fuel, oxygen and an ignition source (heat). Take any leg of the fire triangle away and the fire goes out.

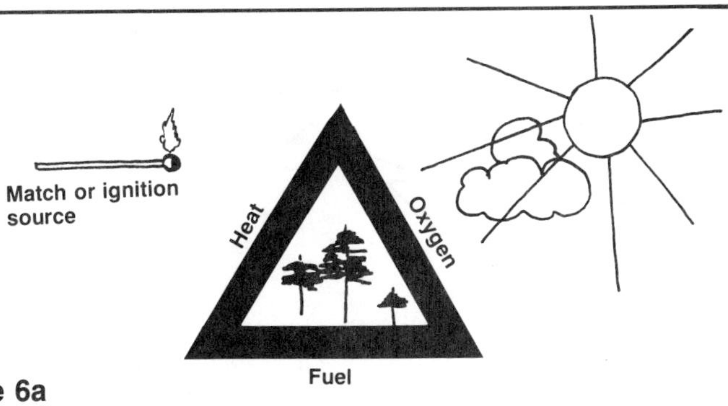

Figure 6a
The fire triangle

IGNITION PROCESS

Most wildland fuels are classified as either *woody* or *herbaceous* (non-woody). Woody fuels are primarily composed of cellulose. Cellulose is mostly water and glucose – the chief components of the cell walls of plants. In addition, woody fuels have lignin and minerals. Lignin works with cellulose to bond cell walls. It has been estimated that 75 percent of woody fuel is cellulose, 15 percent is lignin, and the remaining 10 percent is oils, waxes, resins, turpines and minerals.

Minerals found in plant tissue include nitrogen, potassium, calcium, magnesium, phosphorus, sulfur, iron, manganese, zinc and copper. The above percentages will vary from plant species to plant species, but from the combustion standpoint, the important point to remember is that 10 to 15 percent range, usually made up of waxes, oils, resins or turpines, is the first to volatilize and produce a flammable mixture near the fuel's surface. Sufficient preheating must occur to vaporize water (cellulose) prior to sustained combustion. Even though these elements comprise a small percentage of the woody plant makeup, they produce a high thermal output (BTUs) per pound of material – twice as much as cellulose.

Grasses (annual and perennial) make up the majority of herbaceous plants of concern to the wildland firefighter. Grasses, especially annuals, are estimated to be 95 percent cellulose. Grasses are classified as hygroscopic, meaning they rapidly absorb and exchange moisture with the surrounding air. Once annual grasses cure, the hygroscopic concept makes for a rapid and free exchange of moisture (relative humidity) and air temperature with the surrounding air (Figures 6b and c).

Herbaceous and woody fuels must be preheated to burn. Obviously, the annual herbaceous fuel with hygroscopic cellular structure is more easily preheated and will require less heat to burn than do woody fuel types. Deciduous leaves preheat more easily than ever-

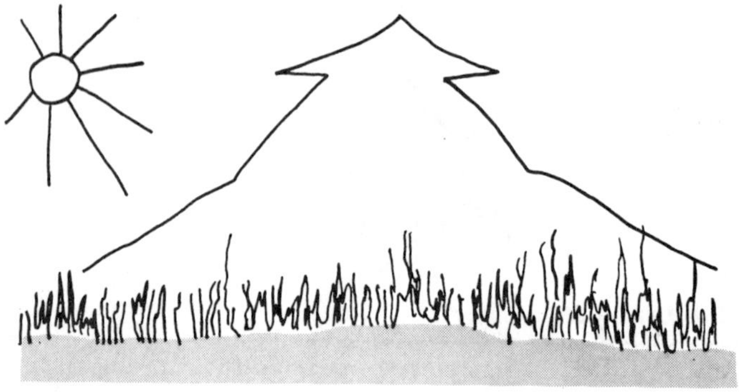

Figure 6b
Annual cured grass hygroscopic exchange — daytime. A rising air temperature and lowering relative humidity means dropping fine-fuel moisture levels. The sun dries out air above the fuel. Moisture present in fuel is freely exchanged with surrounding air.

green leaves; this is because the resin, oils or waxes found on evergreen leaves and needles require more preheating than deciduous types.

The preheating cycle starts with an endothermic process. This is generally associated with the solar influence on the fuel types and their relative position on the ground, as well as the heating of the volatile oils, waxes, resins and turpines after the ignition source has been applied.

Disregarding slope and its relationship to solar exposure, let's look at the surface fuels (layers) and their part in this preheating process. The wildland firefighter is most interested in wildland fuels that are available on the first-flame-front passage, such as fuels that are one-half-inch-or-less in stock diameter.

Three fuel layers are generally found on an undisturbed forest floor. The top layer is formed by free-falling leaves, stems and twigs. Its compactness is generally what we call "fluffy," and it is readily influenced by the endothermic process.

Compactness and soil moisture levels impact the next two layers. Generally, the decomposing layer has been compacted and acted upon by soil minerals, acids and moisture. It may take in heat, but elevated moisture levels makes this layer less available in all but arid soil types. Very little of the third organic layer is influenced by the endothermic process, and it is basically not available. In addition, down-dead limbs and logs over eight inches in diameter are not classified as readily available, although they may exert an influence over the duration of

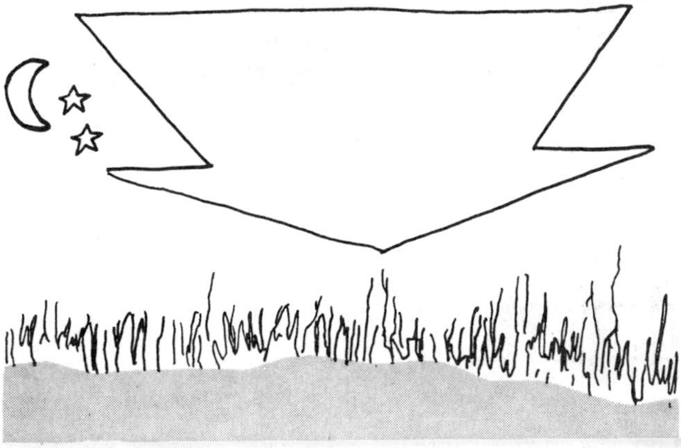

Figure 6c
Annual cured grass hygroscopic exchange — nighttime. Dropping air temperatures and rising relative humidity increase fine-fuel moisture levels. Moisture from the surrounding air is absorbed by the fine fuels.

the fire season.

The herbaceous fuels (grasses) are very important to the endothermic process. The availability and hygroscopic nature of grass, from both the top layer of surface leaves, stems and twigs to the subcanopy of brush or aerial fuels, cannot be understated.

During fire season(s), days are generally clear, warm or hot, dry and long in duration. On a clear, warm or hot day, the sun can transmit radiant heat to the ground, which can mean surface temperatures of up to 150 degrees F (Figure 6d). We seldom acknowledge this extreme temperature because temperature is generally monitored using a weather shelter or belt weather kit, both measuring weather conditions approximately four feet off the surface. Higher surface temperatures advance the endothermic process, especially in the fluffy surface layer and annual grass (all stock diameters under one-quarter inch). Over the length of the fire season, this influence greatly reduces the preheating required in one- and ten-hour-time-lag fuels.

Most wildland fuel types have an ignition temperature of between 400 degrees F and 700 degrees F. By reviewing the above solar influence example where the surface temperature reached 150 degrees F, you can see how this extreme warmth would assist in lowering and preheating fine leaves, stems, twigs and standing grass. When ignition temperature is lowered, we widen the range of possible ignition sources. A higher fuel temperature at time of ignition means less BTUs are expended during the preheating process, leaving more energy for fire-behavior effects (flame heights and fire spread). In other words, the fire becomes very efficient. (Review the topography section in this book to see the impact of slope on the preheating and endothermic process.)

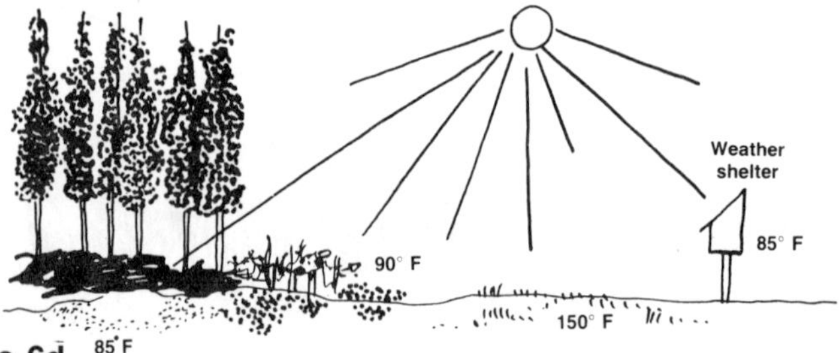

Figure 6d
The effects of shade, fuel types and colors on solar heating. The barren soil may preheat to 150° F. The shade provided by aerial fuel canopy or weather shelter can greatly reduce the solar preheating influences.

As forementioned, solar influences assist the endothermic process, preheating fuels prior to ignition. In some ways, this is the start of the chemical decomposition process of the fuel's living cells known as **pyrolysis** (chemical decomposition with application of heat). Once an ignition source is applied (match, lightning, spark, etc.), volatile compounds move to the fuel's surface and are released into the surrounding atmosphere. Remember, the primary living component of woody and herbaceous fuels is cellulose. Cellulose is mostly water, so a high percentage of these volatile compounds is water vapor. Cellulose is a stable compound until heated to 450 degrees F. At 650 degrees F, rapid pyrolysis takes place. This process involves the releasing of heated vapors and gas, which then blend with oxygen near the fuel's surface to make a combustible mixture as pyrolysis continues.

As the combustion process continues, we find water vapor, carbon dioxide, carbon monoxide, hydrocarbons, tar, resins and ash generated in the smoke. Once free burning starts, live or fine-fuel moisture levels are relative to the percentage of water vapor and combustion. For example, if we take a fuel bed of mixed brush, we can demonstrate the relationship of higher live-fuel moisture (plant moisture), incomplete combustion (not enough heat to drive out and vaporize water in the fuel) and fire behavior effects (rate of spread, flame heights, thermal outputs). The early fire season brush fire with higher live-fuel moistures will produce a fire with more smoke, less canopy burn and lower thermal outputs and rate of spread than a fire burning in the same fuel bed at peak fire season and lowest live-fuel moisture levels.

Once the free-burning process starts, the preheating of surrounding air and fuel types increases rapidly. It has been estimated that forest fuels release between 6,300 and 8,000 BTU per pound of material. In a developing wildland fire, being able to forecast thermal outputs (BTU/sec./ft.) and flame fronts is an important part of estimating fire behavior and making tactical decisions. The incident commander or operations chief must know the limitations of personnel and resources relative to thermal outputs *before* selecting an attack method. The fine composition and structure of annual grass and its relative lack of volatile oils and waxes means that, per pound of material, its heat values are low compared to chaparral brush or pitch pine.

For example, take a developing grass fire, its fuel annual, cured and 12 inches in height, burning on a 40-percent slope and pushed by a 20 mph wind. Fine-fuel moisture level is 5.0. This fire might be able to generate a thermal output of 290 BTU/sec./ft. of flame front. Obviously, the rate of spread will be high, but, in relative terms, most resources and personnel will be able to utilize a direct attack employing a basic flanking action.

However, if we merely substitute chaparral (mixed species), 20-year age class and a 60-percent live-fuel moisture level in the above example, we can estimate the thermal output (BTU/sec./ft. flame front) at 4,200. The woody plant (fine stems, leaves, and twigs) and its waxes, oils, resins and turpines offer more available fuel loading and volatile combustibles than grass. The incident commander or operations chief in our second example should be evaluating the attack quite differently than in the grass fire example.

Down-dead logging slash and old-age-class chaparral in a dense, closed canopy stand make for some of the highest thermal outputs. If, in the example, we use down-dead logging slash of nearly 100 tons per acre, we could exceed 10,000 BTU/sec./ft. of flame front.

As another example, envision one acre (208 by 208 feet) of old-age-class chaparral with a fuel loading of 46.1 tons per acre. Now, somehow ignite the total acre all at once. This could release 737 million BTUs of heat, or the rough equivalent of burning 5,000 gallons of gasoline (8,000 BTU per pound of material, 2,000 pounds per ton). Many an air tanker pilot has gone all out to position a drop exactly where it was needed only to watch the retardant vaporize before it could reach surface fuels. Thermal output potential and the ability to forecast it are very important in regards to tactical deployment of personnel and resources.

In the 1976 publication *Estimating Wildfire Behavior and Effects*[1], Frank Albini graphically showed the relationship between flame length and Byrams[2] intensity (BTU/sec./ft. of flame front), as shown in Figures 6e and f. The wildland firefighter can and should use flame length for field fire-behavior forecasting. It presents the incident commander and/or operations chief with a tool for determining safe operating limits for engine company, hand crew, dozer and aircraft resources. It can also assist in forecasting extreme fire behavior.

Wildland fire thermal outputs are transferred by three methods: **conduction, convection** and **radiation.**

A. Conduction

Conduction is the transfer of heat within the material itself. For example, in a grass fire burning into an area of large down-dead logs, the fire preheats the logs' bark area, then the bark tries to absorb the heat and transfer it uniformly throughout the log. However, wood is a poor conductor, so the transfer generally reduces the heat so rapidly

[1]*United States Forest Service Publication, Int.-30, Ogden, UT.*

[2]*Byram, George, U.S. Forest Service*

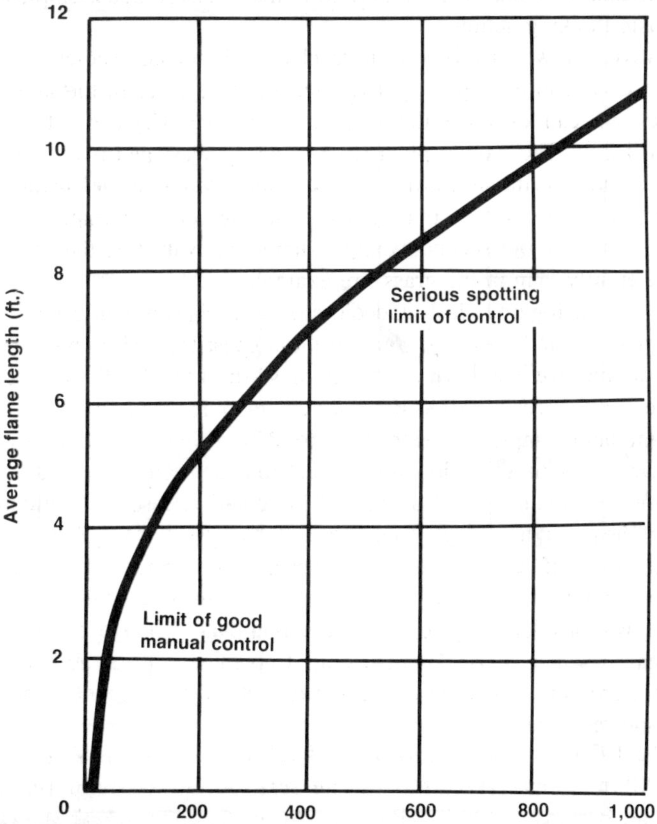

Figure 6e
Byram's Intensity, BTU/sec./ft.

that it's not a factor in fire spread. Occasionally, however, in deep-seated duff and peat fires involving standing trees, the root system can transmit heat, frequently carrying enough heat to ignite leaves and duff across the control line. But, generally, conduction is the least significant method of heat transfer.

B. Convection

Convection is the transfer of heat by liquid or gas. In a wildland fire, convection generally occurs as heated air rises from the burning fuel. This heated convective column will continue to rise to a point where an equilibrium temperature is reached with the surrounding air. A developing fire may produce a cumulus-form convective column over 20,000 feet into the air including the white condensation cap. Convection is also responsible for the introduction of fine leaves, stems, twigs and even wood shake shingles into the convective

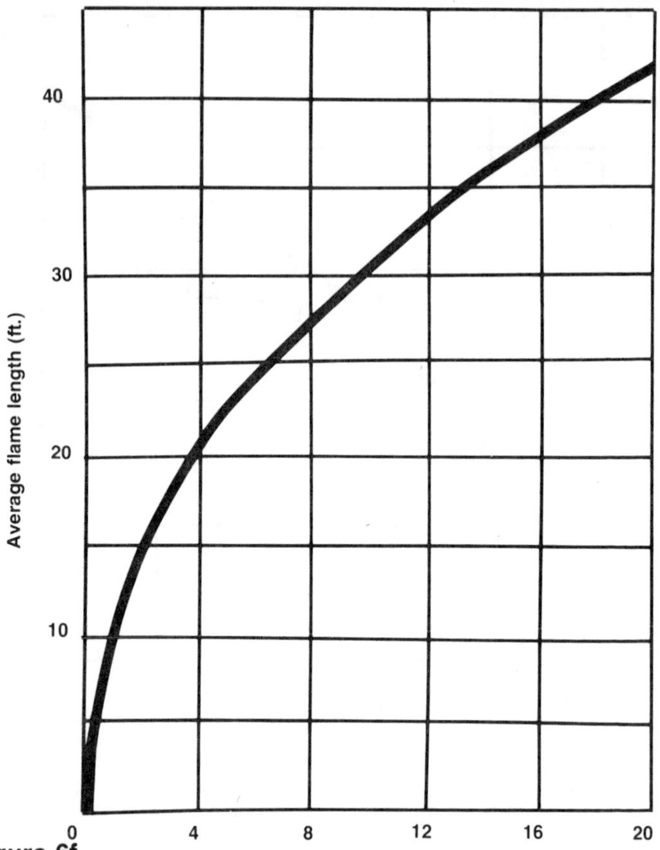

Figure 6f
Byram's Intensity, thousands BTU sec./ft.

column. This addition is responsible for short- and long-range spotting.

C. Radiation

The flame model and burning fuel give off heat sufficient to preheat the surrounding air and fuels. The solar influence on the earth's atmosphere, fuels and water bodies causes radiation heat transfer. Radiant heat transfer decreases inversely with the square of the distance from the fire (Figure 6g).

Radiant heat transfer can be very important, for instance, in a large jackpot of down-dead fuels. The radiant-heat influence transfers heat from log to log, or limb to limb. Radiant heat is also very important to the wildland firefighter, as it is often the cause of many burn injuries, stress and fatigue. The fire shelter, with its aluminum skin, is designed to buffer the radiant heat between the burning fuel and the firefighter

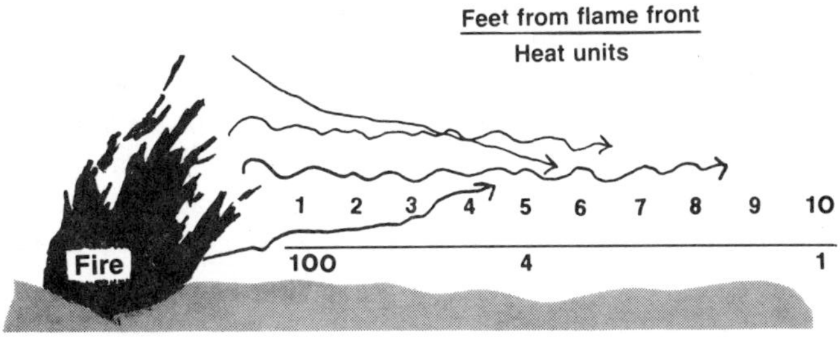

Figure 6g
Radiant heat transfer. Radiant heat rapidly dissipates as you move away from the heat.

inside. Fire-resistive cotton and Nomex protective clothing are also designed to absorb heat and reduce the impact of radiated heat on the working firefighter.

At the wildland fire, we most often see a combination of radiant and convective heat transfers (Figure 6h). Narrow canyons are often associated with area ignition. This fire behavior effect is a by-product of convective heat (preheating ambient air) and radiant heat (preheating adjacent fuel canopies and surface fuels).

When a fire burns in a grass and timber mix, convective heat preheats the aerial canopies, while radiant heat preheats ground and

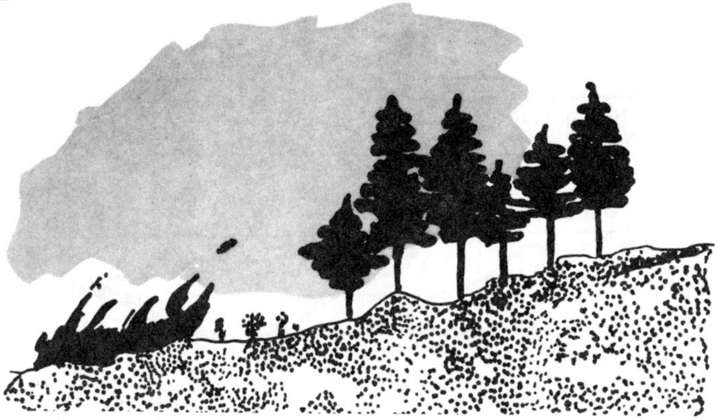

Figure 6h
Slope- and wind-driven fires use convective and radiant heat transfers to preheat fuel canopies in front of the fire. The smoke column provides a good medium for heated convective currents to reach aerial canopies. The flame front provides radiant heat transfer.

surface fuels. A fire that burns on a slope creates a horizontal flame model. In this case, convection also preheats aerial canopies and radiant heat preheats ground and surface fuels. The basic difference between these two fires is that the area preheated in the slope model example is much greater than that of the grass timber mix on level topography. These are important examples, because heat transfer and the influence it has on the available fuels contribute to rate of spread.

Other factors that influence heat transfer and fire behavior.

1. **Fuel moisture and fuel temperature levels**
2. **Nighttime inversions**
3. **Northern aspects**

Fuel Moisture

As mentioned in the fuels section of this book, we are very interested in fine-fuel moisture (FFM) of one- and 10-hour time-lag fuels and live fuel moisture levels (LFM) of 100- and 1,000-hour time lag fuels. Four percent is a critical fine-fuel moisture level and, in live fuels such as chaparral species, 60 to 80 percent is critical. The plotting of fuel moisture levels is helpful in projecting fire behavior effects (Figure 6i).

We are also very interested in the fuel moisture content of dead leaves, stems and twigs – fuels from ¼ to one inch in diameter. These are often called 10-hour time lag fuels and may be suspended in fuel canopies or deposited on the ground. Unlike live fuels, which are impacted by changes in soil moisture, dead fuels are impacted by

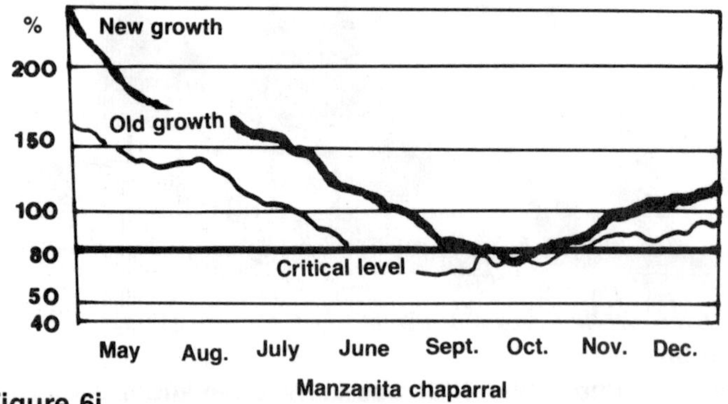

Figure 6i
Live fuel moisture-level plotting. Manzanita chaparral reaches a critical live-fuel moisture level at 80 percent. A fire burning in this fuel type in June or July will react very differently than in August or September.

relative humidity (moisture in the surrounding air). As mentioned earlier, fine fuels such as annual grass are hygroscopic and freely exchange temperature and relative humidity with the surrounding air. These fine dead fuels are classified as one-hour-time-lag fuels because changes in air temperature and relative humidity will impact the fine-fuel moisture within 20 to 60 minutes.

With larger limbs, branches and logs – fuels from three to eight inches in diameter – this change takes from hours to days, depending on the diameter of the fuel.

If a fire burns into an area of large-diameter dead limbs and logs, radiatc and convective heat are needed to drive out moisture near the fuel's surface and convert it to steam. Moisture is converted to steam at 212 degrees F. The kindling point is reached at 400 to 700 degrees F. Raising the temperature of water (moisture) one degree fahrenheit takes three times as much heat as is needed to raise the temperature of wood one degree fahrenheit.

For dead fuels and fine fuels, fuel moisture content is important in relationship to rate of spread. A fuel moisture level of 25 percent is said to be the level of extinction. At 25 percent, the heat source is generally insufficient to drive out enough water vapor to continue to support combustion. To illustrate this, all other factors being equal and assuming the level of extinction is 25 percent (which equals a rate of spread factor of one), we can show that reducing fuel moisture increases rate of spread:

FUEL MOISTURE[3] CONTENT	RATE OF SPREAD FACTOR
25%	1
20%	2
15%	3
10%	7
5%	20
3%	32

From the above comparisons, assuming all outside factors stay the same, we can determine that a wildland fire burning in a fuel type with a 10-percent fuel moisture level will spread seven times faster than in a fuel type with a 25-percent fuel moisture level.

Fuel temperature affects fire behavior in two ways. First, it changes the number of heat units required to raise the temperature of fuel to its kindling point. Second, it determines the rate at which the fuel will burn once ignited. More heat units are required to raise the temperature to the kindling point in a fuel type with a temperature of 60 degrees F than if that same fuel was preheated to 120 degrees F.

[3]*United States Forest Service, Intermediate Fire Behavior Training, Region 5, Boise Interagency Fire Center, ID, 1975.*

Air temperature and fuel temperatures are always trying to reach an equilibrium. Air temperature near the ground is a good indicator of fuel temperature, as this air gets its warmth through contact with the ground and the vegetation cover. Cool fuels in contact with warmer air will tend to become warmer. Cool air passing over warm fuels will absorb some of the heat through convection, thus raising air temperature.

The following graph illustrates that fuel temperatures below 60 degrees F will be accompanied by correspondingly-cool air temperatures and high relative humidity. (It gives 60 degrees F a rate of spread factor of one.)

FUEL TEMPERATURE	RATE OF SPREAD FACTOR
60°F	1
61°F - 70°F	1.2
71°F - 80°F	1.3
81°F - 90°F	1.4
91°F - 100°F	1.5
Over 100°F	2.0

A wildland fire burning in short grass over light soil could produce a surface fuel temperature of 100 degrees F. This would spread at twice the rate than if the fuel temperature was 60 degrees F.

Nighttime inversions

Nighttime inversions are produced by cool air that settles and

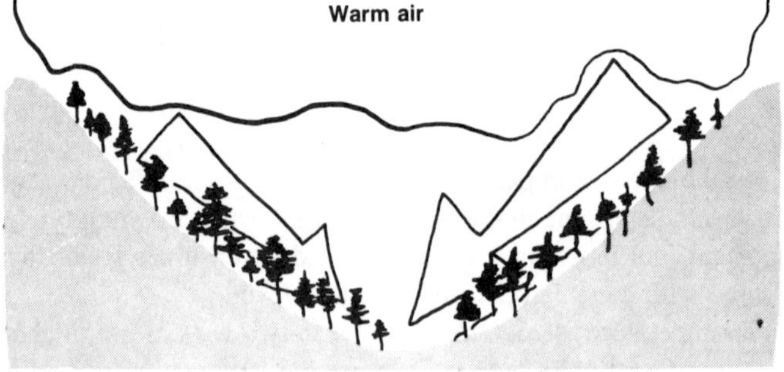

Figure 6j
Nighttime inversion. Under a stable air mass where there is little air mixing, cool air flows downslope to pool in well-defined canyon bottoms. Fire behavior will lessen in the canyon bottom, but the thermal belt may remain active.

pools in defined canyons and valleys where little or no air mixing is taking place. As this cool air accumulates, it becomes stagnant and is overlaid by a warmer air layer (Figure 6j).

The higher relative humidity associated with cooling air promotes a rise in fine-fuel moisture levels. Fires often burn very slowly under this inversion. Above the inversion ceiling, it's warmer, and fires can still burn aggressively. In mountainous areas, this ceiling is often located in the thermal belt (middle one-third of the slope).

Northern aspects

The limited solar exposure and higher fuel-moisture levels found on north slopes will retard heat transfer. Northern aspects have the lowest average air temperature, highest average relative humidity, lowest average wind speed and slowest fuel curing. Live fuel loading is usually very heavy (tons per acre), but the lack of annual grasses and high fuel moisture levels on this aspect keeps most fires small in size.

In well-defined narrow canyons, the combined effects of radiant and convective heat can change fire behavior. Radiant heat preheats surrounding fuels and air currents. This warms cooler air drafts from the canyon bottom, creating a heated convective air cell. The radiant heat and heated convective air cell raise the temperature of ambient air and unburned fuels on the opposite slope. The convective air currents form a cap over the canyon. When buoyant heated air reaches the level of this air (inversion boundary) it cannot go any higher. This cap will allow radiant heat and convective heat to continue to influence air and fuel temperatures in the canyon. If the heat continues to build, however, the cap may be broken, allowing a fresh oxygen supply to reach the fire – which may change fire behavior very quickly.

FLAME DEVELOPMENT

Up to this point, we have discussed the ignition and preheating processes necessary to provide the fuel leg of the fire triangle. Now we will discuss flame development. This process takes place as more fuel becomes available. There are three basic flame models used to describe flame development.

1. No wind, no slope. This model is characterized by a vertical flame that is impacted by radiant or convective heat transfers in only a limited way. The no-wind, no-slope flame model is characteristic of an early-morning fire or late-evening grass fire burning with high humidity, no wind and no slope. A typical fire shape for this model is is shown in Figure 6k. The fire moves out in approximately-equal distances from the point of ignition.

A fire situation can develop when a vertical flame model (ground

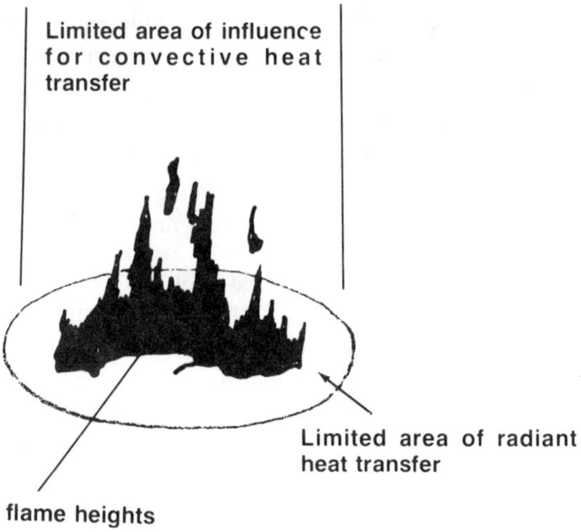

Figure 6k
Flame development. The no-wind, no-slope flame model.

fire) moves under an aerial canopy and preheats it until it becomes a crown fire. This increase in flame length and thermal output could be sufficient enough to step up indrafts of air and rate of spread. The same situation could also occur when a ground fire creeps into a large area of down-dead slash or tree limbs. This tremendous addition of available

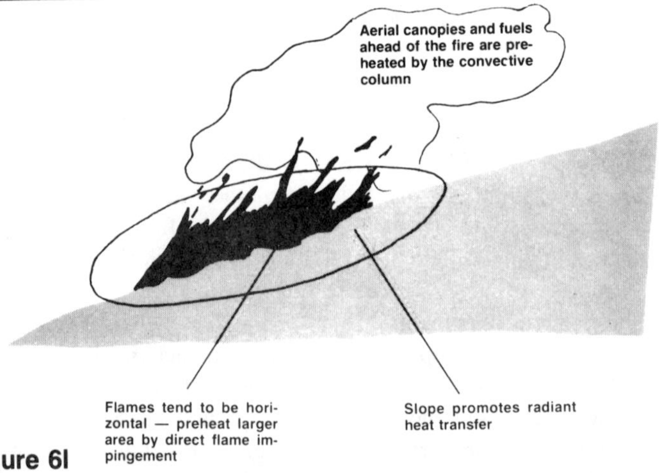

Figure 6l
Flame development. The slope-driven flame model. The change from a vertical to a horizontal flame is important to radiant heat transfer.

fuel could speed up air intake and thermal outputs enough to increase rate of spread.

2. Slope (Figure 6l). The no-wind, no-slope flame model exhibits limited ability to utilize convective and radiant heat transfers to preheat surrounding fuels because it is a vertical flame model. However, the slope-driven flame model has a flame positioned more horizontally than vertically. This difference extends the radiant and convective heat transfers to preheat more fuel ahead of the fire. The slope-driven fire will develop an elliptical shape with a narrow head.

3. Wind-driven model. This model is characterized by a horizontal flame. This horizontal flame allows maximum radiate and convective heat transfer. Wind-driven fires are often associated with **mass flame transport** and **peak thermal pulse** (Figure 6m).

Mass flame transport is a visible indicator of superheated gases in the lower convective column actually flashing over. This requires tremendous aerial temperatures. In peak fire-season conditions, low live-fuel moisture levels, coupled with old-age-class brush, can cause mass flame transport well into the convective column. This mass flame transport phenomenon is also associated with large flame fronts, tremendous indrafts, peak thermal pulse and a free convective state.

The wind-driven flame model can also create some tactical deployment problems, such as:

A. **Head and hot flank too active. Thermal outputs exceed human tolerance. Thermal outputs, convective column exceed aircraft's ability to aerially apply retardant or water. Visibility in the area of the head and hot flank is limited.**

B. **Short- and long-range spotting likely. More fuel is becoming**

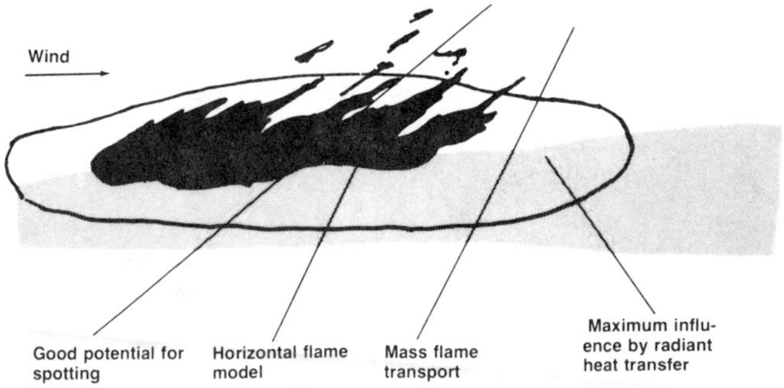

Figure 6m
Flame development. The wind-driven model. Most often associated with extreme fire behavior. Horizontal flame provides maximum influences for radiant, convective heat transfers.

available each additional minute of the burn.

C. Wind-driven, horizontal flames often burn through a fuel bed in stages and cycles. Ground fuels, canopy fuel, aerial fuels or any combination may be involved. (Re-burns possible.)

D. Large unburned islands (fingers) of fuel will be left. Many times, burnout or backfiring must be done to ensure the control line will hold.

For silhouettes of wind-driven models, see Figure 6n. Note that at 25 mph, there's no backing of rate of spread, only forward motion.

A fire that burns in a combination wind and slope model can also create problems by combining slope (horizontally-influenced flame) and wind (horizontal-flame) effects. Unlike the slope-driven model, which has a narrow head, the combined effect of slope and wind create a wide head. There is also a good possibility both flanks will be very active, meaning the possibility for spotting, erratic spread, and high thermal outputs exist on both flanks.

Each flame model and characteristic spread pattern has points that must be evaluated:

A. The early-morning or late-evening grass fire burning with high relative humidity and no wind or slope will burn without a clearly-defined head or hot flank. Its fine fuel moisture (FFM) level is 25 percent. Often, these fires burn out from the point of origin with little or no spread, making it very easy to disregard the importance of having an anchor point – and take the fire for granted. From the fire investi-

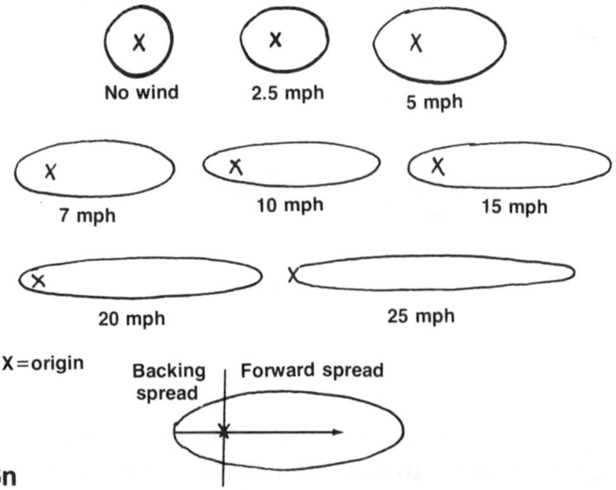

Figure 6n
Silhouettes of wind-driven fires. Note the relationships between forward and backing spread

gation standpoint (cause-origin), many times the point of origin is destroyed by tactical deployment. Since the fire is spreading slowly, some thought should be given to protecting the likely area of origin. This can be accomplished by limiting vehicle and foot traffic into the center area.

B. The slope-driven fire, as mentioned earlier, generally has a narrow head. Depending on the fuel type and resources available, stopping the head should receive a high priority. The slope-driven fire will exhibit some backing spread. Care should be taken to evaluate the area of origin prior to establishing an anchor point and tactical deployment. Depending on rate of spread and fuel characteristics (age class, loading, continuity and fuel moisture level), the flames may be drawn inward as the result of an active head drafting more oxygen from the surrounding area (Figure 6o). This condition often results in large flame fronts and high thermal outputs. Depending on fuel loading, this condition can be exploited by ground personnel, as these indrafts will keep firefighters cooler and out of the smoke. It's

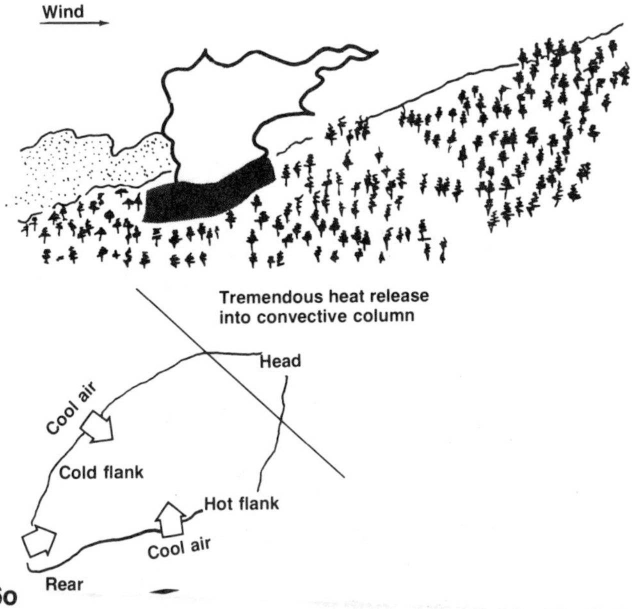

Figure 6o
A rapidly-developing brush and timber fire creates a well-defined head with high thermal energy release. The heated air rises rapidly, forming an impressive convective column. Cooler air is drafted inward from the flanks to fill the void created by the rising air

important, however, to be prepared for changes in this condition, especially in the critical corners closest to the head.

C. The wind-driven fire often has a minimal backing rate. Its area of origin should be evaluated and protected. The wind-driven fire, like some slope-driven fires, will create an indraft situation on one or both flanks. The wind-driven fire, with its horizontal flame model, can interfere with making the corner from the hot flank across the head. Many times, ground personnel and dozers will be unable to make that corner on a single attempt (Figure 6p). The key in a wind-driven fire is to have a good anchor point and work up the flanks, making sure line construction is of high quality and maintaining flanking until aircraft or dozers make the corner or a change in fuel or weather conditions slows the head.

The terms in Figure 6q evaluate and describe flame models and fire spread. Some examples of when these terms might be used are:

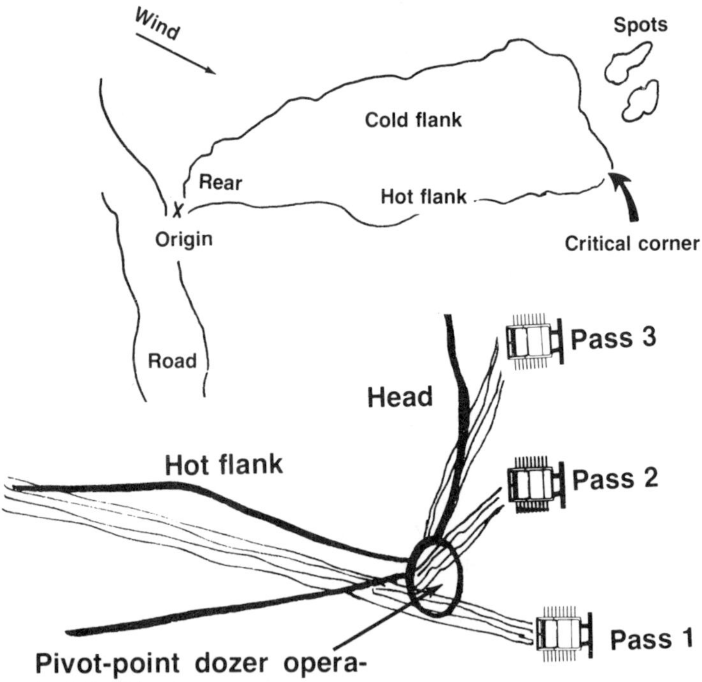

Figure 6p
In this example, a dozer is attempting to make the corner on the hot flank, which may take several attempts. Note pivot point and safety zone.

A. To describe an early-morning fire in light fuel types burning with no wind or slope and a vertical flame model, you might say, "The fire is burning with two-foot flame heights."

B. A fire burning in brush and moving up a steep slope with a horizontal flame model could be described as, "The fire is burning with 10-foot flame lengths."

C. The December 20, 1977 Honda Canyon brush fire in Lompoc, California was pushed down steep-well-defined canyons, and "The peak wind speed of 102 mph produced 75-foot flame lengths."

FIRE SPREAD

The final component of fire behavior is **fire spread.** The key variables of fire spread are **fuels, topography** and **weather.**

A. Fuels

1. **Continuity of fuel bed**
2. **Fuel loading in tons per acre**
3. **Arrangement (vertical vs. horizontal)**
4. **Size and shape of fuel**

Continuity

A continuous fuel bed allows the fire to create its own microclimatic conditions, by increasing ambient air temperature, lowering relative humidity and stepping up microclimatic winds.

Fuel loading is important in regards to rate of spread potential. Note the following examples:

Grass: ¼ to one ton per acre. High spread potential. Erratic rate

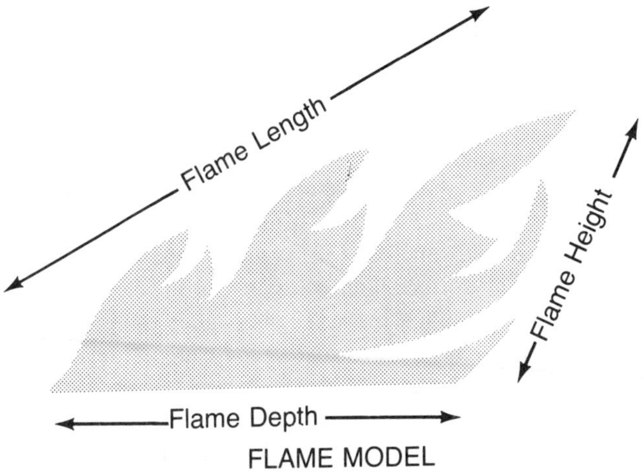

Figure 6q
Flame model terminology

of spread with rapid shifts in direction. Frontal passages, cumulus or orographic build-ups greatly influence grass fire spread.

Sage/Medium Brush: Two to five tons per acre. High thermal output, moderate rate of spread. Spread rates influenced by tremendous thermal output and preheating potential of sage.

Chamise Chaparral: Seven to 15 tons per acre. High availability after age of 20 years. Tremendous thermal output, due to waxes, turpines and resins in plant. Thermal output influences spread rate. High to moderate rate of spread potential.

Heavy Mixed Chaparral: 25 to 50 tons per acre. Generally, lower availability. High thermal output, moderate rate of spread.

Oak Woodland/Grass Understory: Five to seven tons per acre. Low availability in oak woodland. Grass in understory generally short, lacks thermal output to preheat oak canopy. Low thermal output. Spread rate in grass low to moderate.

Fuel Loading

The 1974 edition of the Region I Forest Service Fireline Notebook lists four basic fuel classifications. By fuel type, they are

FUEL TYPE	SPREAD POTENTIAL
Conifer Stand, litter layer, minimal down-dead.	**low**
Conifer stand, medium to heavy down-dead. Could also have slash.	**medium**
Conifer stand, with brush or grass in understory. Medium to heavy down-dead. Could also have slash.	**high**
Grassland. Continuous stands of cured annual grass.	**extreme**

Arrangement and Size and Shape

As mentioned in the fuels chapter, the wildland firefighter is most interested in what fuels are *available* on the first-flame-front passage. This generally includes fuels with a stock diameter of one-half inch or less and surface litter consisting of needles, leaves, stems and twigs with fluffy compactness. Young conifer and pine stands with canopies exposed to grass or brush are good canopy fuels.

The wildland firefighter is most concerned with fuels available on the first-flame-front passage. Generally surface needles, leaves, stems and twigs fall into this category. Young conifer and pine stands with canopies exposed to grass or brush are good canopy fuels.

Some field-use rules of thumb for rate of spread:

1. A fire burning from brush to grass will double its rate of

spread. This is because, once the fire reaches the lighter fuel type (grass), less preheating is necessary to make fuel available to burn. This means more thermal output and intensity is used for rate of spread and fire behavior effects.

2. A fire burning from a brush and timber mix (no crown fire) to grass will triple its rate of spread. The brush/timber mix with no crown fire produces two fire-behavior effects. The brush is mostly available, but requires preheating – which uses thermal output (energy from the fire). The timber has a low availability (bark burn only – maybe scorched canopy) but the canopy (shade factor) allows for decrease in winds in the understory, plus a rise in relative humidity. These factors slow the rate of spread. Once they cease, however, and the fire burns into open grassland, the rate of spread changes dramatically.

3. A fire burning from second-growth timber to brush will double its rate of spread. As with the last example, the lower wind speed and higher humidity associated with timber understory reduce the rate of spread. Also, the timber understory is primarily needles and litter of low-to-average fuel loading. In other words, timber has a low availability.

B. TOPOGRAPHY

1. **Slope**
2. **Aspect**
3. **Position on Slope**
4. **Other Features**

A field-use rule of thumb states that for every 20 percent increase in ***slope,*** *rate of spread doubles.* The steeper the slope, the more convective and radiant heat are able to extend the preheating process to grass and brush canopies. As mentioned in the topography chapter, slope affects a fire in two ways: **draft** and **preheating.** We have discussed preheating already, so we will focus on draft. As the fire moves upslope, more fuel is available as air temperature and fuel temperatures rise and relative humidity lowers. This increase in available fuel means less loss of thermal output (BTU/sec./ft. flame front). More energy is then available for rate of spread and fire behavior. As the rate of spread increases, the convective column builds (heated air rises). As the convective column develops, cooler drafts of air rush in and fill the void left by the rising air, and rate of spread increases.

Now, **aspect.** The north and northwestern aspects[4] have the lowest incidence of wildland fires. The northern aspect has the fewest fires escaping initial attack (Figure 6r).

Position on slope is also important. Most fires that escape initial

[4] *United States Forest Service Region 1, National Forests Statistics, Boise Interagency Fire Center, ID.*

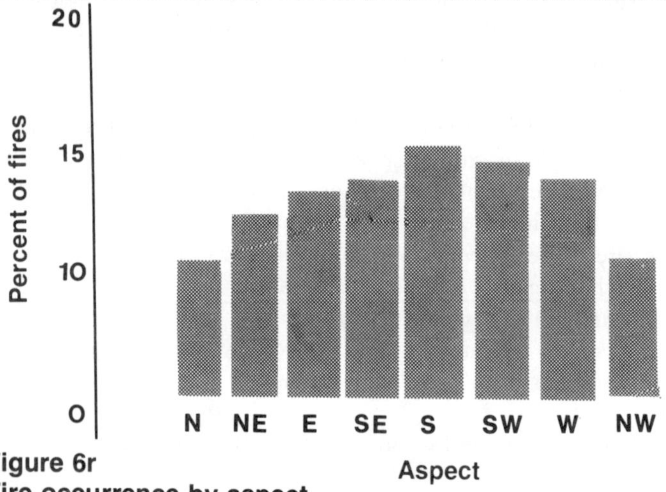

Figure 6r
Fire occurrence by aspect

attack start at the base of the slope.[5] The fewest fires to escape initial attack start at the top of the slope (Figure 6s).

Broken topography **features** such as rock outcroppings can modify fire spread by providing a barrier to spread. These same barriers, how-

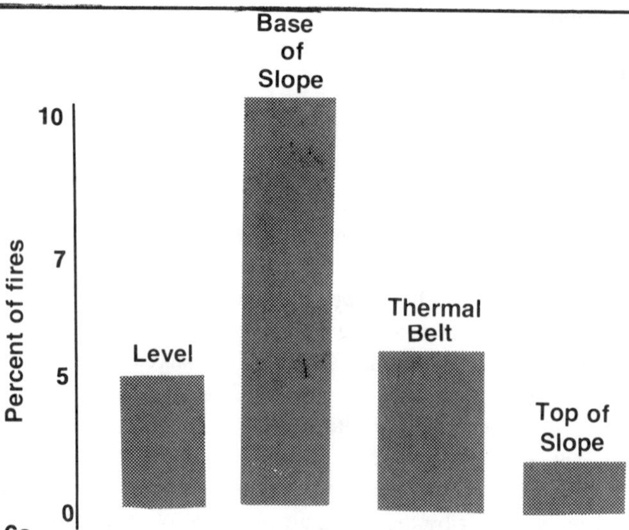

Figure 6s
Fire escaping initial attack size (over 10 acres). Fires starting at the base of a slope reach larger acreages.

[5]*United States Forest Service Region 1, National Forests Statistics, Boise Interagency Fire Center, ID.*

ever, can provide the "trigger" for wind eddies and fire whirls. Features such as passes or saddles through a slope can modify fire spread and generally increase its rate because the wind is squeezed through the passes or saddles, increasing its velocity. Also, the winds flow up the lee side of these features, adding to turbulence and general control problems. Plan for erratic fire conditions along ridge lines where there are saddles.

FIRE BEHAVIOR TESTING

In the summer of 1975, I started conducting some research on rate of spread, flame heights and surface and aerial temperatures.[6] During the period of 1975 to 1981, 19 tests were conducted in annual grass, sage and hard chaparral. The tests were conducted on both wildland training fires and control burns.

The test burns were conducted under the following standards:

Fuel Bed

1. **Good continuity**
2. **Fuel age class, seven to 20 years**
3. **Less than 20 percent of fuel loading down-dead**
4. **Loading:**

    Grass: One-eighth to one-quarter ton per acre.
    Sage: Four to five tons per acre.
    Medium Chaparral: 12 to 15 tons per acre.
    Heavy Chaparral: 40 to 60 tons per acre.

Weather (1300 Hours Average)

1. **Air temperature:** 80 degrees F to 90 degrees F.
2. **Wind speed:** Five to 10 m.p.h.
3. **Wind direction:** West quadrant only.
4. **Relative humidity:** 15 to 30 percent.
5. **Fine-fuel moisture:** 5.7 to 7.0.
6. **Cloud cover:** less than 10 percent.

Topography

1. **No broken topography, saddles or ridge lines.**
2. **No north aspects**
3. **Slopes less than 60 percent, preferably 40 percent.**

Testing performed during the fires included:

A. Soil temperature at first soil horizon. Tempil range 0-550 degrees F. Purpose was to measure hydrophobic soil probabilities in various fuel types/soil series.

B. Aerial temperature at one-foot and two-foot heights above

---

[6] *Wildland Fire Behavior and Fire Spread, Research Paper, Santa Barbara County, CA, 1978.*

first soil horizon. Tempil range 550 degrees F to 2,000 degrees F. Firefighters are usually working directly at these heights, and protective clothing is exposed to radiant heat in these ranges. We were also interested in the relationship of flame height and thermal outputs.

C. Flame heights, utilizing tall, multi-colored metal markers evenly spaced throughout the test burn area to measure flame heights. It's important for firefighters to be able to relate flame heights and thermal outputs to a given fuel type so he/she can evaluate and predict possible fire-behavior effects.

D. Smoke management of airborne particulate matter. During a wildland fire, tons of particulate matter may be released into the atmosphere via the convective column. Leaves, needles, twigs and shake shingles have been carried miles downwind. We were interested in the travel distance of smoke in various fuel types. In addition, sandy and sandy loan soils are fine enough to be moved easily by fire whirls or a developing fire, so we wanted to see if these sands were carried aloft.

E. Fire spread, using the standard mentioned earlier to predict mid-day (peak) fire spread rates under *normal* weather window. From the above test, we were able to develop a basic estimate and one-hour ellipse for the various fuel types, as well as estimate likely thermal outputs. Using the one hour ellipse was important because 90 percent of our wildland fires were controlled during the initial-attack phase, in most cases within one hour.

The key tests, for our county, were those with annual grass and sage. Annual grass is Santa Barbara's key light fuel that transitions into sage or medium brush. Sage and chamise (chaparral) are our problem preheating fuels. These have tremendous aerial temperatures and thermal outputs. Sage and chamise transition into the hard chaparral.

Key Observations During the Grass-Fire Tests:

A. Cured annual grass six inches or less in height very quickly reacts to topography changes (rock outcroppings, drainage). Wind eddies and fire whirls will develop.

B. Cured annual grass can produce aerial temperatures (one- to two-foot heights) to 475 degrees F.

C. Eighty percent of the cured annual grass fuel bed was consumed in the first-flame-front passage.

D. Soil temperature never exceeded 250 degrees F at the surface.

E. Minimum flame height was six inches.

F. Maximum flame height was two feet, six inches.

G. No spotting was observed.

Key Observations During the Sage-Fire Tests:

A. Average height of sage canopy was 30 inches. Species included coastal and button sage.
B. Understory grass was six inches in height. Good transition from grass to sage noted.
C. Sage fuel bed was 60 percent closed canopy.
D. Erratic fire spread, fire whirl developed two minutes after ignition.
E. Twenty-five-foot flame heights exhibited after two minutes of burning.
F. Sage produced aerial temperature of 1,400 degrees F after four minutes of burning.
G. Soil temperature reached 500 degrees F after two minutes.
H. Ninety percent of the sage fuel bed was consumed in the first-flame-front passage.
I. Spotting occurred 100 feet in front of the head.
J. Minimum flame height was three feet.
K. Maximum flame height was 30 feet.

Key Observations in Medium-Brush Test:

A. Medium brush species included baccharis. Baccharis burned in several other tests did not burn easily. Spread was limited during this test.
B. Soil temperatures reached 400 degrees F.
C. Aerial temperatures were between 500-550 degrees F.
D. Minimum flame heights reached five feet.
E. Maximum flame heights were 25 feet.
F. Sixty percent of the medium brush fuel bed was consumed in the first-flame-front passage.

RESOURCE	TACTICAL APPLICATION	BTU/sec./ft. THERMAL OUTPUT LIMIT
Engine Company	Flank Attack	500
Hand Crew	Flank Attack	500
Dozer	Flank Attack	700
Air Attack	Retardant Drops On Head, Hot Flank	1,000

The Southwestern states, including California, have a high percentage of wildland fires in grass, chamise (chaparral) and mixed chaparral. A good portion of these fires start on a slope of from zero to 40 percent. We have previously discussed the tremendous rate of spread and fire behavior characteristics of old-age-class (over 20 years) chaparral. We have also discussed how we can use flame heights to estimate thermal output (Figure 6e and 6f). Thermal outputs are very important in regards to determining limitations of personnel and resources.

The graphs in figures 6t to 6bb combine fuel age class, rate of spread, wind model and thermal outputs. I think it's very interesting to keep in mind the following facts as you review these graphs:

A. Most grass fires burn with a thermal output (BTU/sec./ft.) range of 95 to 400. This range will allow an aggressive flank attack in most cases.

B. Slope increase does not affect rate of spread all that dramatically in grass.

C. For years, fuel management specialists have recommended prescribed and control burns to reduce age class in brush fuel beds. They have promoted mosaic designs and rotational burning to keep fuel age class at 10 years or less. The graphs for both chamise and mixed

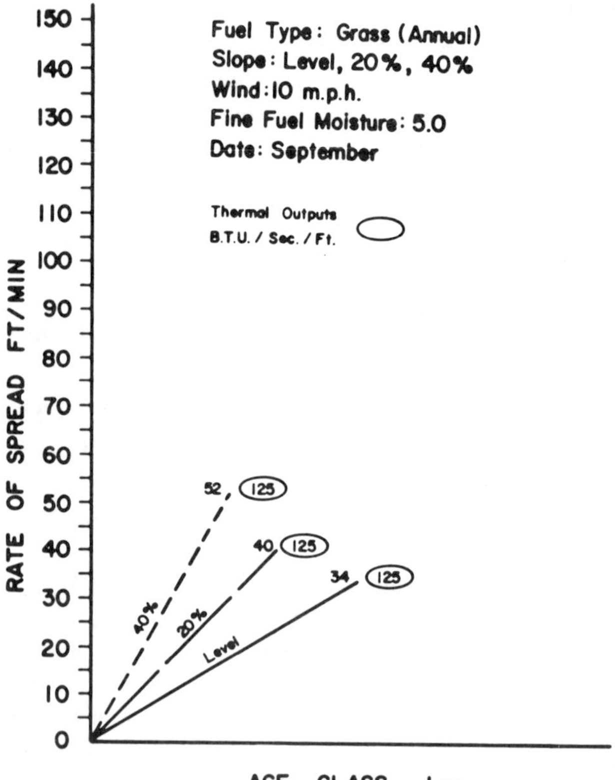

Figure 6t

chaparral illustrate, from the rate of spread and thermal output standpoint, what an age class of 10 years or less means to the wildland firefighter. A less-than-10-year age class not only benefits the wildlife habitat, but also ends large-acreage wildland fires. These facts are great for promoting prescribed or control burning to our citizens and politicians as a way of saving money and reducing the risk to residents and firefighters.

D. The chamise and mixed chaparral graphs illustrate what happens when brush reaches old age class (20 years). The dramatic change in live-to-dead plant ratio results in a canopy with inferior growth leaders and an abundance of decadent stems, twigs, leaves or needles. All of this material is quickly preheated and made available for consumption on the first-flame-front passage. Note the marked change at all wind speeds in rate of spread and thermal output in younger age classes.

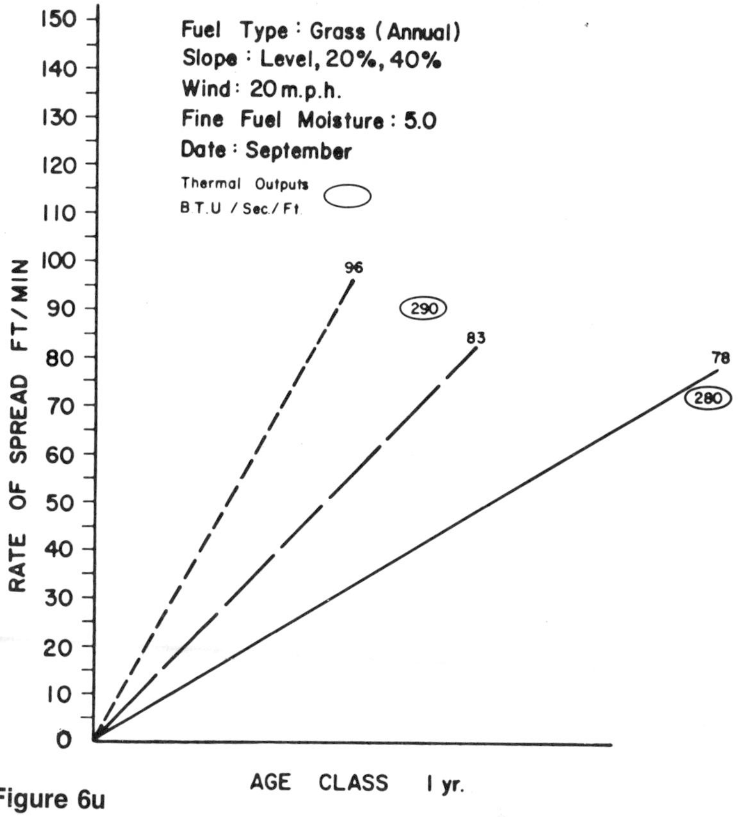

Figure 6u

E. Mixed chaparral, primarily manzanita, chamise, toyon and scrub oak, over 30 years of age exceeds the limitations of almost all resources and personnel.
F. In both chamise and mixed chaparral, a 30-year age class in both 20- and 30-mph wind models will likely produce erratic fire behavior, including spotting (over 700 BTU/sec./ft.). Spotting can be an excellent visual indicator of changing fire behavior.

WARNING SIGNS OF CHANGING FIRE BEHAVIOR

It's very important for firefighters to track the following once fire season is declared:

CONCERN	TRACKING MECHANISM
Weekly live-fuel moisture levels.	**Regional or state live-fuel moisture charts.**
Frontal system passage, especially cold fronts.	**National Weather Service or regional newspapers.**
High-pressure subsidence.	**National Weather Service or regional newspapers.**
Jet stream change(s).	**National Weather Service.**

Changes from normal to extreme fire behavior can be predicted. They are usually triggered by critical live-fuel moisture levels. In the southwestern United States and California, two species of chaparral are tracked, chamise and manzanita. Chamise becomes critical when the live fuel moisture level reaches 60 percent. Manzanita becomes critical at 80 percent.

As live fuel moisture levels drop, the canopy foliage is first to show the change. As leaves, needles, stems and twigs slowly become more available, this increased availability means less heat is required to preheat canopy foliage, so more heat is available to increase the burning rate. As burning rates increase, fire intensity increases. One of the early changes firefighters can visually detect is a higher percentage of the canopy, foliage, stems and twigs being consumed on first-flame-front passage. This increase will produce increased flame heights and thermal outputs.

Spotting may be the next key visual indicator of changing fire behavior. Low live-fuel moisture levels, high air temperatures and low relative humidities promote spotting. Even short-range spotting should be respected – and quickly evaluated. This condition could be your only warning prior to a blow-up.

Spotting starts when thermal outputs reach 700 BTU/sec./ft. and flame heights exceed nine feet.

Generally, a fire that exhibits spotting has a well-defined convective column. This is not always the case, however, because spotting can occur under a smoke-inversion situation in a well-defined canyon.

Fire behavior can change rapidly once spotting starts. Obviously, many outside weather factors must be right to promote a transition to extreme fire behavior. Examples include one or more of the following:

A. Daytime. Long daylight hours with peak burning period still to hit: 1000 to 1600 hours.

B. High-pressure subsidence. If in place for a week or more prior to the fire. Hot, dry days with low relative humidities. Fine fuel moisture levels 4.0 or less.

C. Adverse wind model. Any Foehn wind model or wind speeds exceeding 30 mph.

D. Peak fire season **thunderstorms, cold-front passage.** Gusty, erratic winds and wind shifts.

E. Nighttime. Strong downslope mountain wind (SDMW), such as a Sundowner.

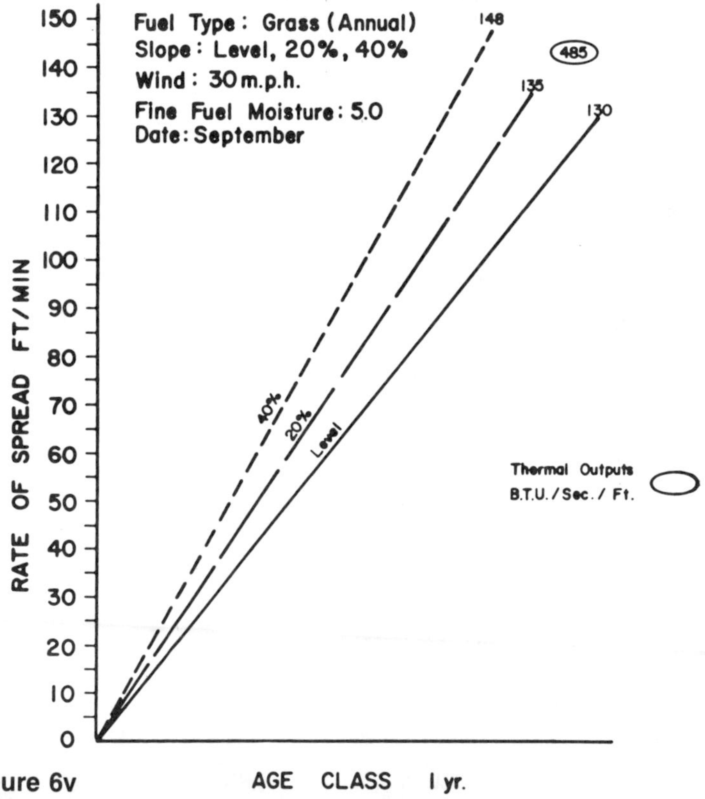

Figure 6v

The next visual indicator – an increase in flame heights, large flame fronts and long-distance spotting – may be hard to evaluate at the onset. An increase in flame heights to 20 feet (4,000 BTU/sec./ft.) can be hard to determine after already evaluating nine to 10 feet flame heights and concurrent spotting (short range). Therefore, the width of the head can be an important and distinct observation at this point.

This time frame in a developing wildland fire is extremely important. I really believe that one of the best ways to monitor these changes is by enlisting the cooperation of the air-attack supervisor. He/she is in an excellent position to notice increases in rate of spread and spotting changes.

The air-attack supervisor can also notice changes in a fire retardant's ability to slow a fire down. Air attack (fire retardant) is ineffective in situations where thermal outputs exceed 1,000 BTU/sec./

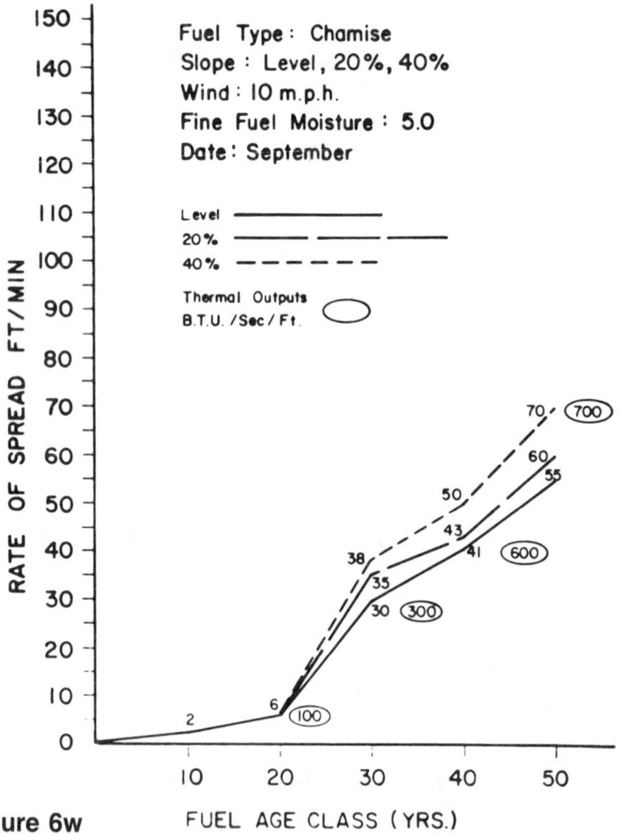

Figure 6w

ft. of flame front (11-foot flame heights).

Depending on weather conditions and fuel type, loading mass flame transport (flashover in convective column) and peak thermal pulses (high aerial temperatures, flame heights) may be visible prior to a fire storm (blow-up). Figure 6cc illustrates this cycle of extreme fire behavior.

In my experiences with extreme fire behavior, these factors were present at the time the fire started:

FIRE NAME	FACTOR(S)	RESULT
Romero Canyon Calif., Oct. 1971	Strong downslope mountain wind (SDMW) "Sundowner." Winds exceeding 60 mph.	Four firefighter fatalities during firestorm; 16,000 acres burned.
Sycamore Canyon, Calif., July, 1977	Strong downslope mountain wind (SDWM) "Sundowner." Winds to 50 mph.	250 homes; 800 acres burned.
Honda Canyon, Calif., Dec. 20, 1977	Cold front, low live-fuel moisture strong downslope mountain winds. Peak wind gust 102 mph. 40-year age class.	Four firefighter fatalities during firestorm; 10,000 acres burned.
Wheeler Canyon, Calif., July 1985	High-pressure subsidence, old-age fuel, spotting, high temperatures low relative humidity.	118.000+ acres 11 homes burned.
Paint Santa Barbara, Calif., June, 1990	Drought stressed chaparral old-age class fuel, "Sundowner" influence, high temperatures, low relative humidity.	4,900 acres, 648 structures.

FIRE BEHAVIOR CONCERNS, BY REGION
Southeastern United States

A. Fire Season(s): Spring and fall.

1. Spring season: March through May.

2. Fall season: October through December.

B. Fire Behavior Problems:

1. Topography associated with Appalachian Mountains. Diverse elevation range from 550 to 6,600 feet (Mt. Mitchell in North Carolina). Many areas of broken topography and outcroppings.

2. Fires generally make good first-day runs in mountainous areas. Heavy ground fuels are present in most areas. Fires in mountains lay down at night. Relative humidity recovery is also good at night.

3. Tactics for mountainous areas emphasize stopping the fire on the ridge line. The ridge line usually is the *only* access for dozers and personnel.

4. Cold front passage is a major threat. With 90-to-180 degree wind shifts, attack *east* flank first for safety.

5. Local residents often set backfires to save their own property. You must watch out for personnel who become trapped between the main fire and the backfire.

6. Some of the fastest and hottest fires in the Southeast are in pine plantations. The layout and design of a pine plantation often makes tactical deployment of personnel and resources difficult.

7. Fires that burn near streams and bottomland burn hardwoods and litter. These fires burn slowly and may be attacked on the head first. Dozers are very effective in these areas. If the head becomes too hot, shift to the flanks for a direct attack and burnout.

8. The Piedmont is developing a large wildland/urban interface. Many summer homes are being built in heavy woodland fuel beds.

9. Thousands of acres of swamp land and low Pocosin are being

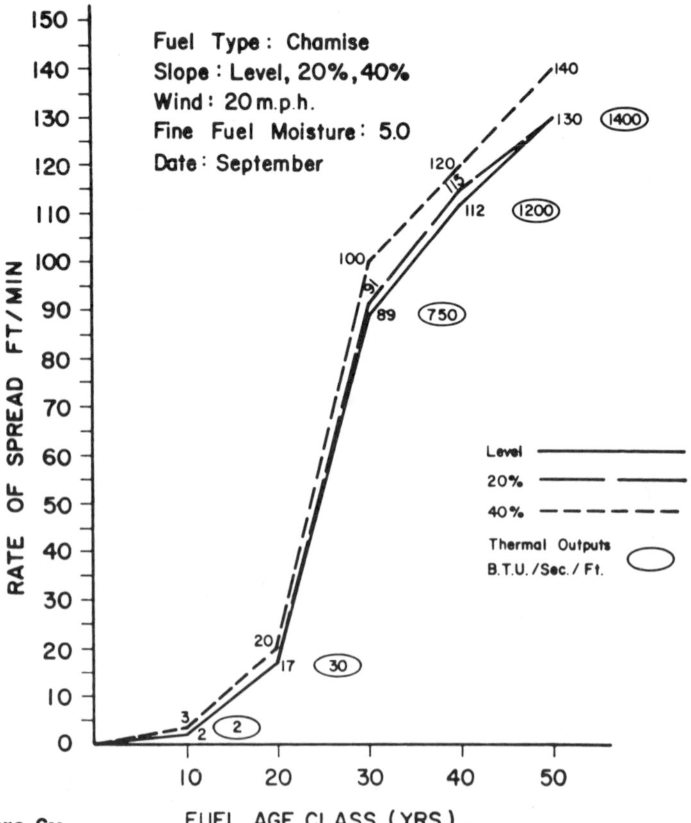

Figure 6x

drained. In their place, pine plantations are being developed.

10. The coastal plains of the Southeast have some of the largest fires in the region. Fires of 10,000 acres are common. Geography is level and dry cold fronts often create severe fire-behavior problems.

Northeastern United States

A. Fire Season(s): April, May and June, September and October.

B. Fire Behavior Problems

1. New Jersey Pine Barrens, which are rated the same as California's chaparral fuel type.

2. Crown fires in Jack and Red Pine stands, producing long-range spotting in the Lake States.

3. Fires run during the day, lay down at night. Good relative

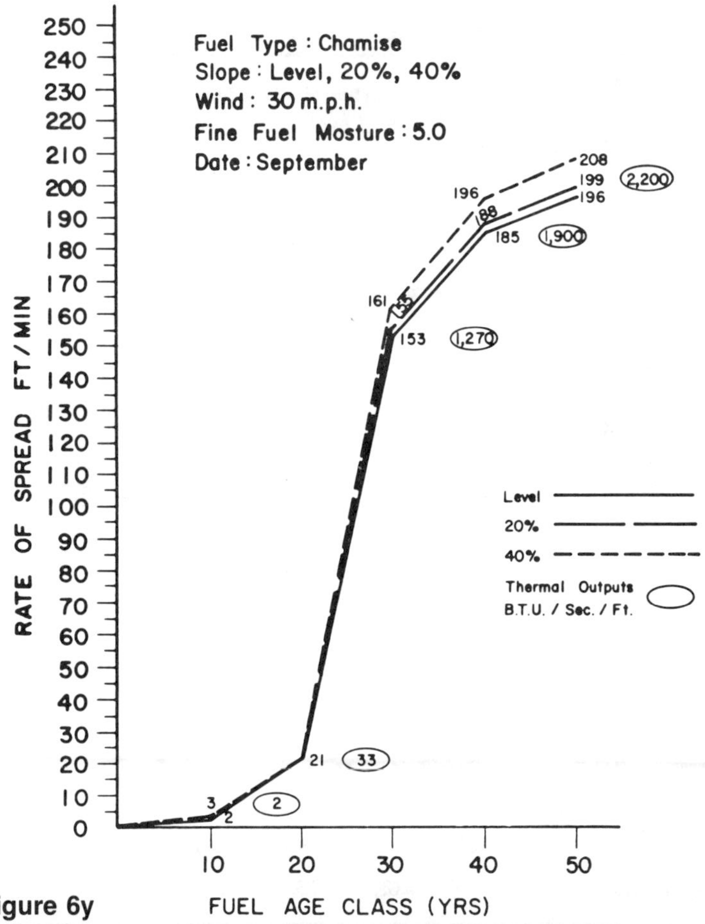

Figure 6y

humidity recovery exhibited at night.

4. Hudson Bay High. This high-pressure subsidence drives out fuels. Low relative humidities common.

5. Mack Lake Fire, in Jack and Red Pines, burned 24,790 acres in six hours, May 5, 1980. Rate of spread the first three hours was two mph (176 feet per minute).

6. It is possible to have a fire running through Jack or Red Pines at speeds approaching six mph (500+ feet per minute).

7. A fire weather forecaster is a must for the Lake States to forecast frontal passages and changing fire behavior.

8. The New Jersey Pine Barrens are rapidly developing a critical wildland/urban interface as subdivisions are built up in the middle of dense pine stands.

Southwestern United States

A. Fire Season: March through December.

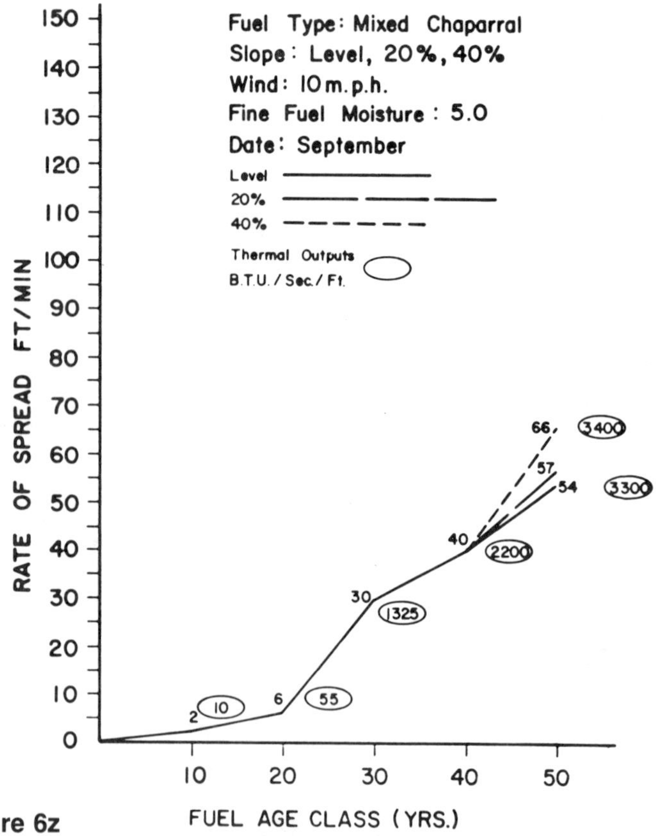

Figure 6z

B. Fire Behavior Problems:

1. Diverse topography conditions. Elevations diverse, from sea level to 14,000-plus feet. Major percentage of north-south drainages.

2. Diverse fuel types:

- Grasslands
- Pinyon-Juniper
- Ponderosa Pine
- Mixed Conifer
- Spruce
- Chaparral (soft)
- Chaparral (hard)

3. Arizona and New Mexico have highest occurrence of lightning in the United States.

4. The Southwest is the fastest growing wildland/urban interface in the nation.

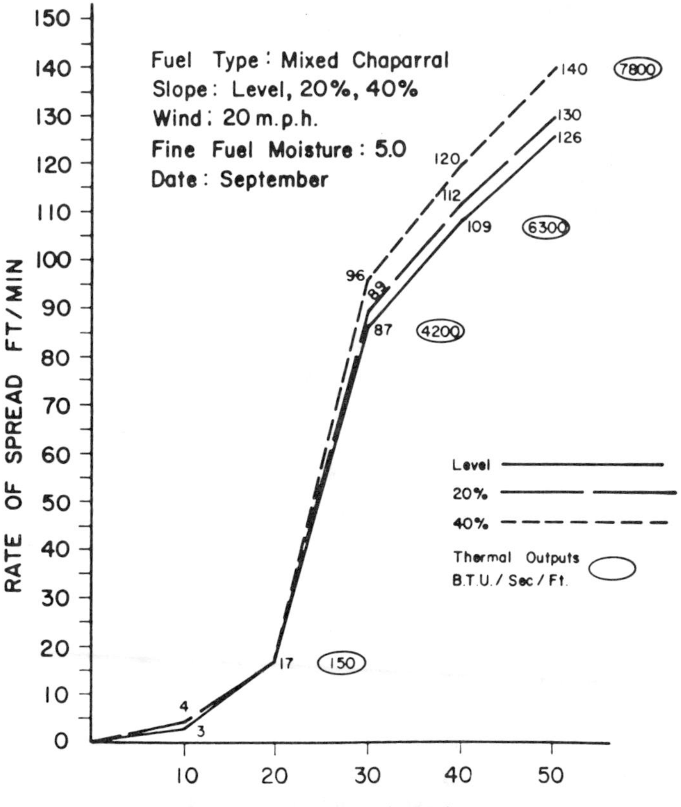

Figure 6aa

5. Santa Ana winds in late fall and spring in Southern California (October, November, December, February and March). Winds to 90 mph and low relative humidities below 10 percent have been recorded.

6. Strong spring winds (March and April) create erratic fire behavior in West Texas, Arizona and New Mexico. Jet stream and frontal activity create these extreme wind conditions.

7. Bermuda High creates thunderstorm problems for southwestern states.

8. Fire behavior conditions can be severe at night in Southern California. Sundowner winds often occur in Santa Barbara and Ventura Counties, often creating adverse downslope fire behavior after 1800 hours. The 1990 "Paint" brush fire near Santa Barbara damaged or destroyed 648 buildings and structures. A majority of these losses occurred within the first four hours as the result of a Sundowner wind.

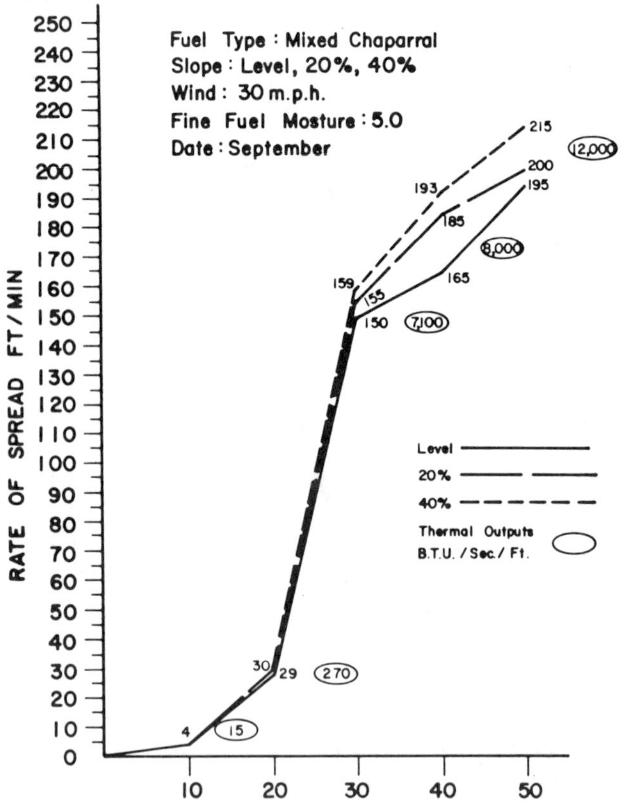

Figure 6bb

A burning structure can modify fire behavior. Burning materials from structures often are carried aloft and cause spotting problems.

Sundowner winds can reach velocities to 70 mph.

The 1971 Romero Canyon fire in the front country of Santa Barbara was a classic example of how rapidly fire behavior can change. At 1900 hours, there was a temperature of 68 degrees F and a 66 percent relative humidity and little wind. Fire spread virtually stopped.

At 1915 hours (just 15 minutes later) the temperature soared to 92 degrees F, relative humidity was 18 percent and a strong downslope mountain wind developed. These conditions remained steady until 0500 the next day. A resulting firestorm was responsible for four firefighter fatalities.

9. Old-age-class fuel beds in chaparral fuel types. A lack of control and prescribed burns has created vast areas of old-age-class fuels. The 1985 Wheeler Fire (118,000 acres) near Ojai, California was a classic example. Prior to 1985, the last major wildland fire in Ojai occurred in *1932*. That burned 219,000 acres. Chaparral fuel of over 20 years in age displays a high resistance to control. As the age class exceeds 20 years, fire behavior characteristics change radically.

Northwestern Great Basin States

A. Fire Season: June through October.

B. Fire Behavior Problems:

1. Critical weather patterns associated with Pacific High or Canadian High.

2. Seventy-five percent of major fires (over 300 acres) occur in July, August and September and are associated with the Pacific High.

3. Foehn winds:

- Chinook - Rocky Mountains.
- Mono - Northern California.
- East - Oregon, Washington, and Utah.

4. Fuel Diversity:

- Prairie grasslands: fast-burning fires
- Vast grain ranges: very fast, hot fires
- Spruce and cedar forests – called "the greatest weight of living matter per acre."

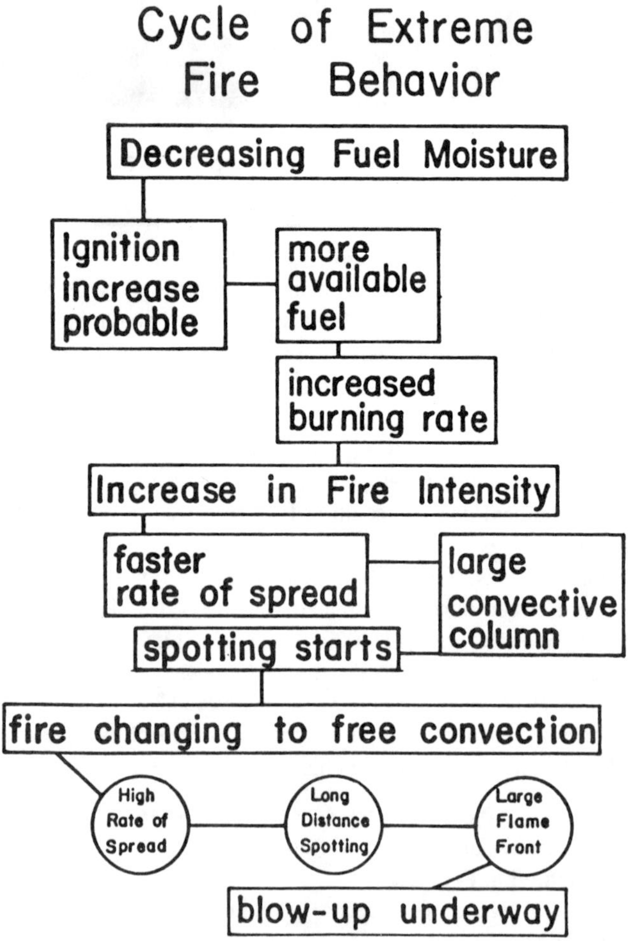

- Oak woodland
- Vast areas of slash/timber stand improvement
- Douglas Fir forests
- Lodge Pole Pine stands

5. Fires at high relative humidities.

6. Fires generally lay down at night, accompanied by good relative humidity recovery and large drop in air temperature.

7. Most wildland fires in the Great Basin burn for only one burn period. However, it is not uncommon to burn 10,000 acres during one burn period.

8. Idaho, Eastern Oregon and part of Utah are developing major wildland/urban interfaces.

FIRE INTENSITY LEVELS

FIRELINE INTENSITY (B.T.U./Sec/Ft)	FLAME LENGTH	FIRE CONDITION	ATTACK
5	1	Barely burning	Envelopment
20 - 100	2-4	Rate of spread under 3 feet per minute	Envelopment
100	4	Low intensity head starts to become active	Flank
300-500	4-8	Head active,hot flank active	Flank
500	8	Head and hot flank very active	Too intense for direct attack by hand crews
700	8-11	Spotting starts	Too intense for direct attack by dozer
1,000	11-15	Long range spotting	Air attack ineffective
3,000	18	Major flame fronts, spotting, crowning	Extreme fire behavior developing
6,500	26	High rate of spread, crowning	Extreme fire behavior
22,500	45	1967 Sundance Fire. Extensive crowning, fire whirls, tree breakage	Extreme fire behavior

Alaska

A. Fire Season: June and July

B. Fire Behavior Problems:

1. Seventy-five percent of Alaska's fires are lightning-caused.

2. Extended daylight: 24-hours in June. Little cooling off in the evening.

3. Daily thunderstorm activity (erratic winds).

4. A unique fuel – Black spruce. Seventy-five percent of Alaska's fires are in this fuel type. Black spruce is extremely flammable and will burn in all 12 months.

5. Alaska's fires generally burn with low fire spread but high thermal outputs (high down-dead fuel loading).

6. Tussock tundra is a very flashy fuel that will burn at high relative humidity and 55 percent "moisture of extinction" level.

Chapter 7

Size-Up

The initial-attack incident commander at a wildland fire must evaluate many things prior to deploying personnel and resources and making fireground decisions. Many experienced officers assist this forecasting process with a mental size-up similar to the structural-firefighting size-up process. I feel, however, that a formal check sheet should be used if the fire has the potential to escape initial-attack size. This formal check sheet can later be used to help formulate control objectives.

THE FIRE-BEHAVIOR CHECKLIST

The wildland fire behavior forecasting sheet can be a valuable preplanning tool (Figure 7a). Many of the evaluation factors can be readily accessed by preplanning fuel beds. The fire behavior forecast sheet evaluates:

A. Fuel Types
B. Fire Weather
C. Topography
D. Fire Behavior Problems

FUEL TYPES

The incident commander must have a good feel for fuel beds, fuel transition zones and age class. In addition, continuity arrangement, percentage of down-dead fuel and size of fuel bed are important.

Wildland firefighters should preplan all fuel beds within their areas and plot old-age-class fuels on topography maps. Fuel transition

WILDLAND FIRE BEHAVIOR FORECASTING

When you are preplanning your wildland areas or even as you initially arrive at the fire scene, answer the following. Your plan of action should reflect your predictions. You must update after your initial rate of spread estimate (1 hour), and then at least every 3 hours.

I. FUEL TYPES ____________
- **A. After 1 Hour ____________**
- **B. After 3 Hours ____________**
- **C. Fuel Age Class (Average) ____________**
- **D. Continuity: UNIFORM ________ PATCHY ________**

II. FIRE WEATHER
- **A. Air Temperature ________°F. B. Relative Humidity ______%**
- **C. Fuel Stick ______ D. Wind Direction ___ Wind Speed ______ mph**
- **E. 12-Hour Prediction ____________**

III. TOPOGRAPHY
- **A. Aspect ________ B. % Slope ________ C. Terrain ________**
- **D. Canyons, Chimneys, Ridge, Bluffs in Area ____________**

IV. FIRE BEHAVIOR PROBLEMS
- **A. % Down dead fuel loading ____________**
- **B. Extreme winds predicted? ____________**
- **C. Limited access? ____________**
- **D. Delay on additional units to arrive? ____________**
- **E. Any spotting taking place now? ________ Predicted? ________**
- **F. Any fire whirls observed? ________ Predicted? ________**
- **G. Large flame fronts? ____________**
- **H. More than (1) head developing ________ Is it possible? ________**
- **I. Frontal activity in area? ________ Predicted ________**
- **J. Is rate of spread increasing rapidly? ____________**
- **K. Is the fire likely to burn into the next burn period? ____________**
- **L. Is indirect attack and backfiring being used? ____________**
- **M. ____________**

Figure 7a **PERRY 1975**

zones should be noted. These fuel transition zones (grass to sage, sage to chamise, chamise to ceonuthus, ceonuthus to oak woodland, grass to timber mix, grass to pinyon, etc.) are key points to consider when developing the incident action plan and control objectives. It's important to hold a wildland fire to the lightest age class possible.

Age class is also very important because old fuels (over 20 years) have a high percentage of decadent stems, twigs and leaves in their canopy and sub-canopy regions and require little pre-heating to burn. Old-age-class fuels burn hot, with moderate-to-high rates of spread and thermal outputs (BTU/sec./ft.) often exceeding limits of fire-control resources.

Most initial-attack fires are controlled within one hour, but what if the fire requires an extended attack? What types of fuels lie ahead of the fire? To plan personnel and resource needs, you must be able to answer these questions.

FIRE WEATHER

This is the most critical evaluation element. All wildland firefighters should be familiar enough with their areas that they know local conditions. This knowledge should include answers to the following:

A. What are local wind speeds?
B. What is the average local wind direction?
C. When do local winds start to peak?
D. What is daytime average temperature at 1300 to 1400 hours?
E. What is daytime average relative humidity at 1300 to 1400 hours?
F. Are there local canyons, ridges, passes or geographical areas that exhibit erratic winds or weather?
G. When does humidity recovery start?
H. Does marine influence (fog) affect fire weather?
I. During fire season, are there daily cumulus build-ups? (If so,

Figure 7b

The belt weather kit consists of a hand-held wind meter, compass and a wet & dry bulb thermometer set called a sling psychrometer for measuring air temperature and relative humidity.

when do they start (time), and what sort of effect as far as erratic winds do they initiate?)

The answers to these questions are essential in order to evaluate incident fire conditions versus normal. Most firefighters who have been in a given location for at least five years will have such knowledge. I highly recommend that every engine company assigned to a wildland area carry a belt weather kit so local conditions can be evaluated frequently during an incident. (See Figure 7b, belt weather kit.)

During fire season, it is also important that firefighters review statewide weather forecasts to look at fronts, winds and lightning activity for the next 12 to 24 hours. Areas of concern should also include lowering barometric pressure (below 29.92), and high-pressure subsidence.

TOPOGRAPHY

Other important components of fire behavior that relate to deployment of resources are aspect, slope and broken topography. Aspect is the direction the slope faces. Fires burning on a southern aspect generally have a greater potential to escape initial attack than ones on other aspects. Slope is important to fire spread, as it aids preheating and rate of spread. A basic rule of thumb states that rate of spread will double for every 20 percent increase in slope. Most bulldozers cannot traverse more than 65 percent upslope or 50 percent side slope. Most brush trucks are limited to under 40 percent upslope. Narrow canyons, chimneys, saddles and ridge lines can modify fire behavior and tactical decisions. Broken topography features such as rock outcroppings modify slope winds and create eddies. The fire is also likely to finger in broken topography.

FIRE-BEHAVIOR PROBLEMS

It is important to be able to forecast erratic fire behavior that might threaten firefighter safety. The following factors should be considered:

A. Percentage of Down-Dead Fuels

During your fuels-inventory tour and age-classing survey, note the percentage of down-dead fuels. This one factor alone is often responsible for an initial-attack fire escaping control efforts. Down-dead fuels can provide the sub-canopy pre-heating necessary to drive a ground fire to aerial canopies. Fine twigs and stems in the sub-canopy region or on the ground can average one-to-three tons-per-acre in chaparral fuels, or much higher in forest areas. Down-dead fuels speed up pre-heating of fuel canopies and make close-in firefighting difficult because of high temperatures. Fuel beds with large areas of down-dead fuels, commonly called "jackpots," should be noted and kept well inside potential control lines.

B. Extreme Winds Predicted

If the local fire weather forecast predicts cold-front activity, Foehn winds or dry storms with cumulus build-ups, the incident action plan should have a safety message attached warning all division group supervisors of this. Safety zones should become mandatory in the line assignment, and the attack plan should remain flexible enough to make an immediate change, should winds shift.

C. Limited Access

This is most often associated with large-acreage fuel beds and steep topography. Limited access may hinder deployment of ground resources.

D. Delayed Additional Units

Fire officers should know how long it takes for air attack, hand crews, bulldozers and brush trucks to reach problem fuel beds. The incident commander can't make an effective deployment without the personnel or resources in the quantity necessary to make the attack. Many times, single resources will have to stage at an incident staging area until additional resources arrive to assist them.

Always plan on the worst-case scenario when it comes to delayed resources. Breakdowns, traffic problems or finding an additional fire enroute are all part of the real world. I believe that one of the major benefits of the Incident Command System is that it trains incident commanders and operation chiefs to order by strike team or task force instead of by single resource. This lessens the chances of delay and often gives the incident commander extra resources to hold in staging in case the unexpected happens.

E. Spotting

Spotting is a good visual indicator of a potential for extreme fire behavior and thermal outputs (BTU/sec./ft.) above 700. A fire building in intensity with a large cumulus column and spotting ahead of the fire may dictate that the incident commander pull back crews from an aggressive direct attack. Instead, he/she may want to work the flank well behind the head until the fire runs out of continuous fuel or the weather changes. Remember, with spot fires, it's not the ones you can see that will give you problems, it's the ones you can't see – these could take off any time.

F. Fire Whirls

Fire whirls are another visual indicator of extreme fire behavior. They can be started by erratic winds, broken topographic features or free-convective-state burning. All these should be a cause for concern. They are most often seen on the head or hot flank of the incident. Fire whirls and spotting typically occur in old-age-class fuel beds with continuous fuels across broken topography features. Fire whirls can also occur when large flame fronts move across unbroken old-age fuel beds.

G. Large Flame Fronts

These are associated with a fire burning across a large, unbroken fuel bed. Often, thermal outputs (BTU/sec./ft.) will be above 1,000, making air attack ineffective in slowing the head of the fire. When the fire's head is broad (over 300 feet), it is often more effective to work the flanks with an air attack and let the head run until fuels change or weather conditions improve. This may first require an initial air drop across the head to evaluate if the fire's thermal output is too far gone to slow at that point. The air-attack supervisor can make this evaluation if so requested.

H. More Than One Head Developing

In steep, narrow topography with intersecting drainages, it is possible for a fire to develop with two heads. If this appears to be happening, the incident commander should make every attempt to use air attack to prevent the second head from developing. Usually it is too hot to use ground resources to accomplish this.

If a second head develops, you will almost always need to give up the fuel between the two heads. *Caution:* In this situation, personnel working near the upper flanks and heads should stay clear of the "island" area between the heads. This situation may dictate burning out the island if the fire's initial pass is so rapid it doesn't carry the fuels between the heads.

I. Frontal Activity

Keep current on the fire weather forecast. Be very alert for cold fronts or predicted dry storms. A marked drop in the barometric pressure may be your only advanced warning.

J. Changing Rate of Spread

This can be an indication of increasing winds or a general worsening of fire-weather conditions. It can also indicate the fire is moving into an older-age-class fuel bed. A rate of spread change may also indicate a slope change. If the fire moves from a heavy fuel type, such as a timber mix, into open grassland, a marked increase in rate of spread will result.

K. Fire Likely to Burn Into the Next Burn Period

Extended-attack or major incidents often burn into the next burn period. Fires starting in daytime and burning into evening present a unique problem for the command team. It is next to impossible to get accurate fuel-typing, topography, slope and rate of spread projections at night. Personnel working line assignments face additional safety problems such as rolling rocks and poor vision that make it impossible to see saddles, narrow ridge lines, safety zones and snakes. Rate of line construction for hand crews and bulldozers generally slows, for much the same reasons. Make sure the incident action plan has a safety message reinforcing safety points and topography hazards.

L. Indirect Attack and Backfiring Being Used

If the fire is burning in a continuous fuel bed being fanned by winds, it may be too risky to deploy resources and personnel directly on the fireline. In this case, the command team may decide to buy time and back off to a favorable wide ridge or a lighter fuel type where a backfire can be utilized. Any time a backfire is used in conjunction with an indirect attack, extreme caution must be exercised. Timing and firing sequences are especially critical. A backfire should not be confused with burnout. Some states, such as California, recognize the hazards associated with backfiring and set strict guidelines under the Public Resources Code (Section 4426). *Only qualified personnel should set and supervise a backfiring operation.*

Make sure the firing team and holding crews have safety zones and escape routes planned. Communication among division supervisors, firing team and holding crews is a must.

M. Other Considerations

Many wildland areas will have additional considerations that should be listed. Add, delete or change the preceding list to meet your specific needs.

Many fireline fatalities and injuries can be attributed to failure by personnel to recognize fire-behavior changes. The initial-attack incident commander must evaluate potential fire behavior before developing an incident action plan (IAP) or committing to an attack method.

Weather, topography and fuel types are what create fire behavior. However, many times, there are advance warnings, called **visual indicators,** that should be evaluated before a heavy commitment to an attack method takes place.

The importance of these advance indicators cannot be overstressed. Unheeded, they not only pose a life-safety threat, but can make even the most cost-effective and efficient attack fruitless. These visual indicators are few in number but important to watch for. How many of these are exhibited in your area?

WEATHER-RELATED INDICATORS

Weather is the key element in forecasting potential fire behavior and fire spread. Wind direction and velocity are easily observed, either by using a belt weather kit, trees or smoke column. Additional weather indicators are listed below:

A. Fair-weather Cumulus Building over Drainages

This visual can be a forewarning of fully-developed cumulus cells and violent down drafts that will erratically spread fire in relative proximity to the path of these cells. This condition, when visible before noon, indicates a good chance for afternoon thunderstorms. Incident commanders should plan an attack safe enough to allow for potential clockwise wind shifts from 90 to 180 degrees. The incident action plan safety message should alert all personnel to this potential (Figure 7c).

Figure 7c

B. Alto Cumulus Linticularis (Lens Clouds) Over Ridge Lines

Alto cumulus linticularis are bands of clouds with an appearance like jet con-trails. They indicate high-speed winds aloft that could potentially surface and affect fire behavior on ridge lines or in drainages. Incident commanders noting this visual can monitor the smoke

Figure 7d

column to watch for a radical smoke fracture that will show the lower limit of the wind. These winds may exceed 50 mph and change elevations rapidly. The incident commander should alert all personnel to this condition (Figure 7d).

C. A Surfacing Downslope Wind

A SDMW is generally characterized by a well-developed smoke column hugging topography features. This very-common wind pattern is associated with the classic fall winds – Santa Ana, Devil, Chinook, East and Mono.

The incident commander working against a downslope wind model often must shift the attack from offensive to defensive to protect structures in the urban interface and valued natural resources in front of the fire. Additionally, it is hard to get to an anchor point to start an attack method.

As in any wind-driven incident, the incident commander must refrain from a tendency to "air attack the incident to death" as a reaction to the rapidly-spread fire. Though it is tempting to hope that the magical flying machines will miraculously stop the fire, in truth, wind-driven fires (over 30 mph) severely limit accuracy of drops and are not cost effective. In addition, pilot safety may be compromised. The incident commander should rapidly evaluate what is in front of the fire and order resources to cover these exposures. Think strike teams, not single resources, if exposures are multiple. Some consideration must also be given to rapidly attacking the flanks once the wind slacks, or the spread will move back upslope (Figure 7e).

D. Lightning Activity with Dry Storm

This is characterized by fully-developed cumulus cell(s) with virga visible. Many times, these cells exceed heights of 40,000 feet, with massive dark-gray bases. As the front moves through an area, it

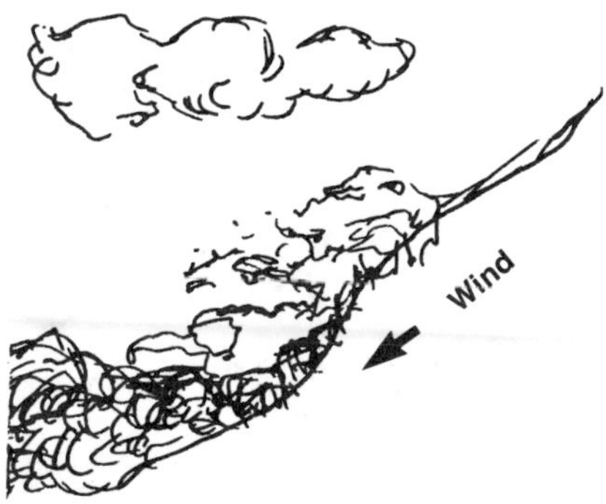

Figure 7e

is important to evaluate if sufficient moisture has reached the surface to extinguish or reduce to a spot down-strikes in dry fuels. If the front is a dry storm, it is important to note its path and start aerial reconnaissance as soon as the pilot feels it is safe. The incident commander faced with a frontal passage must plan for a rapid and radical shift in wind direction and velocity. All personnel should be fully aware of the likely possibility of shifts. Plan ahead and make sure safety zones are frequent and adequate. (Figure 7f).

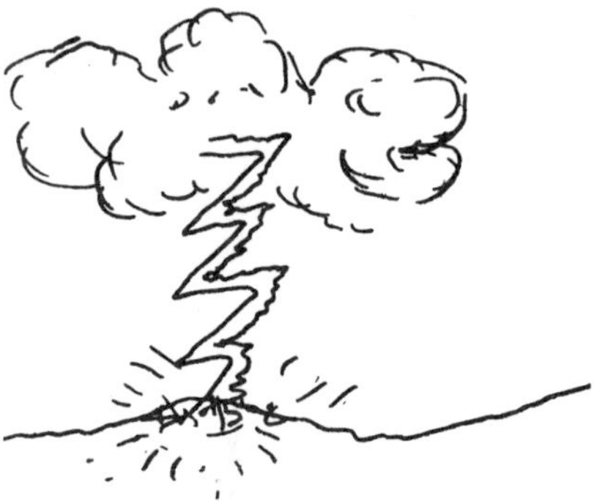

Figure 7f

E. A Stable Air Mass Over a Fire Area

This can be visually identified by a smoke column that rises and starts to stratify with smoky drainages. Overall visibility is limited, and mountains are hard to see clearly in the background. A general rise in relative humidity and a corresponding drop in air temperature are

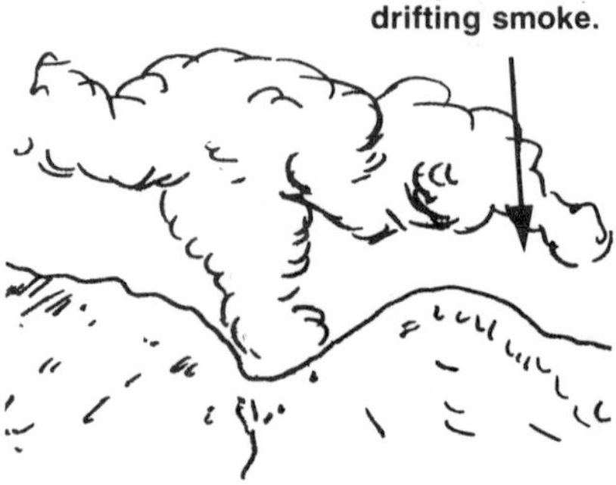
Drainages fill with
drifting smoke.

Figure 7g

associated with stable air. This reduces rate of spread because the condition is usually found in low wind speed models that fail to clear drainages. Incident commanders should be very wary of inversions and their potential for wind changes. Attack methods should take advantage of stable air conditions (Figure 7g).

F. A Smoke Column that Continues to Rise and Is Exhibiting Clear definition (Indicates Unstable Air) (Figure 7h)

This may be associated with low barometric pressures, a front, an adverse wind model or old-age-class fuels. Smoke columns with a large plume and no burning grass are also a likely indicator of high thermal outputs (BTU/sec./ft.) and a moderate-to-high rate of spread. Unstable atmospheric conditions will produce almost unlimited visibility outside the fire area.

Watch for upper-level winds that fracture the column, which could change fire-spread direction. Incident commanders should caution personnel making an aggressive attack on the hot flank in this situation. They should also be alert to the potential for long-range spotting.

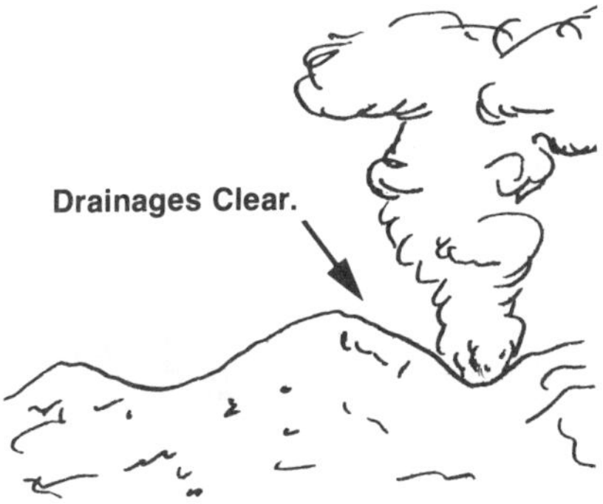

Figure 7h

FUEL-RELATED INDICATORS

A. A Jackpot of Down-dead Fuels in the 100- to 1,000-hour Time-lag Class

These fuels greatly contribute to thermal outputs and often alter attack methods because hand crews are unable to assist in breaking up jackpots prior to constructing a control line. The incident commander should preplan all fuel beds and note the potential for problems associated with poor timber operations, slash piles and snow or pest kill (Figure 7i).

B. A Good Fire Ladder

Figure 7i

Any fuel bed that transitions from grass to medium brush to heavy brush or woodland mix has the potential for exhibiting high rates of spread and thermal outputs. Continuity and arrangement are key variables in this situation. Incident commanders can expect high resistance to control by ground attack. Preplanning will help identify these problem fuel beds.

Fuel beds that have a good transition into aerial fuels often limit ability to utilize air attack because of closed canopies (Figure 7j).

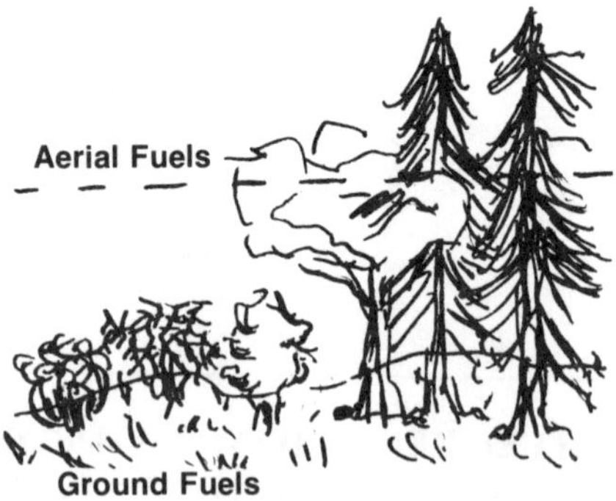

Figure 7j

TOPOGRAPHY-RELATED INDICATORS

A. Saddle Regions

A saddle region is a topographic depression between two high points. Saddles are paths of least resistance. Tremendous heat and high rates of spread into narrow canyons and saddles require incident commanders to evaluate fire spread and potential for the fire to burn when dealing with saddle regions. Hand crew personnel, or dozers working along ridge lines should be alert in these regions and plan safety zones away from saddles (Figure 7k).

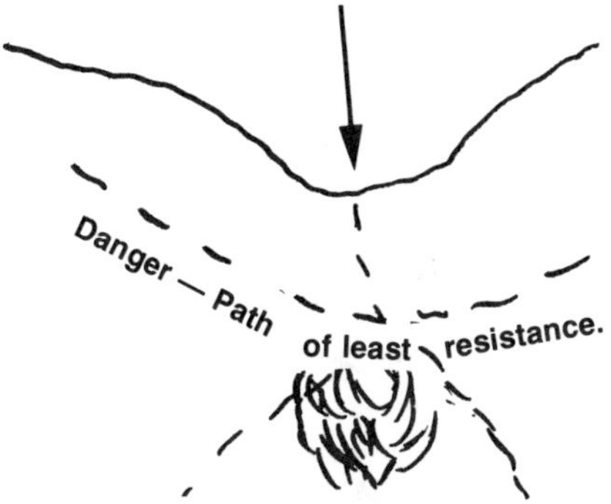

Figure 7k

B. Steep Slopes (Over 50 percent)

Steep slopes can limit or prevent personnel, dozers and brush engines from accessing a fire. More critically, steep slopes modify the flame model, changing a vertical model to horizontal, thus increasing preheating of fuels in front of the fire and rate of spread. (Figure 7l.)

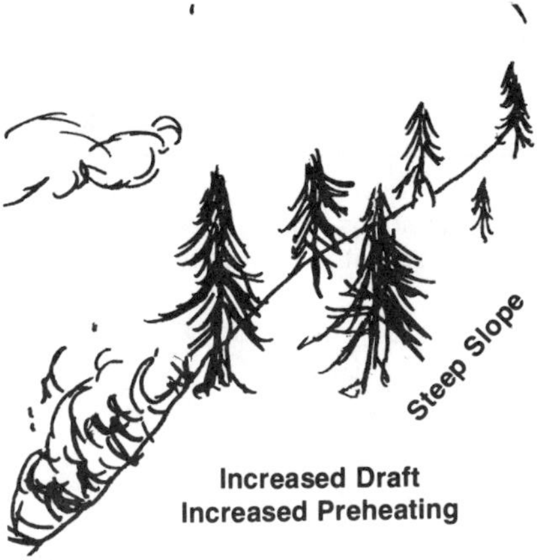

Figure 7l

FIRE-BEHAVIOR-RELATED INDICATORS

A. Dust Devils, Fire Whirls or Fire Storms

These are indicators of instability, triggered by unstable air, intense land heating or broken topography. Fire whirls can greatly modify fire behavior. Even dust devils in the "black area" should be noted, because they may indicate microclimatic instability, which can affect control efforts and an aggressive attack (Figure 7m).

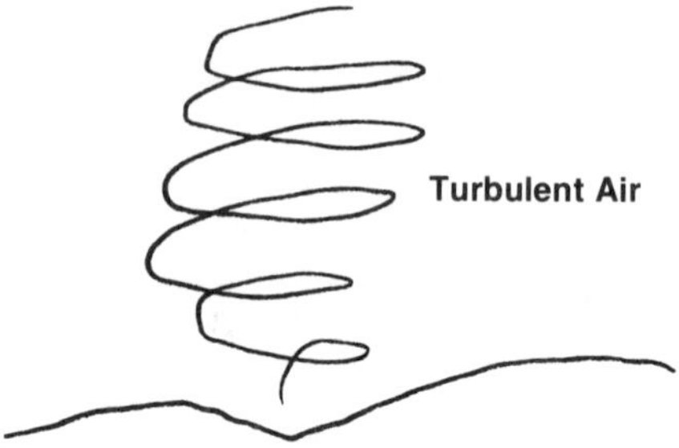
Turbulent Air

Figure 7m

B. Spotting

Spotting ahead of a fire can be an advance indicator of extreme fire behavior. Generally, low live-fuel moistures are associated with this situation. Incident commanders should be extremely conservative in attacking fires in continuous fuel beds of 10-, 100- or 1,000-hour fuel types that exhibit spotting. Be just as cautious about sending hot spot teams to work on these spots. Evaluate winds carefully and, if possible, utilize air attack rather than hand crews if spots are long-range (over one-half mile) ahead of the fire (Figure 7n).

Fuel stems, twigs, leaves,
carried hot in convection column.

Figure 7n

Figure 7o

C. **Smoke Inversion (Figure 7o)**

Be extremely cautious about a fire burning in a well-defined drainage with an inversion forming or present. Inversions allow large-area preheating of fuels, causing fuel ignition temperatures to be lowered and increasing the potential for spotting. If wind conditions change, clearing the inversion or adding oxygen to the fire, change in rate of spread is very likely. Ground personnel should also watch for headaches, fatigue, nausea, vision problems or dizziness – all indicators of low-level carbon monoxide exposure. The incident commander should monitor any injuries occurring in canyon fires extending past one burn period as possibly being caused by carbon monoxide. Establish a safety officer to monitor the situation, if you feel a potential problem exists.

The above are a few key visual indicators that should be evaluated prior to selecting an attack method or deploying personnel. Evaluating these factors will take only a few minutes for the experienced wildland fire officer, but they may be the most valuable minutes that can be spent before assuming command of the incident.

A good portion of these indicators can be preplanned by touring fuel beds prior to fire season. Additionally, topography and access routes should be noted for hazards. Visual indicators may change frequently and be different at every incident, so don't be locked into an aggressive attack method you can't modify should fire behavior change.

Chapter 8

Tactics and Strategy

Prior to discussing tactics and strategy, it's important to review how fireground decisions are made. There are two key factors in good decision making: judgment and potential.

A. JUDGMENT: You need the confidence to say, "Based on my judgment, the situation is of initial attack size/an extended attack/a major emergency." *Make a decision, but be flexible enough to allow for unexpected changes.*

Don't be rushed into early deployment or freelance firefighting actions if you are unsure. Stage the resources, then get a second opinion from the next-in officer. Judgment should not be thought of in terms of good or bad, but rather, *experienced* or *inexperienced.*

B. POTENTIAL: Don't underestimate the fire's potential based on present conditions (weather, topography, fuel, response times, etc.). Order resources and personnel for the worst-case scenario – you can always turn them around.

Tactic and strategy development can be based on an eight-step decision-making process:

1. **Evaluate data** (size-up factors)
2. **State your objectives** (ICS form 201, 202)
3. **Develop an alternate plan** (EFSA)
4. **Anticipate the unexpected** (fire behavior forecast, equipment breakdowns, etc.)
5. **Select a tactical plan** that ensures highest probability of success consistent with personnel safety (EFSA)
6. **Implement the decision** (incident action plan)
7. **Monitor progress** (get feedback, hold briefings and meetings)
8. **Take corrective action, if necessary**

Since wildland fire is a dynamic, ever-changing entity, the incident commander must continue to review decisions and facts as conditions change. The incident commander should consider the following:

1. **Size-up** (evaluate factors, weather probabilities)
2. **Exposures** (wildland fuel bed and structures)
3. **Confinement** (topography factors and access)
4. **Extinguishment** (resources and personnel available)

Once the above items are evaluated, the incident commander can select the most appropriate attack method or combination of methods.

ATTACK METHODS

There are three basic attacks that may be used, either alone or in combination: **direct, indirect and parallel.**

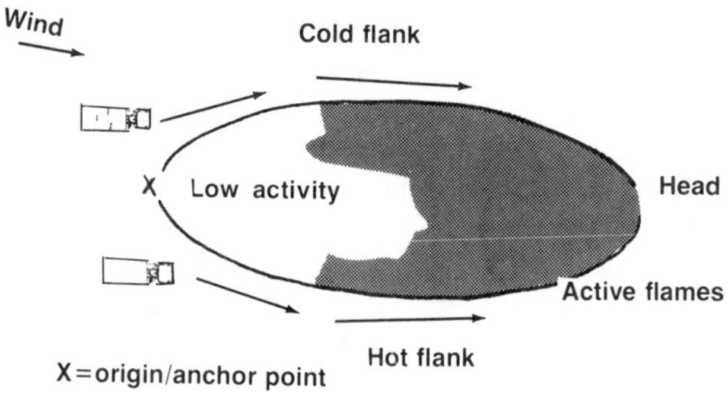

Figure 8a
Direct attack method. Two engine companies working close in with wet lines.

A. DIRECT ATTACK (Figure 8a)

Personnel and resources work close in on the fire's edge. The key features of the attack method are:

1. Cost effectiveness
2. A high degree of firefighter safety
3. By working close in, firefighters are able to monitor thermal limits and fire intensities so as not to over extend safety limits.
4. No additional personnel and resources are required for standby on unburned fuel pockets.
5. Backfiring not necessary
6. Generally, 40 to 50 percent of the burning edge will be low-intensity burning. This usually permits personnel to establish a good anchor point and make progress up the flanks (Figure 8b).

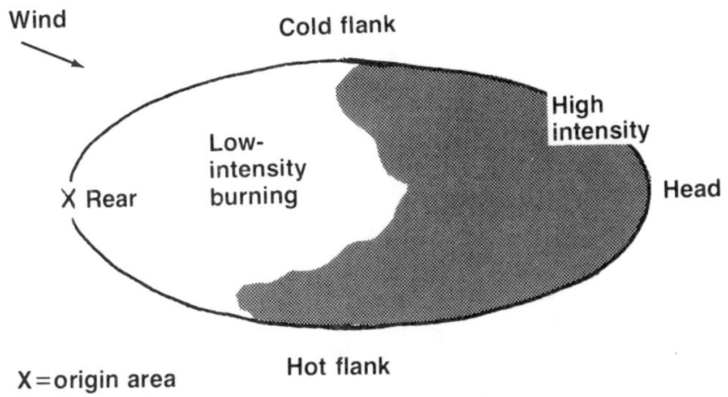

Figure 8b
Fire intensity levels

There are, however, some factors that should be evaluated prior to using the direct attack:

1. Personnel safety

As mentioned earlier, firefighters work close to the fire's edge, and thus are exposed to smoke, heat and super-heated air. This exposure may have little effect, or it may fatigue a crew. If the fire is a developing one and you need initial attack crews for a full shift, the risk of undue fatigue as a result of heat and smoke should receive serious consideration.

2. Increased line construction

The irregular fire associated with a direct attack will create more work and more exposure to heat and smoke.

3. Barriers to fire spread

The direct attack may not take advantage of barriers to fire spread such as creeks, rock outcroppings, old burns, roads or fuel breaks.

4. Reaction to fire-behavior changes

The direct attack affords little time to react to a sudden wind change or short-range spotting that might develop as a line is being constructed.

5. Requires personnel to be in good physical condition

Injuries, fatigue and heat exhaustion could result if the crew is not well conditioned.

The direct attack is generally accomplished by using one of the following methods:

1. Flank attack

Work hot flank, envelop head, complete control line on cold flank (Figure 8c).

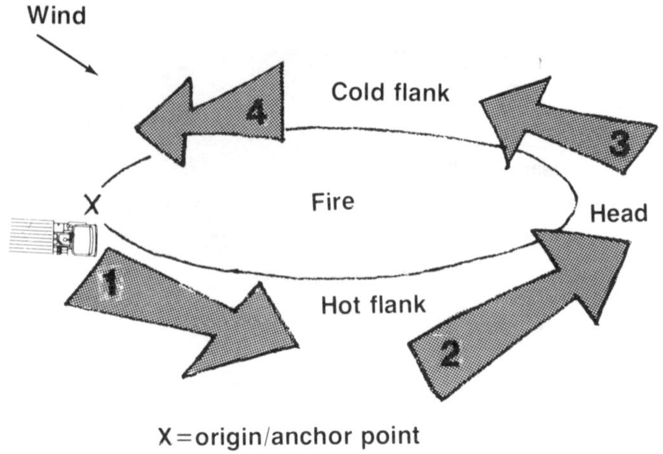

Figure 8c
Flank attack priorities

2. Pincer action

Split crew or resources from common anchor point, slowly reducing width of head (Figure 8d).

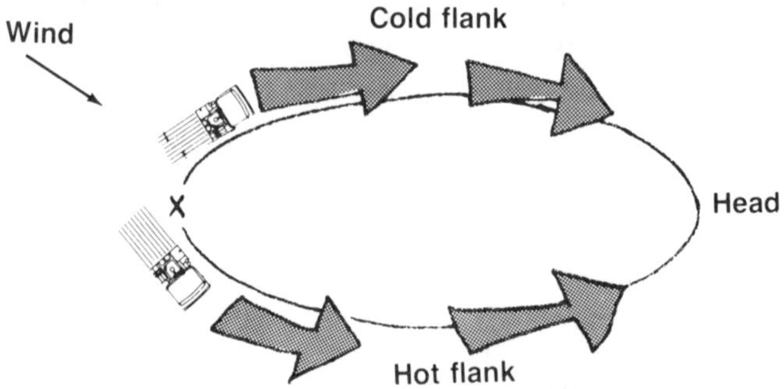

Figure 8d X=origin/anchor point
Pincer action with two engine companies

3. Envelopment

Use multiple anchor points. Work on head (not flank), cold flank simultaneously (Figure 8e).

B. INDIRECT ATTACK

Many times, fire behavior, fuel types, resources and personnel available preclude an aggressive direct attack. The indirect-attack method allows the incident commander to back off and use (Figure 8f):

1. Natural barriers

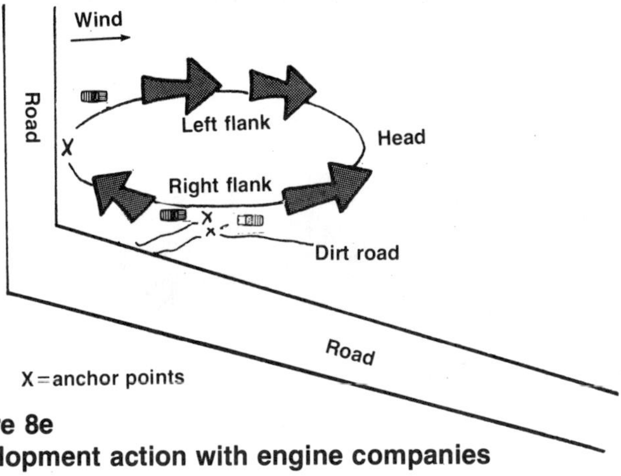

Figure 8e
Envelopment action with engine companies

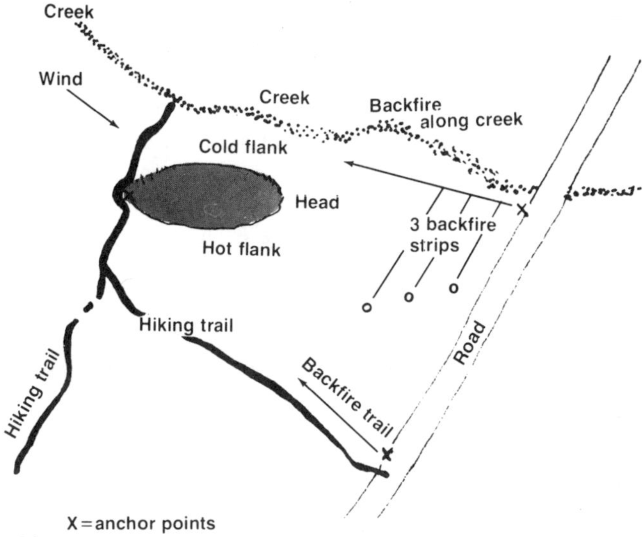

Figure 8f
Indirect attack using natural barriers and backfiring

2. Backfiring

3. Personnel and resources (without undue smoke and heat exposure)

4. More planning as the incident develops

The indirect attack can be a very effective tool for an incident commander who has pre-planned fuel bed(s). Backfiring can be used to reduce personnel's risk of exposure to heat and smoke. It should

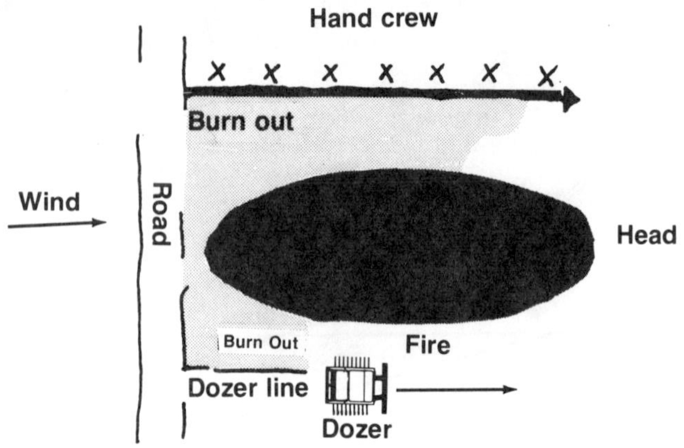

Figure 8g
The parallel attack using a hand crew and dozer burn out.

be noted, however, that some regions have restrictions on backfires.

Backfiring must be coordinated and carried out by seasoned, experienced wildland firefighters. Timing firing sequences and coordinating with other personnel and resources are critical.

The indirect attack allows the incident commander time to acquire more personnel and resources in the staging area prior to launching the attack. Some factors that must be evaluated prior to the indirect attack include:

1. Resource values

The fuel bed may be valuable timber or watershed. The negative impacts of letting it burn may far outweigh the positive effects of backfiring the fuel.

2. Fire behavior

A basic field rule of thumb states, "As fire history doubles, rate of spread doubles." The longer the fire burns, the more chances for adverse fire behavior.

3. Risks associated with backfiring:

- **Wind changes**
- **Timing**
- **Assuming proper firing sequence**
- **Speed of firing operation**
- **Holding resources and personnel**
- **Exposure of personnel, if things go badly**
- **Once you start to backfire, it's hard to shut down**

C. PARALLEL ATTACK

This attack method is primarily made by hand crews and bulldozers when intense heat and/or fire spread preclude direct attack. Hand crew(s) and/or dozers back off five to 50 feet and parallel the flank (Figure 8g).

The parallel attack is used in conjunction with **burnout.** The key to successful and safe use of this attack is a good anchor point and not getting too far in front of the firing team. A parallel attack reduces the length of control line and overhaul time. The only real concerns associated with this attack method are:

1. Risk to personnel working in unburned fuel.

2. Experienced personnel are essential to conduct burnout. Timing and speed of firing are important.

3. Coordinating the attack.

BURNOUT

Burnout is used to strengthen and straighten control lines by eliminating fuel between the control line and the fire's edge by burning it (Figure 8h). The black-line concept states, "A fireline is not complete

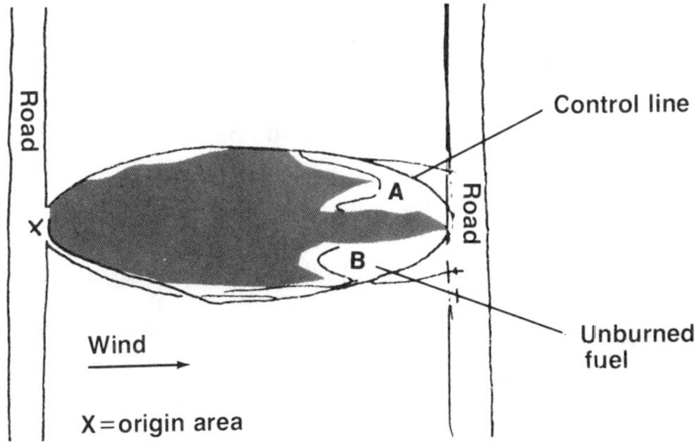

Figure 8h
Burn out. Once the control line is completed, burn out pockets of unburned fuel (A,B) to prevent a reburn.

until the fuel between the fire's edge and the control line is removed (black)." Generally, this is best accomplished by locating the line directly on the fire's edge.

Other methods of removing fuel include cold-trailing, cutting and burning fuel.

Every company officer and crew supervisor should be trained in and responsible for performing burnout as a part of line construction. Burning out should not be delayed; it must be accomplished concurrently with line construction. Avoid leaving this task until after the line is constructed.

By tying control lines to the fire's edge or to natural barriers, several crews may burn out at the same time. Each crew supervisor must assure coordinated communication and the safety of adjoining forces.

Burning out can be effectively used where construction of a direct line on the fire's edge is not reasonable because of fire intensity, fuels or topography, or there is a shortage of control forces to complete the line.

Burning out eliminates fuel concentrations adjacent to the control line, reducing re-burn or spotting potential. Cutting a line across "fingers" or around two or more outside spot fires and then burning out the remaining fuels will shorten the line and reduce the total line-construction assignment.

Being able to recognize situations that lend themselves to burning out will help in constructing narrower lines. It is best to burn in fuel types with less resistance to control such as open spots or grassy areas. Another good line-location practice is to take advantage of existing natural and man-made barriers such as roads, trails, streams or rock slides. Properly-accomplished burning out will reduce the number of holding forces required and minimize mop up or cold trailing.

Elaborate equipment is not required to burn out. Take advantage of the resources at hand by carrying burning materials on a shovel or dragging yucca stalks or other burning natural fuels across areas to be ignited. Fusees, drip torches and other firing devices are also fine, if available.

The features of burning out are:

A. Burn out can be accomplished where it is not feasible to locate a

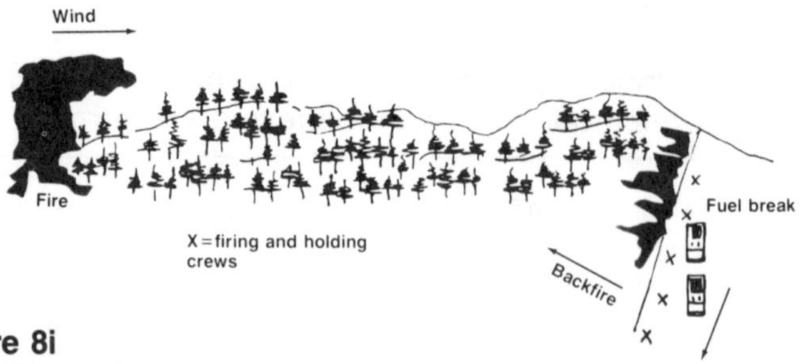

Figure 8i
Backfiring. A rapidly-developing timber fire with spotting visible. Backfiring is initiated from a fuel break well in advance of the fire front.

line on the fire's edge.

B. It strengthens the line by eliminating adjacent fuel concentrations.

C. It straightens the line by cutting across fingers and around concentrations of spot fires.

D. Locating the line in lighter fuels allows for a narrower line.

E. It encourages taking advantage of natural and man-made barriers.

F. It can be used when needed as part of the line-construction assignment.

G. It should not be delayed – burn out must be accomplished concurrently with line construction.

H. Properly accomplished burning out will reduce the amount of holding forces required and minimize mop up and cold trailing.

BACKFIRING

Backfiring is a technique associated with the indirect attack method and typically used against rapidly-spreading fires (Figure 8i). The area between the control line and the fire's edge is intentionally fired, (1) to eliminate fuel in advance of the fire, thus widening the control line, (2) to change the direction of the fire and (3) to slow the fire's progress.

Backfiring requires considerable preparation, organization and coordination. The decision to backfire is normally made by the incident commander, through operations, and put into effect at the division level. Under special circumstances and in emergencies, company officers (initial attack company) are authorized to initiate backfiring.

Safety must be given first priority. No backfiring action, regardless of strategic importance or other critical factors, is worth risking human life. Calculating the risks, including results of backfiring or failing to fire, is necessary, as backfiring can result in loss of control line. Knowledge of when and how to conduct backfiring is essential, since many fires with conflagration potential can be successfully controlled in the early stages with only limited suppression forces using this technique. Overall fire strategy must be clear to all personnel employing backfiring, since fire behavior or fire control operations on adjacent division(s) are likely to be affected.

When to backfire

Backfiring should fit incident fire behavior. When the main fire is burning intensely, backfire aggressively. If the main fire is not spreading rapidly, usually other tactics, such as direct attack or cold trailing, are preferable.

When weather, fuel and topography combine to allow successful backfiring, the operation should proceed without delay. Too many fires are lost by waiting for approval by a higher authority, more preparation or additional holding forces. Sometimes, immediate firing action is the only chance to control the fire.

Organization

One experienced and qualified individual should be responsible for managing and coordinating the entire firing operation. All personnel involved must understand this. This individual should not personally carry out firing but should give undivided attention to supervising the firing team. He/she must keep aware of fire intensity and any changes in the weather as well as stay in communication with the team firing boss at all times.

A minimum number of skilled people should be assigned to the firing team. Depending on the technique (strip or line firing), this number may be anywhere from three to seven, excluding holding personnel. They must be supervised closely by the firing boss. Constant communication, pre-planned escape routes and safety zones are necessary.

Personnel assigned to the line holding crew should never be ahead of the firing team. The holding crew will burn out the line behind them for an escape route. Using large crews for this activity should be avoided, since control of many personnel is often difficult and more time is required should they be forced to temporarily abandon a section of line.

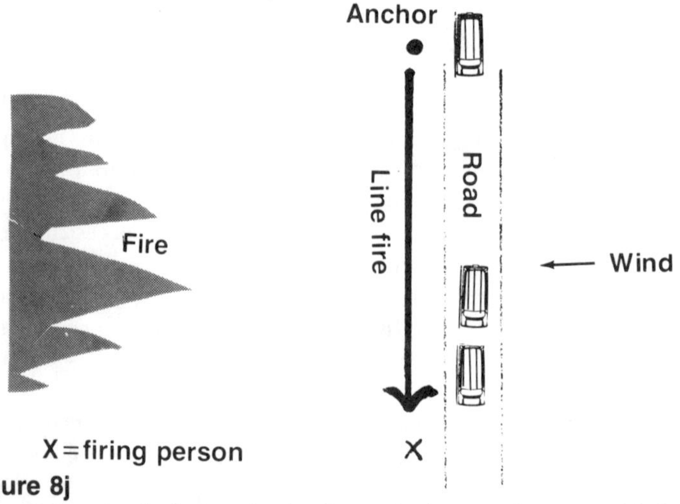

Figure 8j
Line firing technique. A single strip is set three to 10 feet off the road or natural barrier. Wind speed will determine strip width.

Effect of Using Fire on Fire

Active fire (either backfire or main fire) is "magnetic," that is, it attracts other fires, or, rather, they attract one another. Larger, more-intense fires have a stronger, greater-distance effect than do smaller, slower-burning fires.

Firing Methods

A. Timing or Starting

Backfiring against the advancing heads of the main fire, when draft from the main fire is noticeable, will cause backfire to be sucked away from the control line.

B. Line Firing

A single strip fired from a road or natural barrier is most effective when wind aids the backfire (Figure 8j).

C. Strip Firing

Firing strips of fuel inside the control line will draw final backfiring (set after strip is ignited) away from the control line. Stagger progress of personnel burning strips so that the person closest to the fire is in the lead (Figure 8k).

Firing concentrations of fuel inside control line may create favorable indrafts, allowing successful backfiring from control lines in fuel too light or with too much moisture for clean burning. These indrafts may minimize spot fires from the backfire.

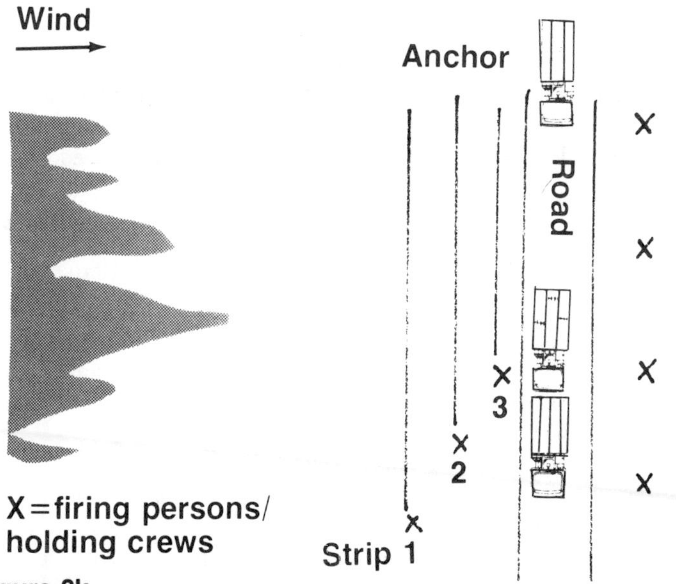

Figure 8k
Strip-firing technique

Backfiring Considerations

A. Backfiring must not jeopardize the safety of personnel or equipment or invalidate suppression action on adjacent divisions. *Determining this is absolutely mandatory prior to firing.*

B. Most successful backfiring is conducted from completed control lines. These are best located at a break in the topography. The lee side of the ridge tops is often the best choice. Canyon bottoms are the second choice and road crossings in thermal belts the third. The third choice – road crossings in thermal belts – is dangerous from the personnel safety standpoint, and requires the most skill and understanding of fire behavior.

C. If necessary, and time allows, concentrations of fuel adjacent to and inside the control line should be removed or scattered prior to backfiring. Snags may be felled or ringed. Fuels inside the line should not be wet down prior to firing.

D. Fuel concentrations outside the control line may be removed, scattered, covered with dirt, wet down or treated by ground or aerial retardant applications.

E. Holding forces should be augmented by pre-positioned hose lays, brush trucks, portable pumps, bulldozers, extra hand crew personnel and/or air tanker support. It's also a good idea to have an air attack supervisor stationed over a backfiring operation to evaluate and assist the firing supervisor/division supervisor.

F. Critical points such as hooks in the line, saddles or "V" shaped canyons will require extra reinforcement.

G. If fuel is insufficient to develop the heat needed for a clean burn, things can be helped along by rearranging existing fuels inside the line or cutting and stacking additional fuel to be fired where needed.

H. Occasionally, backfiring can be successful with minimum preparation. For example, grass to be fired from a wet line or a cow trail with brush truck or crew support and favorable wind.

Firing Order

Backfiring must start at, and proceed from, an anchor point. This may be the intersection of a control line and/or road, stream, rock outcropping, or cold burn. Sometimes an anchor point will have to be constructed.

Firing should progress along control lines without interruption, if possible, usually starting adjacent to the head of the fire and proceeding around toward flanks. It's again important to stress that once the decision to fire has been made, no delays should take place.

Normally, in broken topography with the main fire spreading uphill, backfiring should start at higher elevations and proceed along control lines to progressively lower levels. This limits the intense uphill runs from backfire that occur if lower portions are fired first (Figure 8l). In some situations, if strong downslope winds overcome

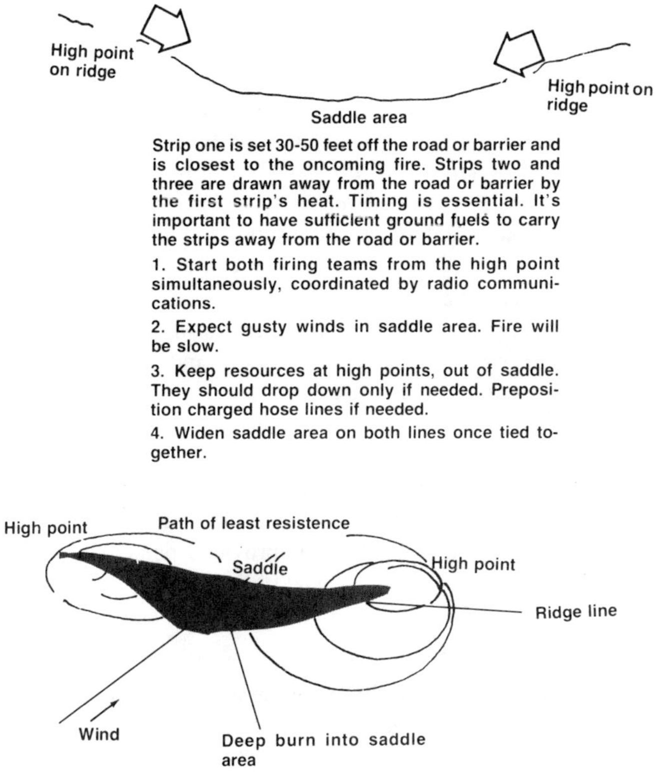

High point on ridge
High point on ridge
Saddle area
Strip one is set 30-50 feet off the road or barrier and is closest to the oncoming fire. Strips two and three are drawn away from the road or barrier by the first strip's heat. Timing is essential. It's important to have sufficient ground fuels to carry the strips away from the road or barrier.
1. Start both firing teams from the high point simultaneously, coordinated by radio communications.
2. Expect gusty winds in saddle area. Fire will be slow.
3. Keep resources at high points, out of saddle. They should drop down only if needed. Preposition charged hose lines if needed.
4. Widen saddle area on both lines once tied together.
High point
Path of least resistence
Saddle
High point
Ridge line
Wind
Deep burn into saddle area

Figure 8l
Firing off a ridge into a saddle

the effect of terrain and fire is spreading downhill, lower elevation control lines should be fired first, again with the purpose of avoiding hard-to-control runs from the backfire.

Progress of the main fire may prove to be uneven, approaching the control line at different points. These may require firing out of the planned sequence. Critical points (saddles, hooks in line, narrow canyons or structures) may dictate firing order.

Rate of Firing

Backfiring can be carried forward only as fast as the line being fired can be held. Holding crews should not be exposed to intense heat and smoke for extended periods, as fatigue and heat exhaustion may preclude the crew's ability to react. If wind, topography and fuel factors are favorable, control lines should be fired quickly, even with minimum holding forces. If the wind changes while you wait for more support, you may have a more difficult job on your hands, even with the extra crew, equipment and preparation.

Adequate backfire development is necessary *before* the main fire reaches the control line. Fuel concentration adjacent to the control line must be reduced to improve chances of successful holding. If the backfire is too late, the impact of the main fire on the control line may be worsened. *The objective is to draw the backfire to the main fire, with the impact area at a safe distance from the control line.* "Safe distance" is a matter of judgment, based upon topography, fuel type, wind and fire behavior. (The smoke column can also be used to estimate potential for spotting.)

Firing at critical points should be done cautiously, at a rate consistent with the number of holding crew(s) needed and available. Generally, only short sections of line are fired at a time, since spot fires across the line are easier to control in smaller sections involving fewer spots.

If it becomes apparent that the control line is likely to be lost due to spotting or too rapid progress by the main fire, often the best course of action is to proceed with backfiring, provided personnel safety is assured. This action may narrow the head of the fire or reduce its intensity, allowing easier control. The key is adequate safety zones and escape routes for personnel.

Firing under conditions adverse to control

The single-most effective key to successful backfiring under severe conditions is to regulate heat from the backfire.

A. Severe Wind

When backfiring against the wind, sparks may be carried across the line or flame may lay over the line. Strip-burning short sections (kept under control by holding crews), constructing the line at right angles to the control line and hot spotting will help reinforce control.

After sufficient strip burning is accomplished, "pie slices" are cut deeper, involving enough fire to create indrafts and draw the final backfire away from the control line.

B. Adverse Slopes

When firing from the top of a slope, strip burning is again employed in a manner similar to that used against severe wind. Care must be taken to limit both length and width of strips, so volume of the fire adjacent to the line can be handled by available holding crew(s). Guard against fire rolling downhill into heavy fuels, as this will result in an intense run back uphill against the control line. As strip firing reinforces the control line, progressively larger strips can be involved.

C. Extreme Turbulence

When the atmosphere of the fire area is unstable, minor changes resulting from backfiring may trigger erratic fire behavior. Fire whirls and intense backfire or main-fire runs may result. Locating lines further away from the main fire sometimes minimizes this problem. Pre-laid, pre-charged hose lines, careful choice of order and extent of firing and avoiding rapid burning of heavy fuel concentrations may also be helpful.

D. Fuel

1. If backfiring threatens to crown in timber when the main fire is mostly on the ground, if possible, fire so backfire progresses downhill against the wind, thus slowing the backfire. Also, if time allows, remove intermediate fuel (cut reproduction and prune poles) inside the line.

2. If you want to keep the crown fire from backfiring, as in a situation where the fire is burning only ground fuels but drying out crowns (thus setting up conditions for a re-burn – a situation to be avoided), fire so backfire progresses uphill or with the wind, if possible. This will speed up and intensify the backfire. Adding fuel, re-arranging existing fuel or using firing devices that add fuel, such as diesel, may be employed.

Critical points

These should be identified in advance of firing, and extra precautions taken against loss of control. Generally, their effect is minimized if the firing team can inspect the line to be fired in advance, during daylight. Often, a few minutes invested in either general or aerial inspection is worthwhile.

A. Saddles

Saddles are critical because they invite increased, erratic air movement, influenced by terrain, prevailing weather and the effect of the fire.

These are generally fired downhill from each side simultaneously, meeting at the low point in the saddle to avoid intense uphill runs. Anchor points are necessary on each side prior to start of firing. A wide control line is desirable. Wind eddies should be expected and may create spotting problems in the saddle.

B. Hooks, Sharp Turns or Square Corners in the Line

These, especially around a ridge, may expose line around the corner to spotting from the backfire. Strip firing well inside the control line may draw sparks and flame away from the line. Simultaneous

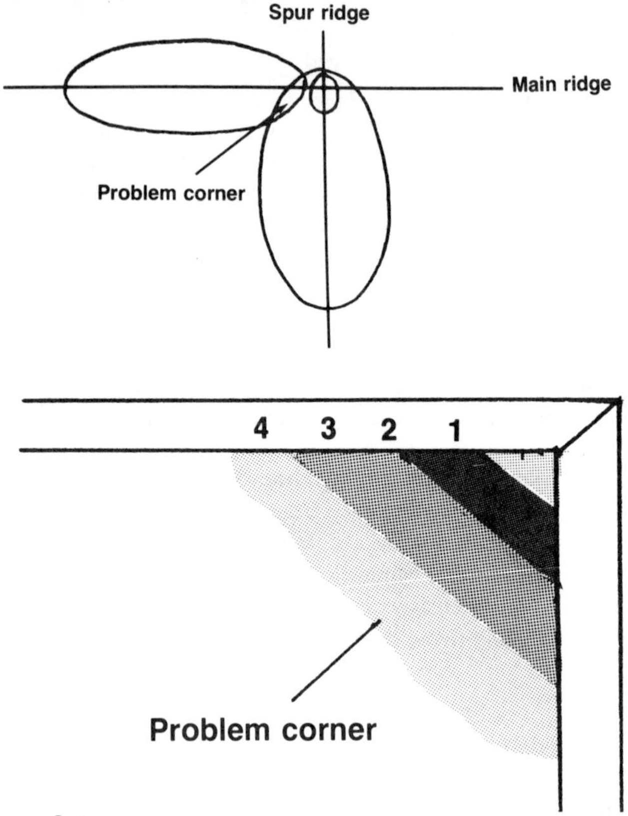

Figure 8m
Firing out a problem corner

firing from both sides into a hook, as in the saddle situation, is sometimes employed (Figure 8m).

C. "V"-shaped Canyons

Should the control line cross a canyon, the situation may become critical due to exposure of fuel outside the line to spotting. Again, careful strip firing or simultaneous firing from each slope at the top progressing into the canyon bottom – or combinations of these – may be successful. Hot runs from backfiring are to be avoided, to minimize spotting and slop-overs.

D. Structures and Improvements

If these are located inside the area to be fired, take special precautions. Exposure, value and type of construction should be taken into consideration in addition to normal fire calculations. If possible, locate the line to exclude these. If this is not possible, firing around these first may minimize damage, or loss of homes, etc. *Never* fire so as to involve these until positive that residents have been evacuated. Often, when structures are numerous and valuable, their presence forces a change of tactics.

Unexpected Situation Requiring Backfiring

Occasionally, a situation may develop requiring an immediate backfire. Company officers and crew supervisors should be authorized to initiate backfiring, provided:

A. The action does not jeopardize safety of personnel or invalidate action on adjacent divisions.

B. Action of the fire, change in weather or fire behavior requires this course of action.

C. The incident commander, operations chief or division supervisor cannot be reached within allowed time limits for a decision.

All three of the above conditions must be present before the experienced company officer or crew supervisor should backfire without orders. In this situation, the company officer or crew supervisor personally directs backfiring and informs the division supervisor of the change in tactics as soon as possible.

Chapter 9

Air Resources

Air attack resources consist of fixed or rotary wing aircraft used to support ground operations. Air attack can be most effective when used as an initial-attack tool.

Efficient use of air programs must start with response criteria based on weather models, response times or incident potential. If air attack is not going to be dispatched with the initial attack, weather models provide a good basis for responses. This requires some research to study the past 10 years of wildland fire history and weather. Determine the number of high fire weather days per year (days over 90-degrees F with 20 percent or less relative humidity or a wind model over 15 mph). During these days, the response of air resources should be automatic during initial attack.

Additionally, company officers should have the responsibility and authority as initial-attack incident commanders to request an air attack. During annual pre-fire planning, the company officer should visualize where air attack could be used to support ground operations. Some key points for determining this include:

A. **Fuel Type**
B. **Fuel Age Class** (brush)
C. **Canopy** (closed/open)
D. **Fuel Loading**
E. **Topography**
F. **Elevation** (above sea level)
G. **Hazards** (power lines, dwellings)

Air-attack resources are most effective in light fuel types like grass or sage. The lack of canopy in grass and the open, fine canopy in sage allow for good retardant penetration and coverage. Company officers should remember this when selecting a line location for an indirect attack or pre-treatment.

As the fuel-bed age class increases, fuel canopies will thicken and close up, making penetration and coverage difficult. Penetration and coverage will also be difficult in mature timber species.

Fuel loading is closely related to age class in importance when considering brush species. Most grass or light fuel types have fuel loading under three-quarter tons per acre. This loading generally produces flame lengths of one to three feet, with thermal outputs as low as 95 to 125 BTU/sec./ft. of flame front. Under these conditions, water or retardant dropped from the air can be effective.

As fuel loading increases, effectiveness drops. Most chaparral species are capable of 10- to 35-foot flame heights and thermal outputs of 700-to-7,000 BTU/sec./ft. of flame front. These conditions can create adverse fire behavior and super-heated air above the canopy region. This will often modify and/or dry out water or retardant before it reaches the fuel canopy. Down-dead chaparral or timber species can also create super-heated air above the fuel canopy.

Broken topography, narrow drainages and hog-back ridge lines must also be evaluated. Broken topography features can create wind eddies – which may cause air turbulence for helicopters or air tankers. Narrow, steep drainages are tough targets for aircraft. Narrow hog backs can also be very turbulent, as lee side winds affect the rising convective column.

Helicopters are affected by air density. When high air temperatures are coupled with landing elevations above 5,000 feet, load capacity is reduced significantly. Elevation can also force air tankers

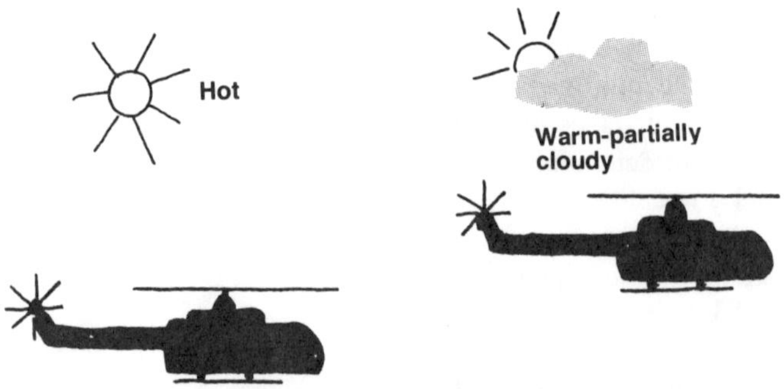

Density altitude is used in calculating the capability of an aircraft to support a load in flight. The more dense the atmosphere, the more weight it will support. Hot, dry days cause download.

Figure 9a

to download from normal retardant capacity. (Figure 9a.)

Hazards come in several forms. High-tension power lines top the list. Housing subdivisions are also hazards. Cumulus clouds above drainages are also dangerous, because of down drafts.

Air attack is very costly, often exceeding $1,000 per hour. The company officer must prepare in advance in order to use this resource cost effectively. Important considerations include:

A. Contacting radio frequency
B. Contacting supervisor by call sign (e.g., "Fox Operations")
C. Orienting over incident (e.g., north-south or landmark)
D. Setting tactical objectives for aircraft (pilot(s) oriented to the fire)
E. Briefing pilots on tanker/helicopter hazards (towers, wires, other aircraft assigned to the fire)
F. Allowing for safe helispot(s) (Figure 9b).

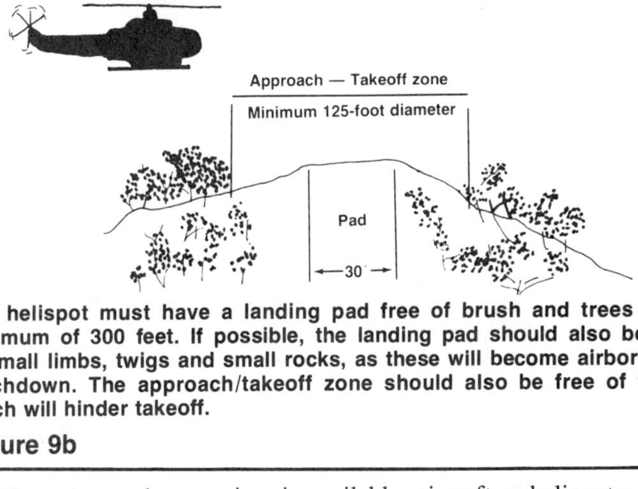

The helispot must have a landing pad free of brush and trees for a minimum of 300 feet. If possible, the landing pad should also be free of small limbs, twigs and small rocks, as these will become airborne on touchdown. The approach/takeoff zone should also be free of trees, which will hinder takeoff.

Figure 9b

If no air attack supervisor is available, aircraft or helicopter pilots should answer directly to the operations chief or incident commander. The contact frequency for this individual should be given with the request for air attack, for instance, "Contact Fox Operations on 154.280."

It's important that "orbit time" be reduced over an incident. To accomplish this, review tactical objectives. Once objectives are set, orient the pilot(s) over the incident as they arrive on scene and ask for information. Most pilots will initiate radio contact three minutes prior to arrival to remind you they are available. For the most part, pilots are very experienced and know their aircraft's capabilities and limitations. The company officer should review his/her tactical objectives with the pilot and ask for an opinion. (This assumes no air attack supervisor is available. If on scene, the AAS should be consulted.)

Smoke conditions, air turbulence, fire behavior, topography and hazards are easily recognized by aircraft pilots. It may be necessary for them to make several observation orbits to fulfill your request, however.

Some key guidelines for dealing with pilots include:

A. **Have all ground personnel out of target area prior to final run.** (This is an often-violated rule.)
B. **Advise all bulldozer operators in the area of drops so they can be prepared.**
C. **Don't request uphill runs.**
D. **Don't ask pilots to fly into a smoke column.**
E. **Honor the pilot's professional judgment.**
F. **Don't argue with the pilot.**
G. **Keep radio traffic to pilots at a minimum.** (After you give the pilot(s) the assignment, let them ask questions until the drop run is complete. This is very important.)
H. **Give pilot(s) feedback on drop accuracy and effectiveness *after* the run is complete.**
I. **Utilize scene flight rules**

If the fire escalates into an extended attack or major incident, Federal Air Regulations Part 91.91 (air space restriction) can be used to secure air space over and around your incident. Some information you will need to provide includes:

A. **Restricted Area Size** (i.e., a circle five miles from the center point of the incident).

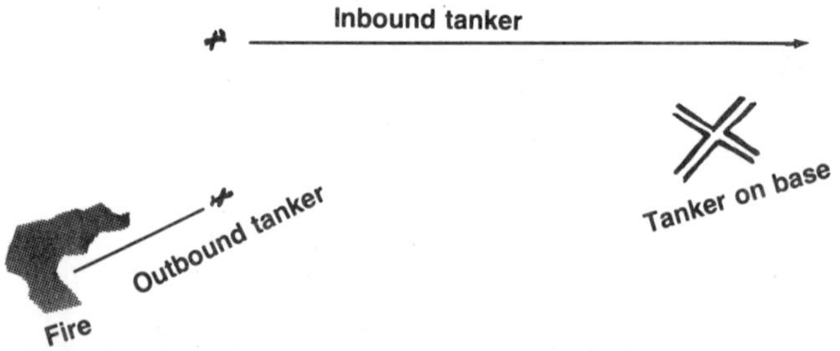

To keep an air tanker constantly over the incident, you will probably need three air tankers, assuming your reload base is 15-20 minutes from the incident. In the above example, one air tanker has dropped its load and is outbound to the tanker base (reload). The second air tanker is on base reloading and the third is inbound to the incident.

Figure 9c

B. Ceiling Elevation of Restriction (i.e., 2,500 feet above ground level).

Remember to cancel the restriction after the incident. Local airport officials can give you exact procedures for requesting this advisory.

Some regions have adopted a wise safety policy of issuing dozer operators and hand crews "red smoke" grenades. These grenades are used in an emergency to signal for an immediate air drop. Pilots should be advised that red smoke gets immediate priority over all other non-life-safety tasks. Pilots and AASs should always be alert for red smoke while flying over an incident.

Incident Command System Aircraft Resource Typing

TYPE 1	TYPE 2	TYPE 3	TYPE 4
AIRTANKER			
2,000 gallons retardant capacity	1,000 gallons retardant capacity	800 gallons retardant capacity	600 gallons retardant capacity
HELICOPTER			
16-person capacity, 700 gallons retardant/water capacity	10-person capacity, 300 gallons retardant/water capacity	5-person capacity, 100 gallons retardant/water capacity	3-person capacity, 75 gallons retardant/water capacity

Obviously, it is important to use the right aircraft for the tactical objective. Realizing however, that you have to use what resources are available, we can develop some basic guidelines:

A. To keep one air tanker over your incident you will probably need to assign three (Figure 9c).

B. Helicopters are very effective in supporting hand crews and dozers on an active portion of the line.

C. Helicopters are very accurate and effective on spot fires.

D. Helicopters are a very good resource for aerial reconnaissance.

E. Twin-engine air tankers (Type 2 or 3) with 800-to-1,000-gallon retardant capacity and four to six doors are very effective for direct-attack, split-load applications and supporting crews and dozers on active portions of the line.

F. Twin-engine air tankers (Type 2 or 3) with the same capabilities listed in E are excellent for picking up spot fires.

G. Twin-engine air tankers (Type 2 or 3) are effective in narrow canyons. (Use pilot discretion.)

H. Multi-engine air tankers (Type 1) with 2,000-to-3,000-gallon retardant capacity and six to eight doors are excellent for making a long trail drop on a flank or ridge line.

I. Multi-engine air tankers (Type 1) can be very effective to pre-treat an area prior to backfiring.

J. Multi-engine air tankers (Type 1) can be effective in penetrating some heavy canopies.

K. Multi-engine air tankers (Type 1) are very effective on multiple targets (spots).

When using two or more air-attack resources, request an air attack supervisor if one has not responded. The air attack supervisor flies in a light plane and directs air traffic and air tanker operations (and helicopters). *If an air-attack supervisor responds, he/she is your contact rather than the pilot.*

Let's consider some tactics for air-attack resources. Say, for instance, the fire is in a grass and sage mix, burning upslope. Wind is from the southwest and under 10 mph. The fire is seven to 10 acres in size, with a narrow head. No aircraft hazards exist in the fire area (Figure 9d).

The first drop priority is to cool the fire's head while pre-treating unburned fuels ahead of the fire. This will slow the combustion process and reduce short-range spotting potential ahead of the fire.

Depending on the size of the air tanker, this first priority may be

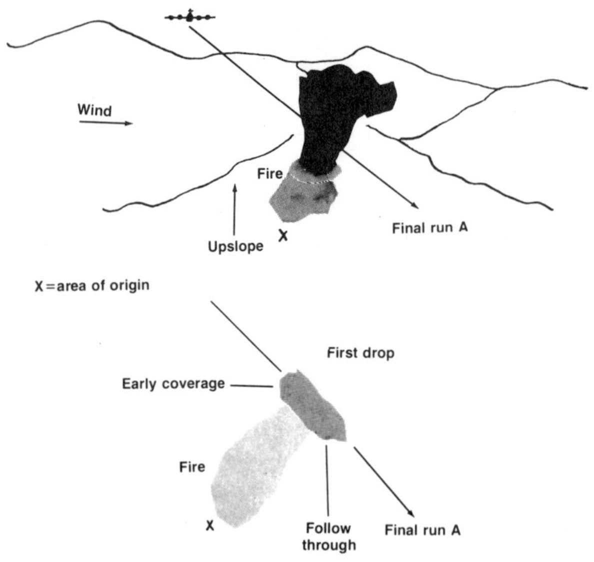

Good early coverage and follow through are important for subsequent runs down each flank. Note high percentage of drop in unburned fuels (pretreatment).

Figure 9d

accomplished with one split load (two-to-four doors) or several single-door passes. Door selection may be based on fuel type, air turbulence or pilot or air-attack supervisors' judgment.

In the example, the need for additional drops is dependent on what progress personnel and resources have made up the flanks. Let's assume the hot flank (east) is burning at too high a temperature for personnel and a dozer working that flank. The personnel move back down from the projected target area (Figure 9e). Now the second

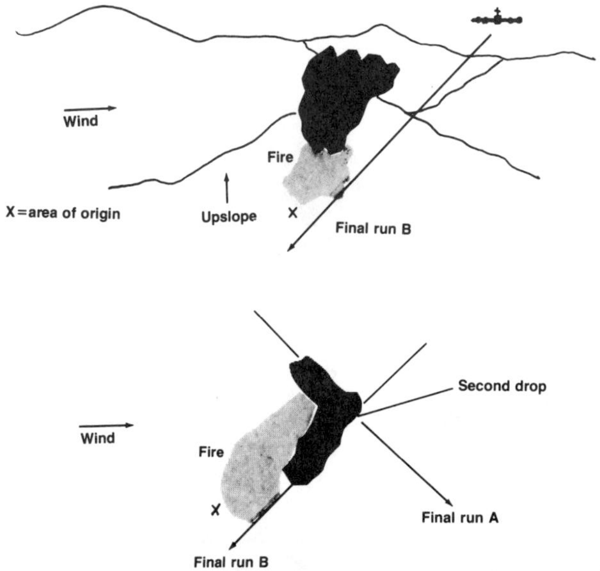

Second run moves down the hot flank. The key to this drop is to adequately tie into the follow through from the first drop.

Figure 9e

drop overlaps (ties into) the first drop, which is placed across the head. This tie-in is important if you want to keep the fire from fingering through the retardant and you plan to place personnel in target areas to complete the control line.

If conditions warrant, and personnel safety can be ensured, the cold flank can be tied into the head as illustrated above (Figure 9f).

In an air operation such as the one in the example, you could probably accomplish all three tactical objectives with one Type 1 air tanker (2,000-to-3,000 gallons retardant). A Type 2 air tanker (1,000 gallons) may only be able to accomplish the first and second priority without a re-load.

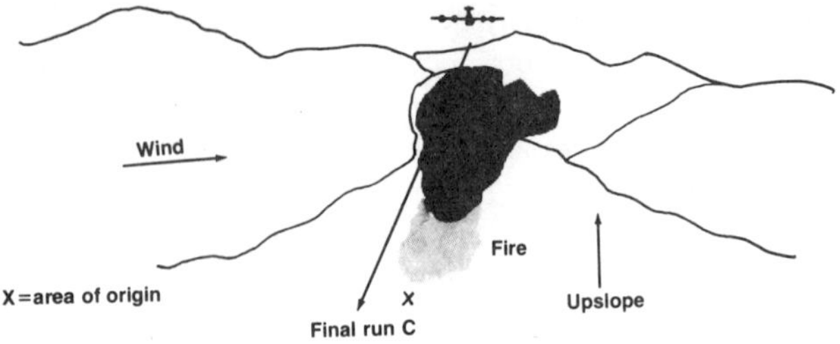

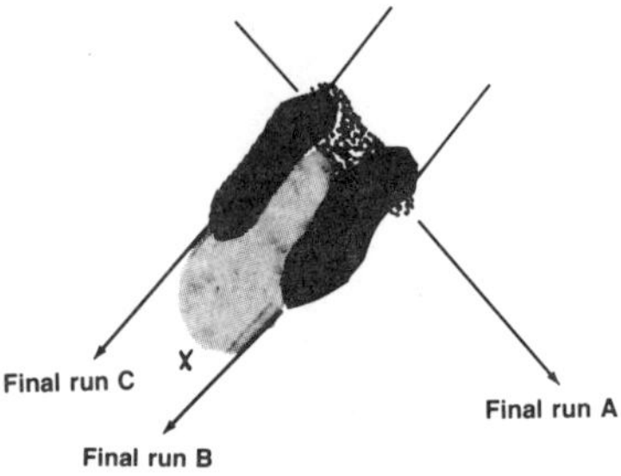

The first drop on the spot fire is intended to stop forward spread. Depending on spot size, this drop may exhibit sufficient cooling and accuracy to pick up the total spot. A second drop will guard against any lateral spread and finish cooling down the spot. Depending on weather conditions and rate of spread, these drops may assist in picking up the hot flank of the main fire.

Figure 9f

When planning for a developing seven-to-10-acre grass and sage fire with good potential like the one in the example, I recommend that you formulate your basic incident control objectives and envision how retardant might assist you in accomplishing them. A basic guide to retardant length and width drop patterns is found in Figure 9g.

Of course, the above are just guidelines – air temperature, relative humidity and wind speed will all affect the drop's characteristics and effectiveness. You can use a topography map to measure and plot drops and coverage areas.

Once a basic overlay of potential drops is plotted on the map, you can estimate drop patterns and need for aircraft. For example, on a grass fire, the retardant coverage may require only a one-door aircraft to assure the width necessary for the retardant pattern. This means that a twin engine (Type 3) aircraft carrying 800 gallons of retardant could give you several drop combinations, depending on fuel type, canopy coverage and fuel loading.

DROP DATA FOR FIELD APPLICATION

AIRCRAFT TYPE	ICS TYPING	RETARDANT CAPACITY	SALVO	TRAIL	SPLIT
S-2F	III	800 gal. 4 DOORS	200x90	400x45	200x45
F-7-F	III	800 gal. 2 DOORS	200x90	400x45	200x45
B-17	II	1,800 gal. 6-8 DOORS	450x90	900x45	450x45
C-119J	II	1,800 gal. 6-8 DOORS	450x90	900x45	450x45
DC-4	I	2,000 gal. 8 DOORS	500x90	950x45	500x45
C-123K	I	2,000 gal. 8 DOORS	500x90	950x45	500x45
DC-6B	I	2,800 gal. 8 DOORS	750x90	1,500x45	750x45
DC-7	I	3,000 gal. 8 DOORS	750x90	1,500x45	750x45

1,500 x 45 A trail drop approximately 1,500 feet long by 45 feet wide. The call for this drop would be 1 x 8. (One door sequentially fired eight times.) The 45-foot width provides good coverage for light fuel types. Heavy fuels require the 90-foot width. As a field guide, figure one-half the load capacity for trail drop length, one-fourth capacity for split or salvo length (ft.).

Figure 9g

A **1 x 4** sequence refers to one door used four times on small spot fire(s) or a series of hot spots. This sequence could also be used to tie a series of drops together, much like the trial drops used by heavy air tankers.

A **2 x 2** sequence means two doors used twice. This is effective on larger spot fire(s) or to cool down a flank hot spot ahead of personnel.

As a basic planning guideline, figure one door width covers 45 feet of grass fuel types; two door widths covers 90 feet of brush.

To communicate your request for a drop (assuming no air attack supervisor is on scene) you could say, "My first drop priority is to slow up the head. I'd like one door four times tied in sequence from the cold flank towards the hot flank."

Another example is where a spot fire is developing in brush. The call might go something like, "I'd like two doors twice on the spot fire on the hot flank." (If the first two-door run is all that's needed, you can hold the last two doors.)

Twin-engine aircraft (Type 3, 800 gallons retardant) is well adapted for canyon runs and spot fires in difficult slope positions (Figure 9h).

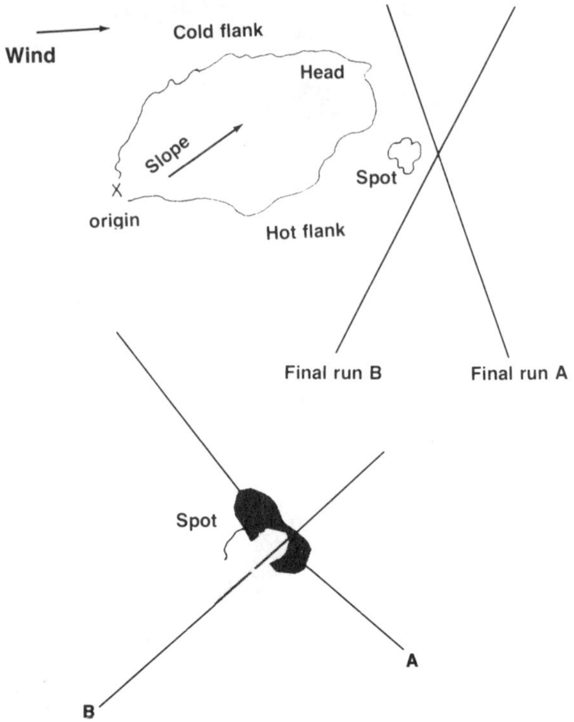

The third run ties into the first run, across the head and moving down the cold flank. Ground personnel can now follow up retardant line.

Figure 9h

For a developing spot fire, the first drop is placed with emphasis on the upper slope side of the spot. The second drop emphasizes the lower slope side of the spot. *The overlap is very important.*

Say, a developing grass/brush fire is moving up a moderate slope and short-range spotting is visible (Figure 9i). Smoke and heat are too intense to aggressively work on the fire's head. Spots are clearly visible 100 yards in front of the head. In this case, a series of well-placed drops may accomplish two objectives: (1) to keep spots from developing multiple heads and (2) to slow the developing main fire head moving upslope.

A series of two-door runs by a twin-engine (Type 3) aircraft, or a six-to-eight-door trail drop by a Type 1 air tanker can accomplish the above goals. If the first series of runs was successful, a second series could serve to reinforce initial drops prior to starting the second priority flank run(s) (Figure 9j).

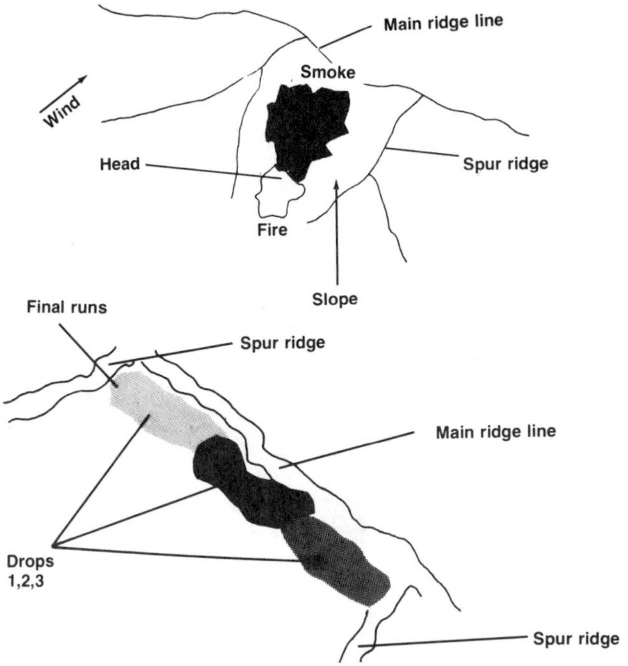

A fire is well established in a drainage of light and medium brush moving towards the main ridge line. First priority is to hold it to the main drainage.

Figure 9i

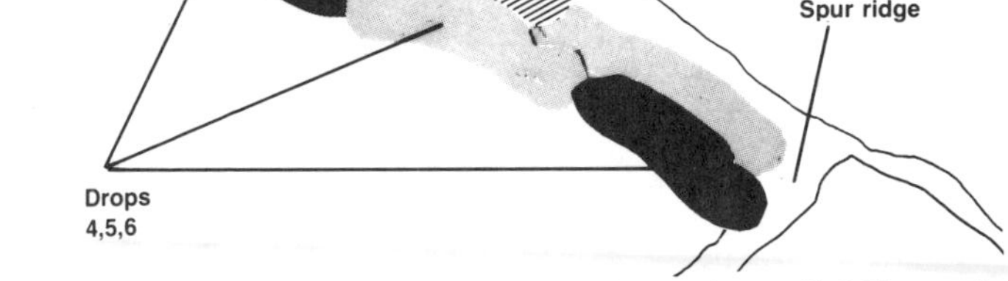

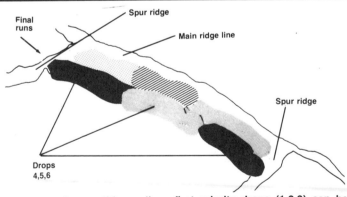

If time and smoke conditions allow, first priority drops (1,2,3) can be reinforced by extending the retardant line deeper down in the canyon. This also allows for deeper coverage in the corners of spur ridges.

Figure 9j

Photo by Jim Allan

A PB4Y2 air tanker makes a drop on a problem spot fire. Fire personnel should stay well out of target area.

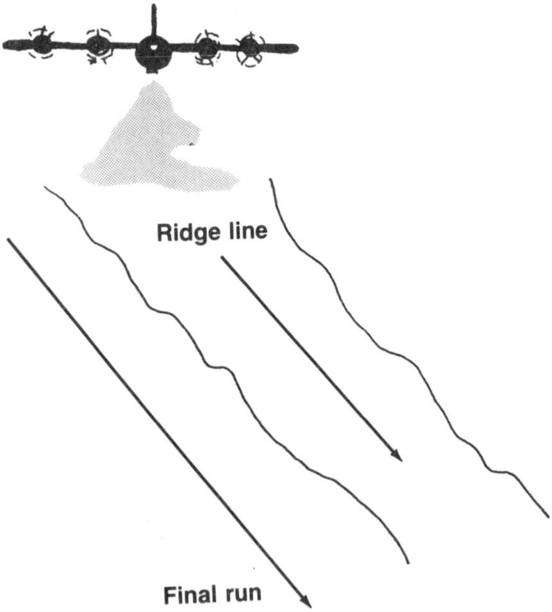

Let's assume this Type 1 (heavy) air tanker has 3,000 gallons and eight doors set up for a trail drop. We could estimate an effective trail drop of 1,500 feet long by 45 feet wide.

Figure 9k

The Type 1 air tanker (2,000 to 3,000 gallons) can be very effective on a ridge line situation requiring a long line of retardant when ridge width (narrow) or fire intensity is such that personnel cannot be safely deployed. In the example, a Type 1 air tanker makes a 2 x 4 drop, in other words, a trail drop two doors wide sequentially timed four times (Figure 9k).

Figure 9l shows a developing fire in light fuel types. The basic

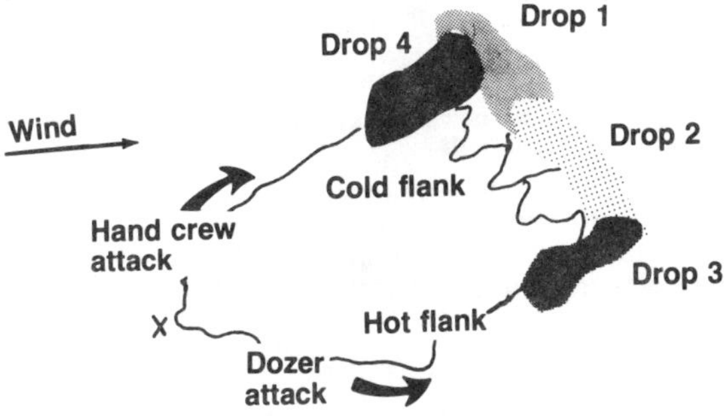

X=Anchor point

In this example, a hand crew and dozer are working a fast-moving fire in light fuels. The air tanker can slow up the developing head and make the corners on both flanks. This also keeps the tanker out of the "personnel zone." Flank runs will cool down the fire in front of the crew and dozer, but drops will end prior to contact with either resource.

Drop 1: Started early enough so fire will not outflank retardant

Drop 2: Tie into drop 1, extend drop so the next run will make corner on hot flank.

Drop 3: Tie into drop 2, extend down hot flank. End run prior to contact with dozer (or have dozer move out of target area).

Drop 4: Tie into drop 1, extend down cold flank. End run prior to contact with hand crew (or have crew move out of target area).

Figure 9l

flank attack is being accomplished by a dozer on the hot flank and a hand crew on the cold flank. Note the drop sequences and objectives of each drop.

The Type 1 air tanker is a must in heavy, closed-canopy situations. Figure 9m illustrates a heavy air tanker making a run down a wide canyon.

The air tanker can be a valuable tool during an indirect attack,

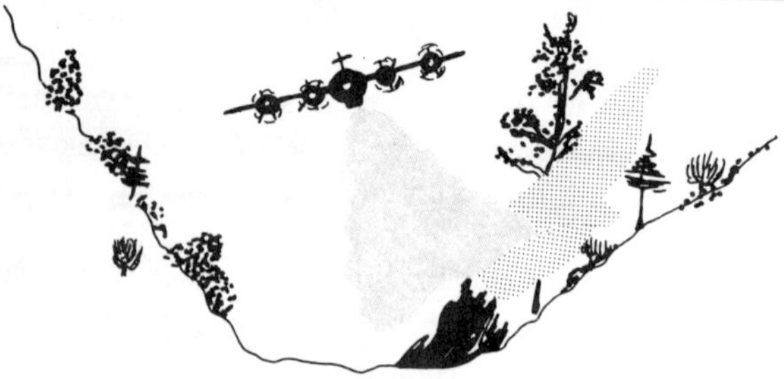

A heavy (Type 1) air tanker can be used effectively when a ground fire is burning beneath a heavy brush or tree canopy.
The larger payload can break through canopies to slow the fire. It's important to have all personnel out of the target area prior to the drop.

Figure 9m

where backfiring must be employed to widen a fuel break or anticipated control line. Figure 9n illustrates a strip-firing operation, where a narrow fuel break is being widened ahead of an oncoming fire. The air tanker can assist this by pre-treating the lee side of the fuel break. This reduces the threat of spot fires from the backfire and possibly (depending on time frame and weather) reduces the spotting potential

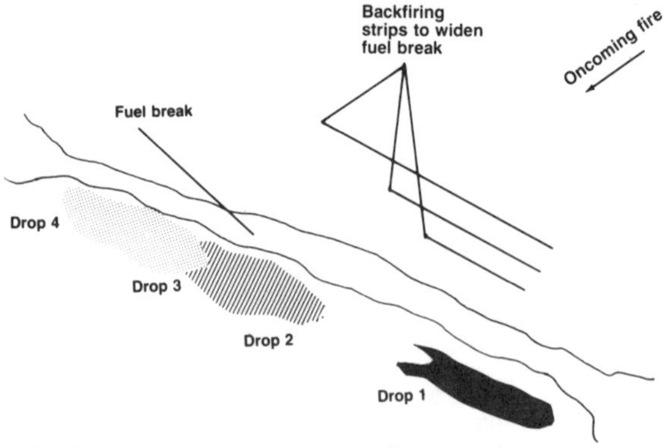

In this example, a fuel break is being widened prior to the arrival of the fire (indirect attack). Widening is being accomplished by strip firing. In addition, firing and holding crews have received support in the form of a retardant drop to reinforce the opposite side of the fuel break and minimize the chance of spot fires. depending on timing, this sequence of drops may prevent oncoming fire from spotting across the control line.

Figure 9n

USFS photo

The helicopter is a versatile tool. Personnel must understand and respect all rules associated with loading and unloading.

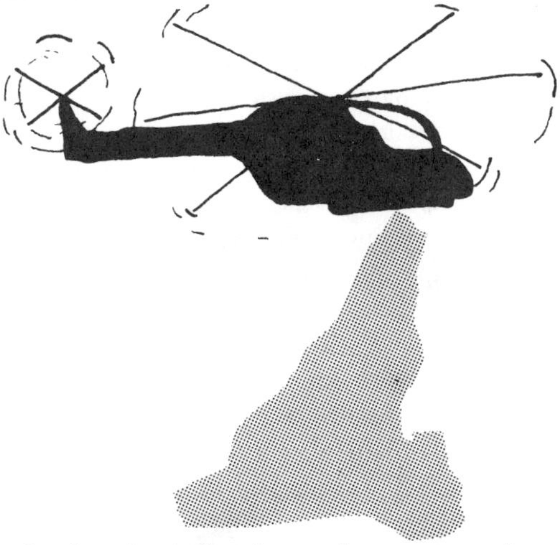

A. A water-dropping helicopter can be very accurate on spot fires.

B. If a helicopter comes with a heli-shot crew, that helicopter should be assigned with that crew.

C. The helicopter can serve to back up a dozer working a hot corner trying to cut off the head.

D. Because the helicopter can safely drop at lower elevations (if no personnel are in target area), there is a high risk of creating wind eddies and turbulence, which can modify fire behavior.

Figure 9o

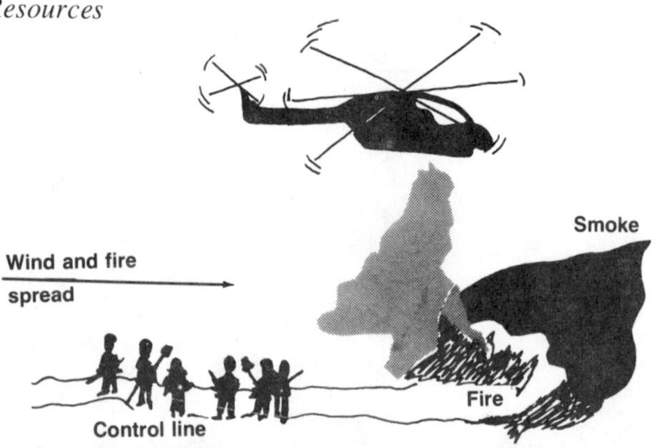

A water-dropping helicopter supporting a hand crew working a flank. The flank flares up, and the crew pulls back out of the target area. The helicopter cools down the hot spot so the crew can return.

Figure 9p

One of the recent improvements available to some helicopters has been the addition of forward looking infrared system (FLIR) called the "fire mousetrap." The mousetrap system uses an infrared camera on the helicopter to cut through the smoke exposing hot spots. A computer gives exact latitude and longitude of hot spots and then transmits the information to ground crews. One of the nation's largest helicopter contractors (Era Aviation, Inc.) has equipped a Bell 206-B (Jet Ranger) with a mousetrap system as follows: a 2000F long wave (8-12 micron) infrared imager; two (2) CRT monitors (one in front and one in rear of aircraft); a super VHS recorder; a portable and an on-board computer. On the ground this system is supported by a video printer to produce high resolution pictures from the video tape. An example of its capability and quality is found in new Figure 9r which shows a firestorm on a wildland incident shot July 29, 1989 in San Luis Obispo County, California. Note the hot spots (light areas). This capability will allow firefighters to focus efforts on key areas saving many hours per incident.

It's important during the initial stages of a developing incident to project your aircraft needs: If you plan on using more than one aircraft or you are going to mix fixed and rotary aircraft, you need an air-attack supervisor. Fixed and rotary aircraft can complement one another, but have differing air-space needs. If both resources will be on scene, make sure that the tanker pilot knows the helicopter is in the area and vice versa.

Figure 9q illustrates an important reminder for all personnel. Every year, you read about firefighters injured by flying limbs and rocks stirred up by a load of retardant. Review with personnel the importance of leaving the target area prior to a final run.

Unsafe, if within 300 feet

Safe if over 100 feet away

Evaluating safety for personnel working in close proximity to air attack resources. Silhouettes can be used to determine safety.

Figure 9q

Figure 9r

The minimum safe drop height for air tankers is 200 feet above ground level. Drop heights may vary, however, because of rapid changes in slope or topography.

Figure 9r points out that tanks should not be dropped below 200 feet. In reality, however, broken topography or ground cover may cause the pilot to drop below this safety standard.

An air attack is many times the key to keeping a small wildland fire from becoming a large wildland fire. To best utilize this resource, remember:

A. Pre-plan your key fuel beds. Ask yourself, how would you use air attack resources?

B. Know where these resources come from. How long is flight response time? Are they automatically dispatched?

C. Remember, air attack is an initial-attack tool, so order early. You can always turn it back.

D. Go to your air attack base or heli-base and become familiar with pilots/air attack supervisors. Ask them how they like to operate.

E. Review safety procedures with all personnel about keeping clear of target areas (Figure 9s).

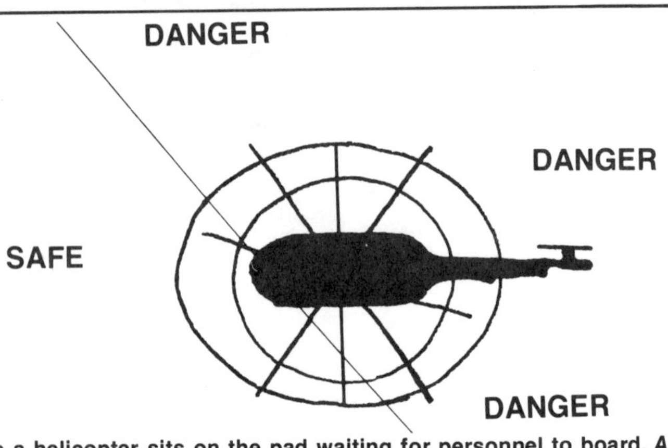

Here a helicopter sits on the pad waiting for personnel to board. *Always* allow heli-tank personnel to direct loading and unloading. Do not approach the helicopter unless in full view of the pilot. Remain at least 75 feet away from the helicopter's main rotor.

Figure 9s

F. Make use of the pilot's experience and judgment.

G. Check out payment procedures for using air-attack resources.

If aircraft/retardant is used on an incident, the operations chief or incident commander should advise dispatch or the coordinations center of total drops/estimated gallons dropped. Make sure contracts are made prior to fire season.

H. Critique all fires where air attack resources were used.

Ask yourself if you were cost effective and safe in your tacti-

HELICOPTER HAND SIGNALS
CLEAR TO START ENGINE
TAKEOFF
RIGHT HAND BEHIND BACK LEFT HAND POINTING UP
HOLD-HOVER
PLACE ARMS OVER HEAD WITH CLENCHED FISTS
MOVE UPWARD
ARMS EXTENDED, SWEEPING UP
MOVE DOWNWARD
ARMS EXTENDED, PALMS DOWN, ARMS SWEEPING DOWN
MOVE RIGHT
LEFT ARM HORIZONTAL
RIGHT ARM SWEEPS UPWARD TO POSITION OVER HEAD
MOVE LEFT
RIGHT ARM HORIZONTAL
LEFT ARM SWEEPS UPWARD TO POSITION OVER HEAD
MOVE FORWARD
COMBINATION OF ARM AND HAND MOVEMENT IN A COLLECTING MOTION PULLING TOWARD BODY
MOVE REARWARD
HANDS ABOVE ARM, PALMS OUT USING A SHOVING MOTION
RELEASE SLING LOAD
LEFT ARM DOWN AWAY FROM BODY. RIGHT ARM CUTS ACROSS LEFT ARM IN A SLASING MOVEMENT FROM ABOVE
LAND
ARMS CROSSED IN FRONT OF BODY AND POINT- -ING DOWNWARD WITH BACK TO WIND
SHUT OFF ENGINE
SLASH ACROSS THROAT

cal applications.

I. Realize that, at a developing wildland/urban interface fire you may need to request a "no divert" policy.

In the peak fire season, air tankers may be a "premium resource." As mentioned above, the air resource is an initial-attack tool. Some regions have a policy during peak fire periods that "New fires take priority over old ones."

If your incident is still developing and you have three or four aircraft assigned, it's not uncommon to have an aircraft diverted to a start elsewhere. If your incident has great potential to damage structures or prime watershed, have the air-attack supervisor request a "no divert."

Don't abuse this policy – release the no divert once the threat is over or tactical objectives for aircraft are met. As part of your pre-fire season preparation, find out what regional or forest policy on aircraft diversion is.

Photo by Keith Cullom

Helicopters are playing a larger role in air attack operations.

The Lockheed P-3A Orion is a Type 1 Air Tanker with 3,000 gallon tank capacity. This aircraft is powered by 4 Turbo Prop Allison engines. This aircraft has good performance and speed characteristics.

Photo by the author

The Lockheed SP-2H is a Type 1 Air Tanker with 2,000 gallon tank capacity.

Mike Hicks Photo

Chapter 10

Brush Trucks

For the purpose of this text, we will classify engines and brush trucks as ICS engine Types 1, 2, 3 and 4 (Figure 10a).

Before deploying an engine or brush truck for either a running attack or hose lay, some key points should be considered. If the first-arriving engine or brush truck is carrying an incident commander who wants to attack the fire, these points are important prior to deployment.

A. Good Size-up of the Incident, Including:

1. **Acreage estimate** (e.g. three to five acres)
2. **Incident potential** (e.g. structures threatened, extended attack)
3. **Wind speed/direction**
4. **Rate of spread estimate** (e.g. slow, moderate)
5. **Fuel type(s)** (e.g. grass, brush or timber)

B. Advise dispatch and responding chief officer of your decision to attack.

Transition command to next company officer or chief officer.

TYPE	PUMP CAPACITY	WATER CAPACITY	1½″ HOSE	1″ HOSE	MANNING STANDARD
1	1,000 GPM	400 gallons	400 ft.	200 ft.	4
2	500 GPM	400 gallons	500 ft.	300 ft.	3
3	120 GPM	300 gallons	1000 ft.	800 ft.	3
4	50 GPM	200 gallons	300 ft.	800 ft.	3

Figure 10a
Resource typing, equipment standards and staffing levels.

C. When evaluating your attack, look for where you can do the most good for the overall incident.

To determine this, it's necessary to know what engine(s), dozers, hand crew(s) and aircraft are responding and their approximate arrival time. To be totally effective, initial-attack engine and brush truck operations should complement the total suppression effort (air, hand crews, dozers, etc.).

For example, it does no good to drop retardant across the head or hot flank of the fire if you don't follow up with hand crew, dozer or engine to establish a control line.

Additionally, if you deploy a dozer on the lower portions of the flanks where hand crews or engines are able to work, you are wasting the dozer operator's time and jeopardizing your ability to slow the head of the fire. A dozer working near the area of origin also stands a good chance of destroying key evidence such as burn indicators.

D. Principles of Initial Attack.

1. **Establish a good anchor point** (Figure 10b).

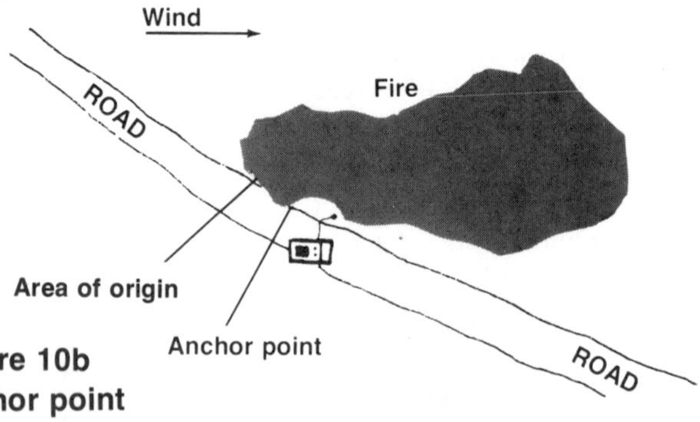

Figure 10b
Anchor point

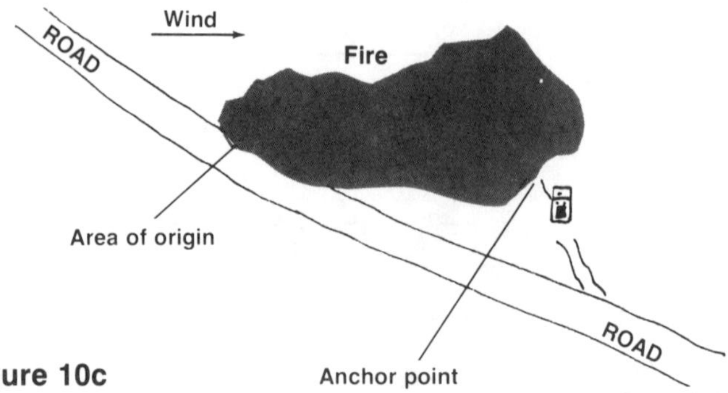

Figure 10c
Anchor point in risky location. Personnel safety not ensured.

2. **Plan the attack in such a way as to ensure personnel safety** (Figure 10c).
3. **Limit fire to lightest fuel type consistent with personnel safety.**
4. **Use direct attack where possible.**
5. **Attack flank with the greatest potential for escape or development** (Figure 10d).

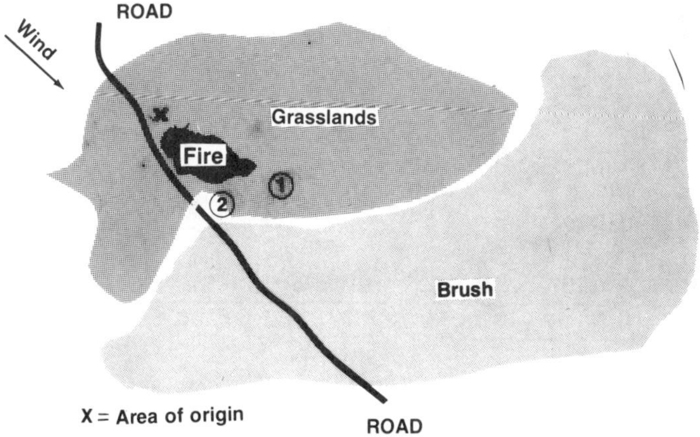

Points 1 and 2 are areas with greatest potential to develop. Engines and brush trucks will probably attack Point 2 prior to Point 1 to establish an anchor point and minimize exposure to personnel.

Figure 10d
Establishing priorities for attack

6. **Burn out islands of unburned fuel near control line(s) if potential for re-burn exists.**
7. **Eschew frontal assaults** (Figure 10e).
8. **Keep out of paths of least resistance areas** (saddles – see Figure 10f).
9. **Be aware of topography hazards** (side hills, steep slopes, down-hill, rocky soils).

Keep fire in lightest fuel type consistent with personnel safety. Two key points are evaluated in Figure 10d. In a coordinated attack, the head can be slowed by air attack or dozers while the hot flank is worked by hand crew and/or brush trucks. After Points 1 and 2 are accomplished, Point 3 will allow full containment of the fire.

Points 1 and 2 have the greatest potential to develop. For maximum effect in slowing the head of the fire, work the hot flank second. Because of the need for an an anchor point, an engine/brush truck may be assigned to work on Point 2 prior to Point 1 (flank attack).

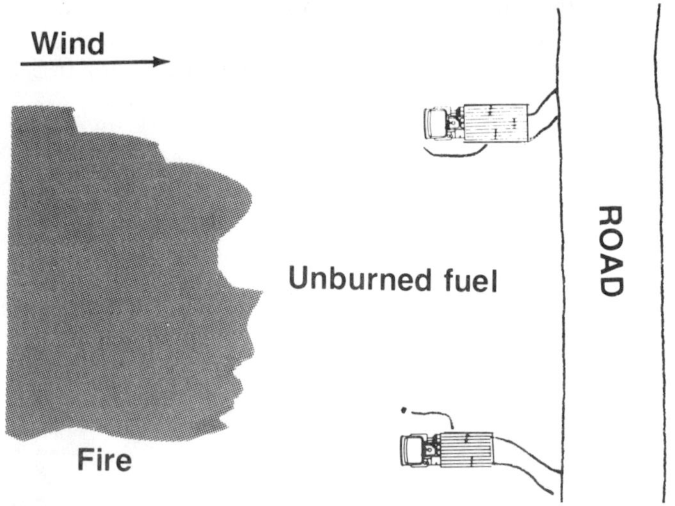

Frontal assault with engines or brush trucks. No anchor points. High risk to personnel. Unsafe attack.

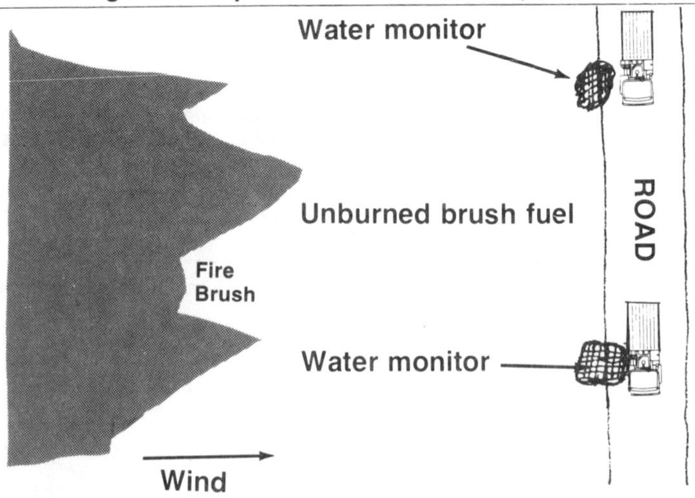

Figure 10e
Frontal assault with Type 1 engines and water monitors. High risk to personnel.

Often, wind-driven fires will leave islands of unburned fuels ("elongated fingers"). Company officers and crew leaders should have responsibility and authority to burn out islands if they lie within 30 feet of a control line and the possibility of a re-burn exists.

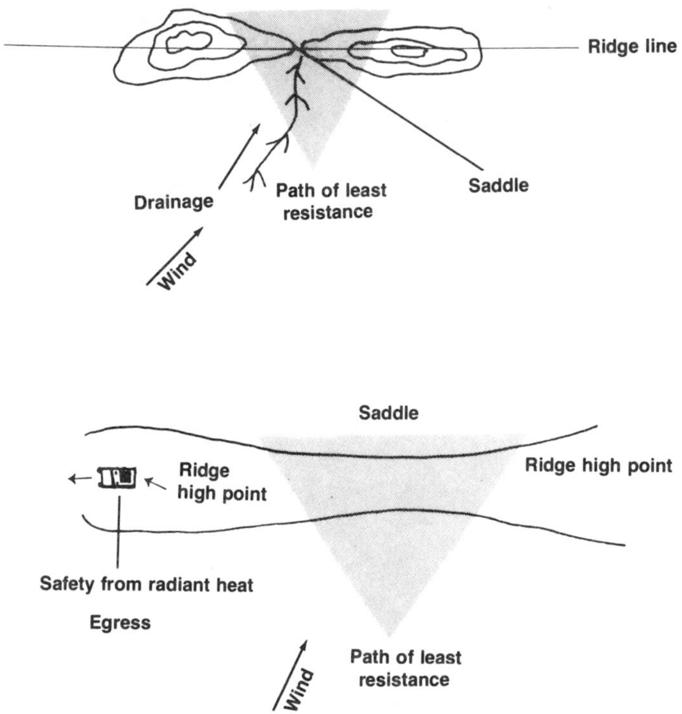

Figure 10f
Path of least resistance. Resource positioning on ridge line.

If the first-arriving engine/brush truck is anticipating an additional engine or brush truck within a few minutes there are three possible approaches (See also Figures 10g and h):

A. **Pincer Action: for Light Fuels**
B. **Tandem Operations: for Heavy Fuels** (brush, low-to-moderate spread)
C. **Envelopment**

PINCER ACTION

In light fuels, fire will exhibit good spread potential but low thermal outputs. This enables an aggressive attack on both flanks and possibly the head. The first engine/brush truck attacks the fire on the wind-driven flank (hot flank), as it has the greatest potential to spread.

The second engine/brush truck then ties into the anchor point and starts an attack up the opposite flank. Both engines keep in constant radio communications. The goal of the pincer action is to work up the

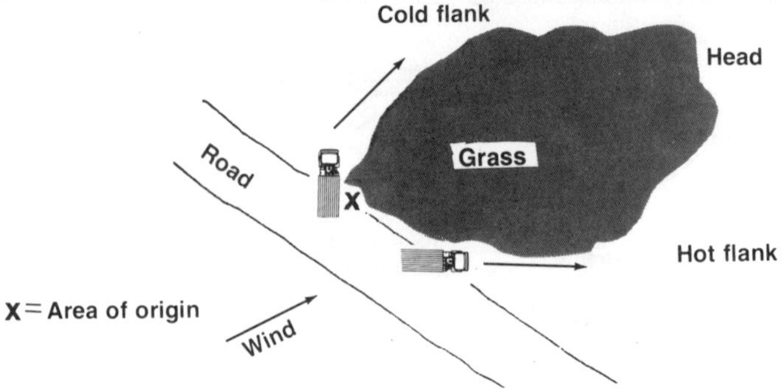

Pincer action

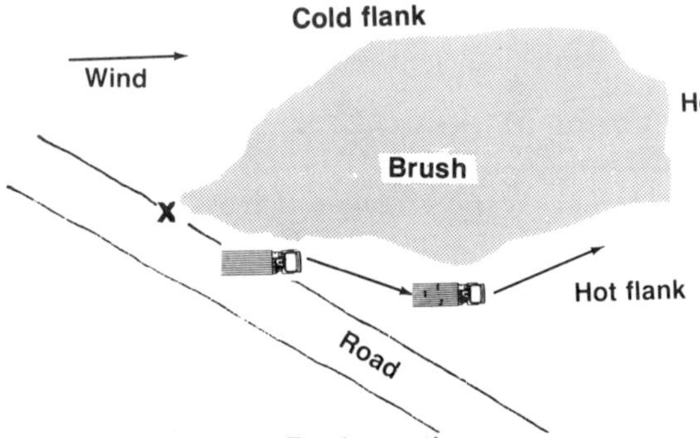

Tandem action

A brush fire burning with slow rate of spread. Tandem action allows the lead engine to take heat out of the fire. Second engine completes the wet line.

Figure 10g
Flanking attacks

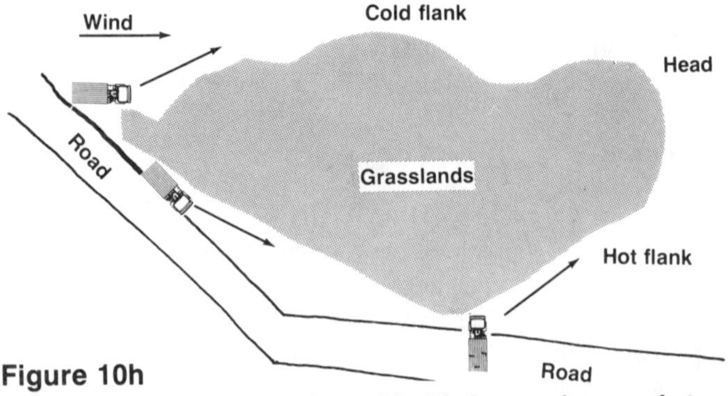

Figure 10h
The envelopment action. Multiple anchor points allow multiple attack points.

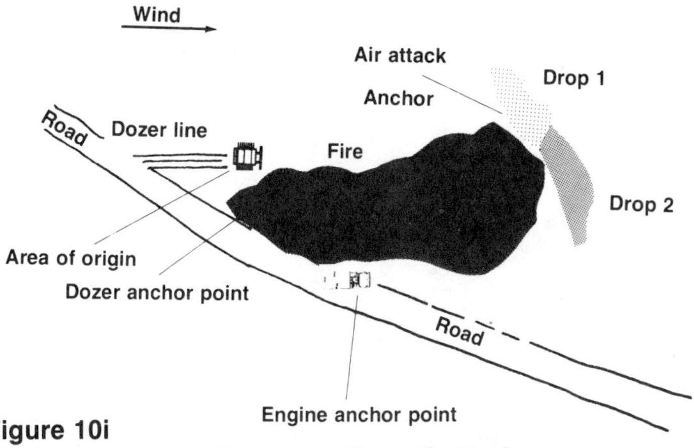

Figure 10i
Multiple anchor points, coordinated attack.

flanks and slowly pinch off the head or reduce its width until it can be safely stopped.

Obviously, in a coordinated attack (Figure 10i) that involves an aircraft or dozer, engines can work the flanks while an air tanker or helicopter concentrates on slowing and cooling the head of the fire. A dozer can bump the hot flank in front of the engine and work on reducing the head's width.

TANDEM OPERATION

In heavier fuel types or in situations where down-dead fuel loading is a problem, the tandem operation may be used. This can also be useful on a large grass or grain fire where the possibility of running out of water exists.

In a tandem operation, the lead engine or brush truck uses a straight stream or 30-degree fog pattern to cool flames and thermal intensity while a second engine completes the wet line and watches for spots.

ENVELOPMENT

If properly coordinated, an envelopment action allows the head and both flanks to be attacked simultaneously. The envelopment action should follow the sequence of the previously-mentioned control objectives, namely, hit the head first, if possible, then the hot flank, then the cold flank.

I am often asked about which is a safer attack for an engine or brush truck to make: an attack in "the black" or "the green." A basic rule of thumb:

A. Engine in green: firefighter in green (Figure 10j).

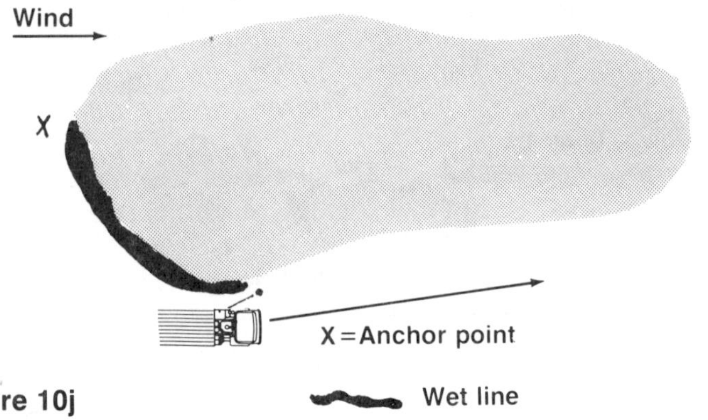

Figure 10j
Engine and firefighter both in green. Allows firefighter to use nozzle pressure to blow embers into black. Black serves as safety zone.

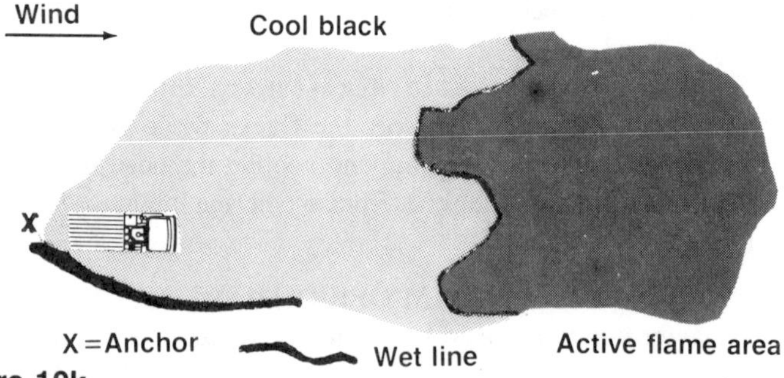

Figure 10k
Engine and firefighter in black area. This action may allow best visibility for engineer. Firefighter must watch so that embers do not spread into green area.

B. Engine in black: firefighter in black (Figure 10k).

I have seen and used both methods, as well as a combination of both, and feel either can be safely used, given consideration of weather and fuel types. For example:

A. Grass and Grain

Use a running attack; engine in green; firefighter in green.

B. Grass and medium brush

Broken topography, running attack. Engine in black; firefighter in black.

Important points for Example A (grass and grain):

1. Do not strip off over 20 feet of hose from the reel. This will

prevent the engine or brush truck from running over the hose. It will also keep the firefighter within the engineer's vision.

2. Black is a safety zone. Grass or grain will cool off quickly. The firefighter can cover his/her face so as not to suck heat into the mouth and nose, then retreat to the black. The engineer can also reposition the apparatus to the black for safety.

3. The firefighter making a wet line should keep black to black and green to green, as there's a low risk of blowing hot embers, burning leaves and needles into the green (unburned) area.

Some considerations for Example B (grass and medium brush):

1. If fuel height or down-dead fuels warrant, the engineer may have better visibility in the black.

2. Unburned fuels may hide hazards to the engine and brush truck such as rocks, barbed wire and holes.

THE GANSNER PACK

Besides the running attack, a progressive hose lay using 1½-inch and 1-inch cotton-jacket hose is widely used. One of the more popular hose packs is the **Gansner Pack.** The Gansner Pack was designed by a U.S. Forest Service engine crew stationed in the Plumas National Forest. Since the pack was introduced in 1977, a number of engine companies throughout the western United States have deployed the Gansner with positive results. The design of this pack gives the firefighter free use of his/her hands, as the trunk line feeds out behind. In addition, the pack gives better weight distribution than preious pack designs.

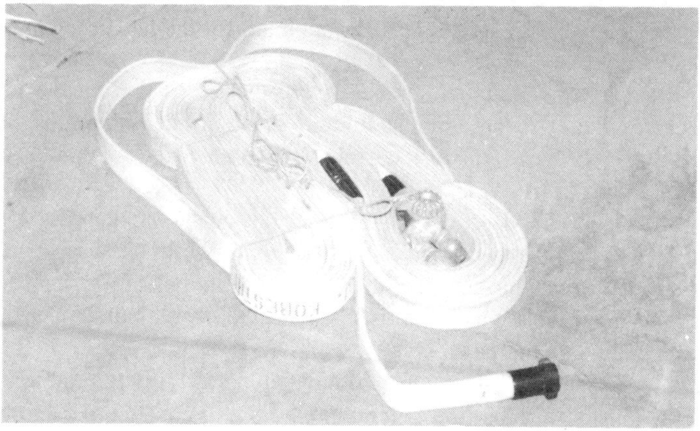

Photo by Steve Hobbs

The Gansner Pack offers a quick method for a progressive hose lay.

A. Equipment Needed Per Pack

1. One 100-foot section of 1½-inch CJRL
2. One 100-foot section of 1-inch CJRL
3. One gated wye
4. One reducer (1½-inch NS to 1-inch I P)
5. One nozzle (twist type) 1-inch KK
6. Nylon P-cord
7. Some means of deflating the hose
8. Wooden box (24 inch x 18 inch)

B. Packing Instructions

1. Connect gated wye to 1½-inch hose. Deflate hose
2. Place cord in box just above gated wye.
3. Begin "horseshoe" packing.
4. Stagger folds around gated wye and on the opposite side so folds are peaked in the middle.
5. Leave enough hose for a "tail." Be sure not to tie the string too tight or the hose won't feed out properly.
6. Connect nozzle and deflate 1-inch hose.
7. Form a circle, with nozzle inside, approximately 2½ feet in diameter, then spin-roll hose in a clockwise direction.
8. When spin-rolling is completed, pull middle opposite side as shown. Leave one side of pack shorter to accommodate a gated wye when the two packs are joined. Remember that the side with the quick-release knots will be in the center of the pack.
9. Shoulder straps are formed by pulling hose from the female end. There should be sufficient space at the top of the pack to accommodate two fists. Be sure to leave enough tail for the lateral to connect to gated wye.
10. Tie top string first, making sure the straps are equal and of adequate size. Second, tie the middle string inside the straps. The third string is tied outside the straps. Use quick-release knots, and make the three strings as tight as possible.
11. Place lateral on top of the first, 1½-inch, bundle with knots inside. Now tie the two bundles together with two more strings, making sure you don't tie up arm straps. Include the tail of 1½-inch with the top string. Notice how the right side of the lateral bundle is shorter to accommodate the gated wye.
12. Figure 101 shows the completed pack with tail under top string. This allows the firefighter enough hose to connect to gated wye on the ground.

C. Using the Pack

1. Pull tail, allowing enough hose to reach gated wye on ground.
2. Connect to gated wye.

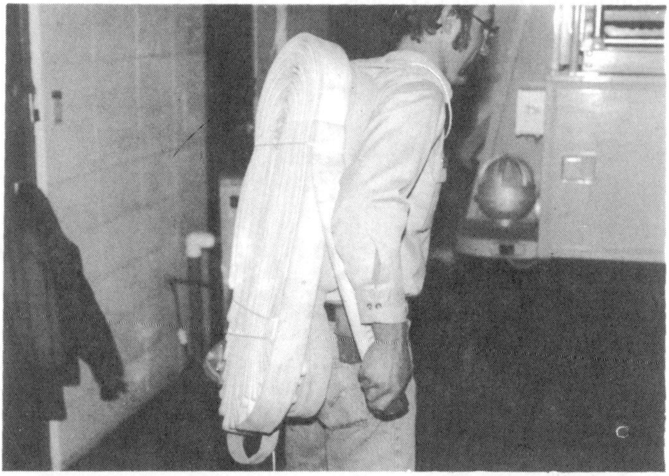

Photo by Steve Hobbs

The Gansner pack allows the firefighter to maintain balance while leaving both hands free to carry a hand tool, if necessary.

3. Proceed up fireline with supply line feeding out behind.

4. Once the supply line has fed out, turn pack over and pull strings, at the same time calling for water.

5. The lateral is now spread apart into a circle and can be charged.

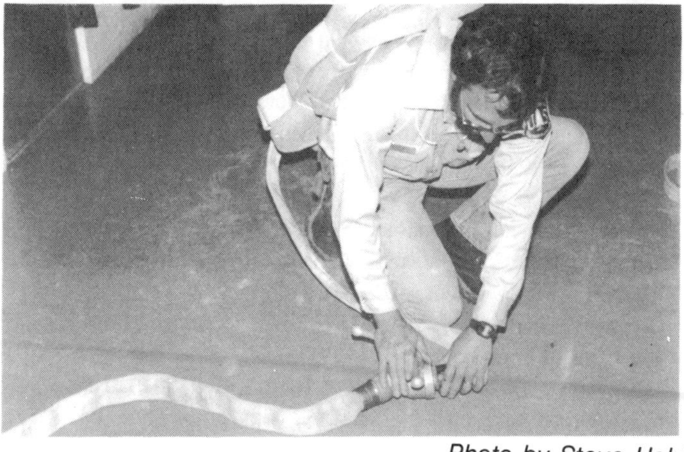

Photo by Steve Hobbs

A gated wye is used to either "branch off" to 1-inch hose or continue the hose lay.

The Gansner pack. A progressive hose lay enables firefighter to also carry a hand tool.

Every wildland fire will have differing circumstances requiring the engine company officer to use one or more of the attack concepts just discussed. In summary:

A. Be flexible

You may use multiple attack methods in the course of the fire.

B. Make sure the apparatus engineer understands his/her role in the attack.

C. Discuss safety zones

D. Think about water usage.

Where will you refill? How long will it take to refill? What effect will it have on the attack? At what point do you refill? (one-quarter or one-eighth tank?)

E. Think personnel safety.

Save some water for protecting apparatus should a breakdown occur.

Chapter 11

Bulldozers

In many parts of the United States, bulldozers are used as initial attack tools at wildland fires. The bulldozer is very effective in completing line construction in varied fuel, topography and soil conditions. It provides a valuable link between engines, hand crews and air attack resources. The key is to know how and when to utilize this resource – and its limitations. Important considerations include:

A. **Realize that the bulldozer operator is the vital link between the bulldozer and your needs. Involve the operator in your planning.**
B. **Know the basic limitations of bulldozers.**
C. **Respect the bulldozer's power and plan safety measures accordingly.**
D. **Good communications are a must.**
E. **Require safety inspections for bulldozers not maintained by fire departments or the Forestry Service.**
F. **Require safety gear for operators.**

Most wildland agencies use the bulldozer as an initial-attack tool. The basic tactic strategy in the western United States is to set up a flank attack to support ground resources (Figure 11a).

In Figure 11a, the basic tactical plan is a flanking action starting from an anchor point. The bulldozer is assigned to direct-attack the hot flank because the unit and its operator can withstand more radiant heat (although operator experience and safety gear may affect this). The cold flank is handled by a hand crew and engine company following the crew with a "wet line." The example in 11a makes good use of a bulldozer and limits ground personnel's exposure to the bulldozer (which will be working in smoke on this flank).

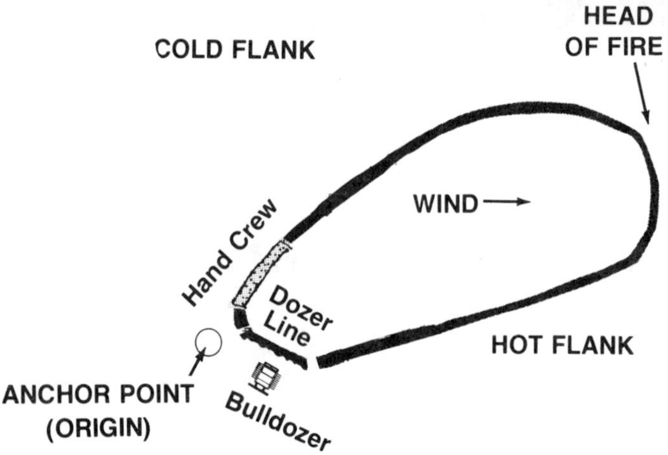

The basic flanking action. In this example, the hand crew is taking the cold flank, while the dozer has started on the hot flank. Both resources have started from a common anchor point. This attack limits ground personnel's exposure to the dozer.

Figure 11a

Ground personnel must be ever alert to the bulldozer as it envelopes the fire. (Communications are imperative.) The bulldozer must have common tactical communications with ground and air resources.

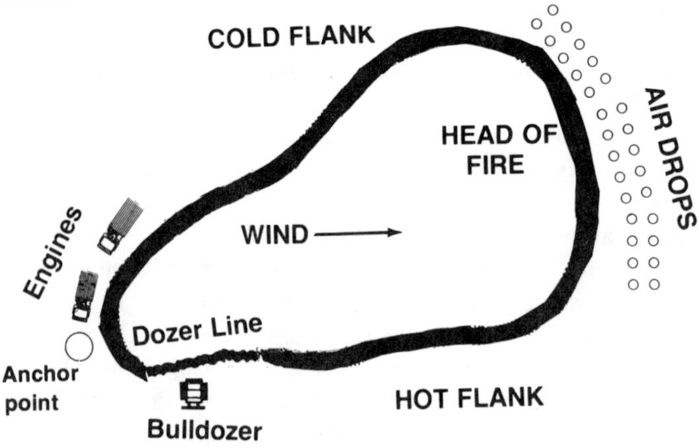

The basic direct attack, flanking action. The cold flank is handled by two engine companies. A dozer is working the hot flank. The head of the fire is being slowed up by air drops.

Figure 11b

Another common tactical application for the flank attack is illustrated in Figure 11b. Here, the basic flanking action using a direct attack is modified. The cold flank is attacked by engines or brush trucks using a progressive hose lay, making for minimal smoke and heat exposure to personnel. The hand crew starts from an anchor point common with the engine(s). To take full advantage of bulldozer capability, it "bumps into the black" and moves ahead of the hand crew. The hand crew will be responsible for tying the hand line into the bulldozer line.

In heavier fuel types, the bulldozer operator should also plan and construct safety zones a minimum of 100 feet in diameter and spaced not more than every 10 chains of line (660 feet). The key is to locate in the lightest fuel type possible and make safety zones as wide as practical. Operators should be trained to look for fuel transition zones or breaks in heavy fuel types that can speed construction of safety zones.

Referring again to Figure 11b, note how an air attack can minimize heat and smoke exposure to the bulldozer operator by pre-treating or directly applying fire retardant across the head. This wet line will provide a measure of safety to the bulldozer, operator or hand crew as they work to envelop and tie back into the cold flank.

The bulldozer can also be very effective in widening a ridge line, old fuel break or natural barrier in an indirect attack. Bulldozers should work in tandem in such a scenario, if possible.

In the northeast states of Maine, Pennsylvania and New Jersey, bulldozers are employed in a basic flanking attack. In the Lake States of Michigan, Minnesota and Wisconsin, bulldozers pulling plow units are used in flanking or pincer actions. Here, the blade is used primarily to push down-dead fuel out of the way while the plow unit constructs the control line.

In the southeastern states, the coastal region and Piedmont, bulldozers are the primary suppression tool. Lines in woody fuel types are constructed by dozers, then are immediately fired by ground personnel. In pocosin, an aggressive head attack is employed, due to this fuel's low rate of spread.

In the Rocky Mountain States and Florida, the bulldozer's use is limited because of sensitive environmental concerns and risks.

Because of the widespread use of bulldozers in the Western United States, the California Dozer Operators Group (CDOG) was formed to educate firefighters and operators about safety practices, fire behavior and protective needs. Since 1976, the CDOG has provided guidelines for the use of bulldozers at "all-risk" incidents.

The principal goals of CDOG are

A. **Inter-agency coordination**
B. **Relating communication needs**
C. **Safety standards for equipment and operator**
D. **Minimum training standards**
E. **Reviewing accidents/fatalities associated with bulldozers**
F. **Educating engine, hand-crew and air-attack personnel about bulldozers**

The California Dozer Operators' Group has these basic standards for wildland fire participation:

A. FIRE OPERATORS
   1. **Protective clothing** (three layers minimum)
   2. **Fire shelter**
   3. **Helmet** (air filtered)
   4. **Emergency air supply**
   5. **Operator health** (annual physical)

B. BULLDOZER
   1. **Fire curtains** (fire resistive)
   2. **Lighting package** (front and rear)
   3. **Rollover protection system (ROPS)**
   4. **Two one-gallon water canteens**
   5. **Seat belt**
   6. **Basic first aid kit** (including burn kit)
   7. **Communications radio**
   8. **Hydraulics** (no cable units)
   9. **Basic tool kit** (wire cutter, etc.)
   10. **Cable** (choker)
   11. **Fire extinguisher** (ABC rated 5)
   12. **Fusees, drip torch or Very pistol**
   13. **Flashlight and extra batteries**
   14. **Hand tools** (axe, shovel)
   15. **Emergency signaling device** (red smoke)
   16. **Service equipment** (lube gun)

C. MINIMUM TRAINING STANDARDS
   1. **Fire Operators**
      - Eight-hour fireline-safety course
      - Eight-hour fatality study course
      - 32-hour fire-behavior course
      - Basic radio communications class
      - 300-hour heavy-equipment safety class
   2. **Dozer Swamper**
      - Eight-hour fireline safety course
      - Eight-hour fatality study course
      - 32-hour fire behavior course

The height and configuration of the dozer allows the operator to work a direct attack in many fuel types. Personnel must be alert to the visibility problem for the operator caused by dust and smoke.

- Four-hour heavy-equipment safety class

Some key reasons for accidents while working around bulldozers:

A. Ground personnel following too close to bulldozer

B. Ground personnel working below bulldozer; material rolls downslope onto crew(s)

C. Limited visibility, poor communications with bulldozer operator

D. Problems loading and unloading bulldozer from the transport

E. Attempting to approach the bulldozer while it is in motion with no visual contact with the operator

Many wildland fire agencies do not employ heavy fire equipment operators, but, rather, contract on an "as-needed" basis. These agencies recognize the value of bulldozers at most wildland fires but do not want to employ full-time operators and maintain costly equipment.

If this describes your situation, or you contract for bulldozers during the fire season, there are key steps you should take prior to agreeing to hire an operator and/or bulldozer. These include:

A. Pre-fire-season inspection

B. Walk-around inspection at the incident

C. Operator briefing

D. Review of liability insurance policies

Pre-fire season inspection

You can save much time and energy by aggressively signing up interested contractors/construction companies well in advance of fire season. The sign-up process starts by advising the company that you would like to look at its equipment. Before you get much past the "I am available" status, make sure the equipment meets the minimum fireline safety standards.

Some important visual observations that will help you determine this include: Does the unit have a rollover protection system (ROPS)? Is the unit equipped with a seat belt? Does it appear to be well maintained? (Ask to see the service records.) Remember, a clean, freshly-painted dozer is not necessarily well maintained. Conversely, a dirty dozer with old paint may be very well maintained. Look at the manufacturer identification plate for year/model data.

Some time should be spent with the company owner or contracting officer discussing in what capacity the bulldozer/operator will be used. Explain the short-notice likelihood and need for around-the-clock availability during fire season. Review and agree on basic rates for operator, bulldozer and transport. Discuss how fuel, oil and breakdowns will be handled. Agree on who is to be liable for workmen's compensation should the operator be injured.

Stress the point that only experienced operators should be given fire assignments. If nighttime assignments are anticipated, only operators with that kind of experience should be assigned. Operators who have never before used a light package in dust and smoke will have lots of problems with glare. If the assignment calls for extensive slope work, then an operator with slope experience should be sent. Slope experience is an important concern especially in the western states. A contract operator may put in years of level pushing, but have never worked a sideslope or steep downslope. This lack of experience will become even more apparent at night.

The pre-fire-season check should be accompanied by a written description of equipment available for contract. This should include year, model, type (D-6, D-8, etc.) and serial number. Do a basic walk-around check and note excessive wear, oil or hydraulic leaks and other problems (broken lights, gauges not working, etc.). You should also inspect the owner's transports for basic safety elements, including good tires, mirrors, good lights, overall condition of trailer, chaining devices, load capacities and service records.

Discuss emergency and non-emergency transportation for contract equipment and permit process for wide loads and/or weight restrictions. Secure the names/phone numbers of local highway patrol or road department officials having jurisdiction over such matters.

Above all, establish a written agreement stating you have inspected and signed up said equipment with listed serial numbers and capabilities and that you have advised the owner of basic requirements for operators.

Once you have come to an agreement on basic pay rates and liability during contract usage and have reviewed the permit process and local limitations for wide loads and/or road surfaces, both you and the owner should sign the basic agreement. Give him/her a copy of this to file. Keep a copy for yourself.

Basic Walk-Around Safety Check for Contract Equipment

Hopefully, you will have made a pre-fire season inspection and need only pull out your contractor's file, check serial numbers and do a quick visual check with the contract operator on the scene of the incident.

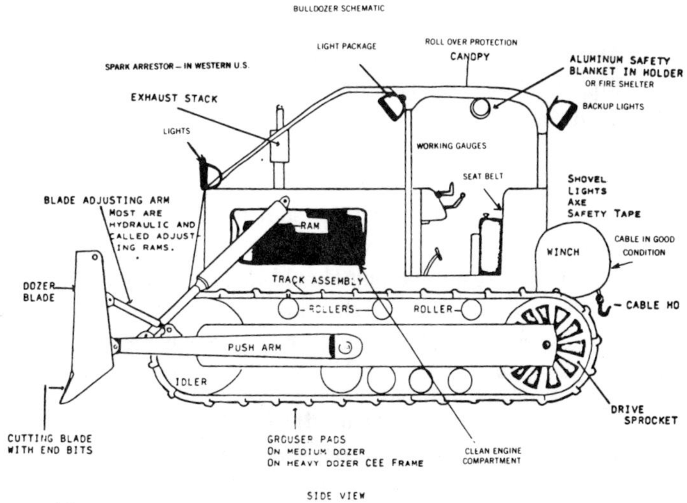

Figure 11c

Review the key check points in Figure 11c. Starting in the front of the bulldozer, check:

1. **Dozer blade** – for cracks, loose bolts at push arm.
2. **Cutting/corner bits** – for looseness.
3. **Radiator** – should be free from dirt, leaves. Radiator level full (no oil in water). Do *not* open warm radiator to check; let cool first.
4. **Hydraulic rams** – make sure there are no visible leaks.
5. **Exhaust stack** – must have a certified spark arrestor in western United States. Stack must be of sufficient height to take exhaust away from operator's air space.
6. **Idler** – not worn or cracked.

7. Engine compartment – should be free from trash, leaves, debris (also check belly pan for same). Fan belts, lights in good condition. No major oil leaks. Recent service on primary air cleaner.

8. Track assembly – should have not more than two inches sag in track between first and second roller (use straight edge on top of track assembly). Check track plates for wear, missing bolts or cracks.

9. Sprocket – should show even wear. Watch out for "chisel-point" wear or fractures in sprocket.

10. Final drives – look for major oil leaks. A major leak can be described as dripping as you watch it.

11. Driver's compartment – must have seat belt. Do gauges all work? Check fuel (should have screen in place in tank). No trash, leaf debris under foot controls.

12. Rollover protection – all bolts are tight. No apparent cracks or broken welds.

13. Winches or rippers – Winches should have good cables, not frayed. Rippers should be free from hydraulic leaks.

14. Hydraulic hoses – All hoses should be free from cracks and leaks.

15. Lighting package – in working condition (front and rear).

16. Start up – have the operator start the unit up after the above inspection. After a minute or two, the initial diesel "black or gray" smoke should disappear. The unit should idle smoothly and all gauges should read "green." Check the dozer controls. (Have operator raise/lower dozer unit.) Have operator shut down the unit after you are satisfied.

Operator Briefing

Hopefully, no contractor or company would send out an inexperienced operator on a fire assignment, nevertheless it's wise to ask the following quesions to evaluate the operator prior to tactical briefing.

1. Does the operator have protective clothing? This should include gloves, eye protection and helmet.

2. How many year's experience does the operator have?

3. Has he/she operated at a fire before?

4. When was the last time he/she operated this unit?

5. Was a daily check performed on this unit today? Any problems?

6. Does the operator have a background in the special circumstances of this fire, i.e., slope experience, nighttime operating experience, timber fuel types?

7. Is he/she under any medical limitations?

8. Are there any commitments that might preclude the operato

Nighttime dozer operations can be extremely hazardous. All personnel must be aware of line assignments where dozers are working. Communication is the key.

from completing the assignment once it starts?

9. Are there any questions?

Other Considerations

1. Assign a birddog or swamper with radio communications for the assignment.

2. Always inspect the bulldozer(s) transport(s) prior to release from the incident. *(This is very important.)* Agree on how any damage will be repaired prior to release.

3. Make sure the contractor has proper road permits (if wide load)

Hand crews and engine personnel often work on a division with a dozer(s). Keep at least a 50-foot distance from the dozer. The rear and sides are natural blind spots. Assume the dozer always has the right of way.

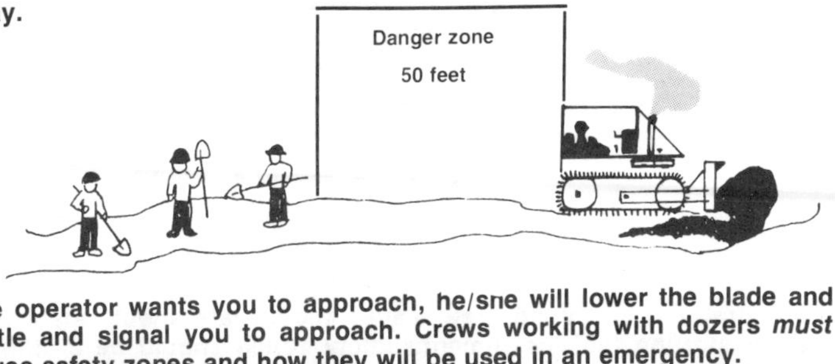

If the operator wants you to approach, he/she will lower the blade and throttle and signal you to approach. Crews working with dozers *must* discuss safety zones and how they will be used in an emergency.

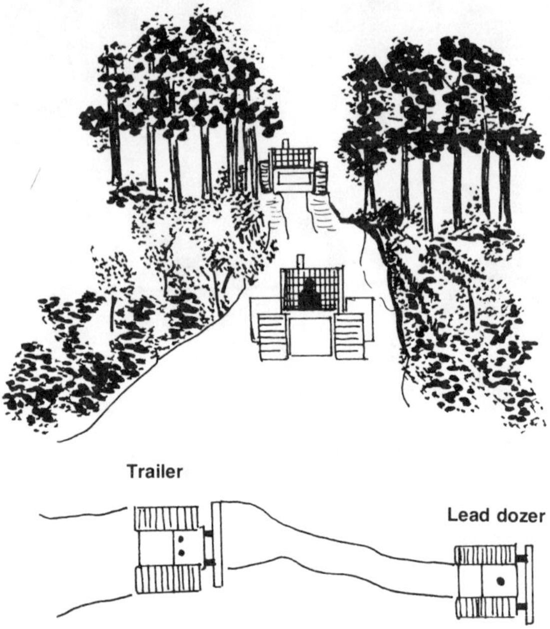

Tandem dozer operation. Very effective in heavy brush and timber mixes. A lead dozer pilots the line; trailer dozer widens, puts in safety zones and broadcasts down-dead or brush piles.

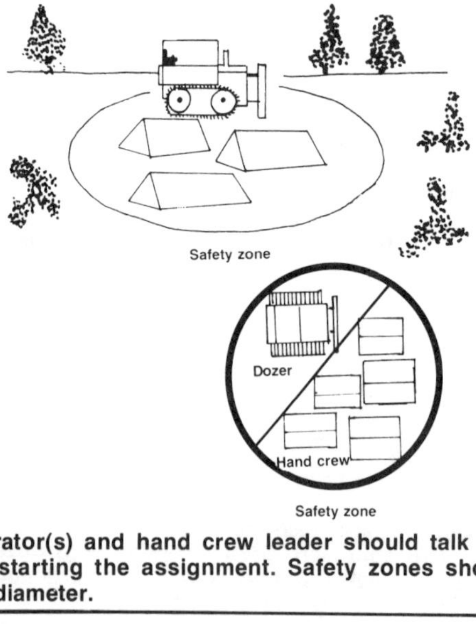

The operator(s) and hand crew leader should talk about safety zones prior to starting the assignment. Safety zones should be a minimum 100 feet diameter.

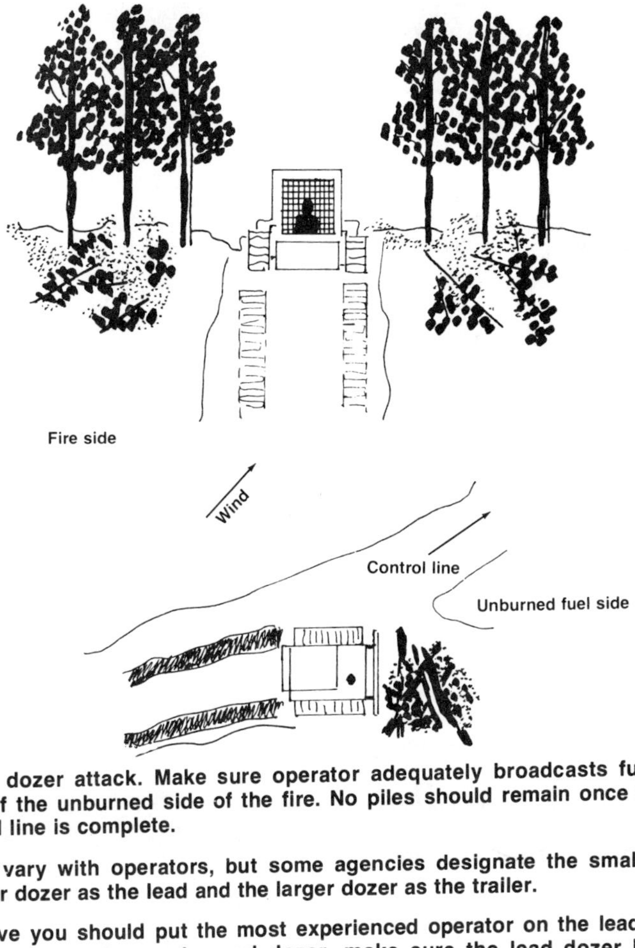

Single dozer attack. Make sure operator adequately broadcasts fuels well off the unburned side of the fire. No piles should remain once the control line is complete.

It will vary with operators, but some agencies designate the smaller, quicker dozer as the lead and the larger dozer as the trailer.

I believe you should put the most experienced operator on the lead. If using a contract operator and dozer, make sure the lead dozer has radio communications.

for trip back home.

Many contractors/companies offer fire departments their services. Take the time prior to fire season to discuss your requirements and safety needs. Most companies will gladly modify their equipment if they know it will be used and you are genuinely concerned about safety. It is your responsibility not to allow unsafe heavy equipment or inexperienced operators at your incident.

AVERAGE SINGLE PASS BULLDOZER LINE CONSTRUCTION FIGURES [1,2,3]

Size of Bulldozer	Footage Constructed One Hour Operating Time	Fuel Type	Upslope Percent
D-6	2,500 feet	Grass	40%
D-6	1,100 feet	Medium Brush	40%
D-6	900 feet	Heavy Brush	40%
D-5	2,000 feet	Grass	40%
D-5	700 feet	Medium Brush	40%
D-5	500 feet	Heavy Brush	40%
D-6	4,000 feet	Grass	0%
D-6	3,300 feet	Medium Brush	0%
D-6	1,900 feet	Heavy Brush	0%
D-5	3,500 feet	Grass	0%
D-5	2,100 feet	Medium Brush	0%
D-5	1,500 feet	Heavy Brush	0%

ESTIMATING CONSTRUCTION RATES FOR BULLDOZERS [4,5]

	Bulldozer Size			
	D-8	D-7	D-6	D-4
1. Walking rates (mph) dirt trail or road	4	5	5.5	5
2. Climbing upslope maximum slope percent blade raised — medium brush — *forward* gear	75	73	70	67
3. Climbing upslow maximum slope percent blade raised — medium brush — *reverse* gear	46	45	44	40
4. Descending downslope maximum slope percent blade raised — medium brush — *forward* gear	75	73	40	67

[1]*Every operator and dozer has differing capabilities and limitations. Use operator's judgment and experience.*

[2]*Wildland Fire Modeling for Initial Attack Planning, Donald G. Perry, Santa Barbara, CA, May, 1982.*

[3]*Most brush and heavy fuel situations will require multiple pass widths. Think strike teams in planning assignments (tandem operations).*

[4]*Trail Building Guide for Fire Planning 20,8, U.S. Forest Service, Washington, DC, 1973.*

[5]*These are* maximum *figures, not averages. Every operator and dozer will have differing limitations and capabilities. Use operator's judgment and experience. Above tests assumed ideal dozer conditions, no rocks or hazards.*

	Bulldozer Size			
	D-8	D-7	D-6	D-4
5. Descending downslope maximum slope percent blade raised — medium brush — *reverse* gear	80	80	80	80
6. Climbing upslope maximum slope percent blade raised — heavy brush — *forward* gear	52	50	48	45
7. Climbing upslope maximum slope percent blade raised — heavy brush — *reverse* gear	35	35	35	35
8. Descending downslope maximum slope percent blade raised — heavy brush — *forward* gear	70	65	65	60
9. Descending downslope maximum slope percent blade raised — heavy brush — *reverse* gear	80	80	80	70
10. Side slope travel maximum percentage medium or heavy brush	50	50	50	50

Chapter 12

Hand Crews

BACKGROUND

Many major wildland fire agencies deploy seasonal firefighters specially trained in the use of hand tools, called "hot shots." These organized and highly-trained crews vary in strength from 10 to 20 personnel plus a crew leader.

The history of hand crews is both colorful and noteworthy. As far back as the Depression era, these crews not only fought brush and timber fires but also constructed roads, trails and structures (fire lookouts, forestry fire stations and forestry camps). In the early days, impromptu hand crews were also formed after a fire started, as forest rangers went from bar to bar or down city streets seeking volunteers. If no volunteers were found, forest rangers had the authority to "draft" healthy, sober young men for the detail.

Today, wildland hand crews are divided into two categories, Type One and Type Two. A Type One hand crew has a minimum strength of 15 personnel plus a crew leader. A Type Two hand crew has a minimum of six plus a crew leader. The Type One crew has no operational restrictions and receives the most extensive training. A Type Two crew generally has some restrictions in regards to line assignments. Type Two crews may be organized by conservation corps, colleges or environmental agencies.

Despite the fact that the age of automation has arrived for the fire service and even though brush trucks, bulldozers and aircraft are now available to the incident commander, there is and will always be a need for hand crews. Once limited to crude swatters, rakes and shovels, today's hand crews are equipped with super Pulaskis and high-tech saws and scraping tools. Crew leaders are trained and

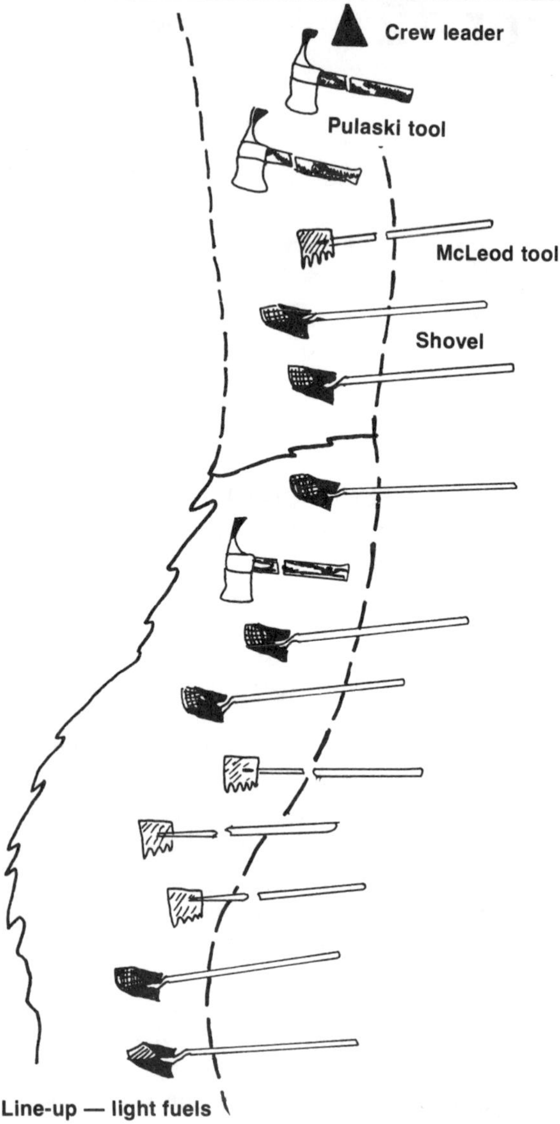

Tool Line-up — light fuels

Figure 12a

skilled at designing a tool lineup to meet the fuel types to be cut and figuring the productivity level necessary to accomplish the job (Figures 12a and b).

Hand crews operate much like a professional sports franchise. You hire people in top physical shape who have a desire to work on a

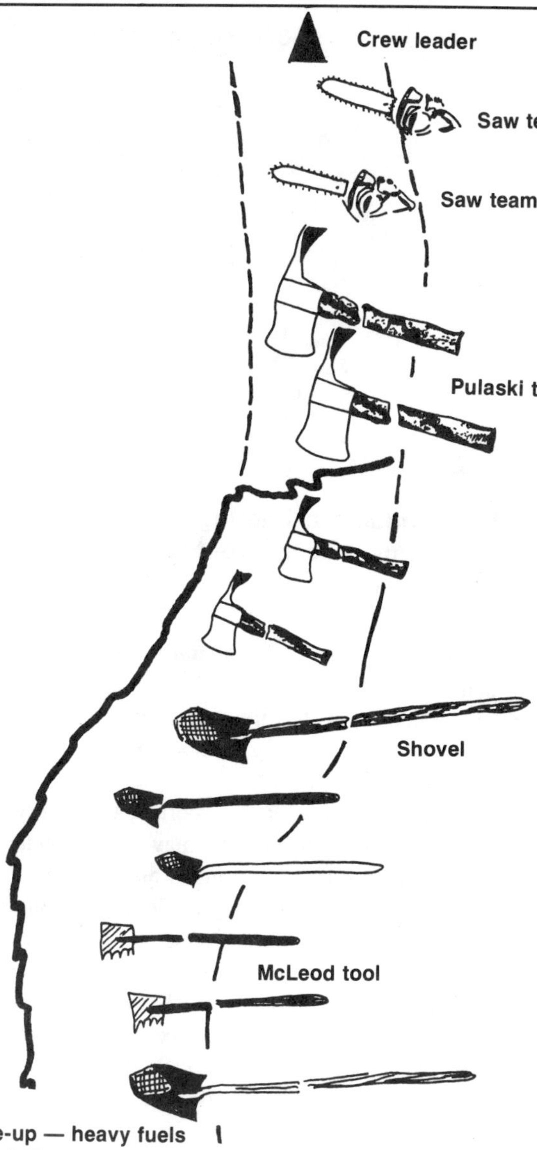

Tool line-up — heavy fuels
Figure 12b

team and develop an "espirt de corps." Call it pride, status or challenge, but it's an honor to have bragging rights as part of a Type One crew. These crews carry legendary names like Indian, El Cariso, Texas Canyon, Fulton, Los Prietos. Del Rosa, L.A. County Camp 2 and Redding Regional Crew. Most of them wear vests or designs

The crew leader conducts a briefing prior to deployment. Performance standards, escape routes, safety zones and fire behavior are discussed.

displaying their crew logo or name. You must earn and prove your worth to wear such a garment.

Hand crews generally begin the fire season with an extensive and rigorous training period. This training varies from what is termed a "Basic 32" (32 hours) to 110 hours.

When organizing a hand crew, it is important that every member understands what fire behavior situations may be encountered, the various fuel types he/she could be working in and burning characteristics. They should fully understand the Incident Command System and how it works. They should be well versed in how fire behavior affects fireground and attack method decisions. It is my belief that if every crew member understood what he/she was witnessing as a fire burned, the potential for panic would be vastly reduced. This would also impart more confidence in the crew leader, as personnel would understand why fireground decisions are made.

TRAINING

I taught my first hand crew academy in 1980. It was 80 hours in length, even so, I didn't acomplish all the goals I had set for the 50 crew members and 10 dozer operators attending. In 1984, I bumped the hours to 110, and that is where they remain today. I feel this is a good academy length, and it accomplishes my theme, namely SQQT.

What is SQQT? It is an acronym I use, meaning Safety first,

Photo by Keith Cullom

Spacing and tool usage are important. Personnel must learn how to best use the tools to prevent fatigue and injury. Scraping tools — McLeods.

Quality of line construction, second, Quantity of line cut, third and Time, fourth. Time refers to being physically conditioned enough to hold up under a full-shift line assignment.

Academy attendees arrive having been through an extensive screening, including a fitness evaluation, agility test and oral board. This ensures that they have a basic fitness level and receptive attitude. It's interesting to note that, over the last six seasons, there has been at least 50 percent return rate, which really solidifies a crew. Returnees average three fire season's experience.

The academy focuses intensely on physical fitness (daily aerobic and flexibility exercising), and all aspects of safety (tools, fireline, injuries, fatality studies, fire shelters, safety clothing and fire behavior). Once a foundation in safety and tool familiarization is established, then quality of line is stressed.

Personnel using cutting tools, such as the Pulaski, should control tool swings to keep the body balanced and footing secure. Tool spacing is also important. Watch overhead canopies.

Many times, hand crews are assigned to direct attack an incident. The line they construct must be a quality line, the first time. Like the crew name or logo, the quality of line becomes part of a crew's reputation. For the most part, a Type One hand crew gets a reputation of either being "animals" or "water buffalos." (The term "water buffalo" is also used for a crew that is continually stopping to drink water or rest.) A first-rate crew will gain regional or statewide status based on a good job, and become known as "animals."

Most training will start with light fuel types, emphasizing good scraping tool techniques. Quality of line starts with correct use of hand tools and learning short cuts that use the tools efficiently. A crew must understand the importance of putting in a quality line – versus doing a slipshod job and leaving a potential problem. It's important to stress to even the seasoned crew member that *pacing* is extremely important. *Quantity* of line will come as teamwork, conditioning and tool usage become second nature.

By starting in light fuel types, crews gain confidence and see improvement quickly. After the crew starts to achieve the necessary quality, it can work on speed. To some degree, physical conditioning, weather conditions, fuel types and topography will vary line quantity on each incident.

It's paramount for a crew to understand and recognize two types of speed. There is one that is driven by a need to get the control line in place prior to a weather, fuel or topography change. Then there is the speed that is accomplished in a light fuel type because of little or no resistance to scraping.

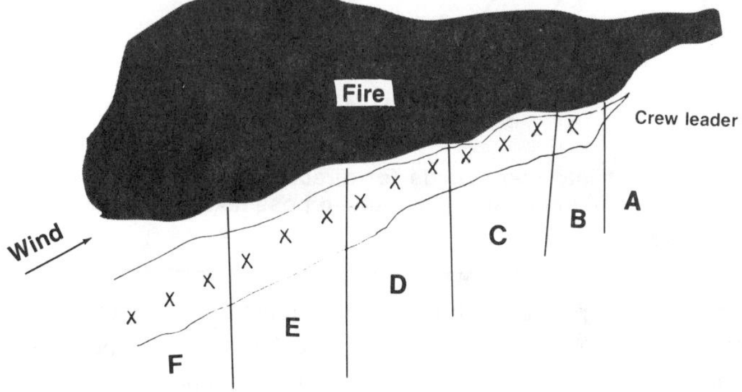

Stages of Line Construction

A. Locate line, manage crew, monitor safety and fire behavior.
B. In grass fuels, lead shovel. Hit 'n' go, one-foot swath.
In brush fuels, lead Pulaski or saw team. Punch a hole in canopy, take out one-foot swath down to six to eight inches from surface. Try not to take too much at this point.
C. In grass, a Pulaski loosens soil, initiates scraping. Two scraping tools widen line (rough width).
In brush, three Pulaskis work on stobs and broadcasting (see Figure 11f).
D. Scraping tools widen and improve line to needed width.
E. In grass, line is improved.
In brush, Pulaskis finish off stobs, check broadcasting.
F. Finishing line. Last person in line is responsible for making sure line is of good quality. Often, the crew squad boss is near this zone and in constant communication with the crew leader.

Crew personnel must have some live fire training so they can become accustomed to the stress of intense bursts of giving 110 percent to prevent that small fire from escaping initial attack. I like to accomplish this by splitting the crew into several smaller squads on one-fourth- to one-half-acre grass fires (Figure 12c). Each three-to-four-

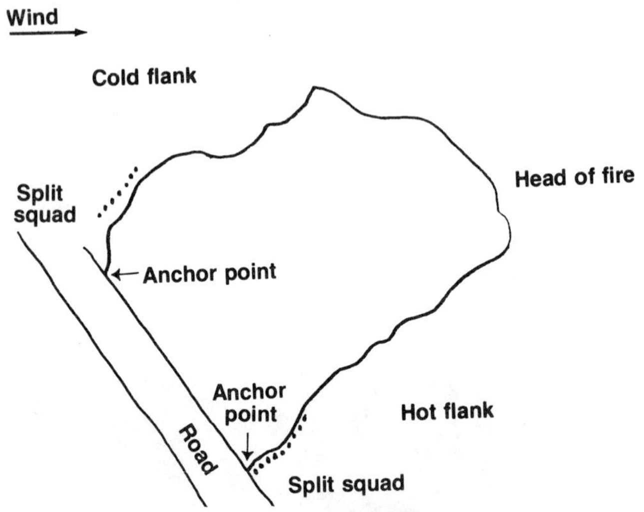

Hand crew split into two squads for direct attack on a flanking action. Crew leader takes hot flank squad; squad boss takes cold flank.

Figure 12c

person squad has a squad boss who designates an anchor point and directs scrapers to try and catch the fire before it reaches one acre in size. These drills build confidence, while exposing personnel to the heat and smoke they can expect at an actual incident. Also, each fire gives the crews a new measure of quality and quantity. The smaller, split-up squads also allow each crew person to experience the squad boss position and the role of being a leader. This confidence-building exercise reduces the likelihood of panic in a difficult situation. However, as with any training fire, it is extremely important to monitor safety practices. We attempt to hold three full days of live grass-fire drills, starting off with one-to-two-person scraping-tool fires (one-eighth acre in size) and working up to two-to-three-acre initial-attack fires with bulldozer or brush truck assistance.

We also make use of these fires to test the crew's ability to deploy the fire shelters under live fire conditions. Shelter drills are practiced twice with a full crew, plus numerous times individually.

A crew must be able to get into the shelters correctly within 25 seconds.

Live fire drills also lend an opportunity to emphasize and monitor good spacing and tool swings (Figure 12d). Initially, spacing will

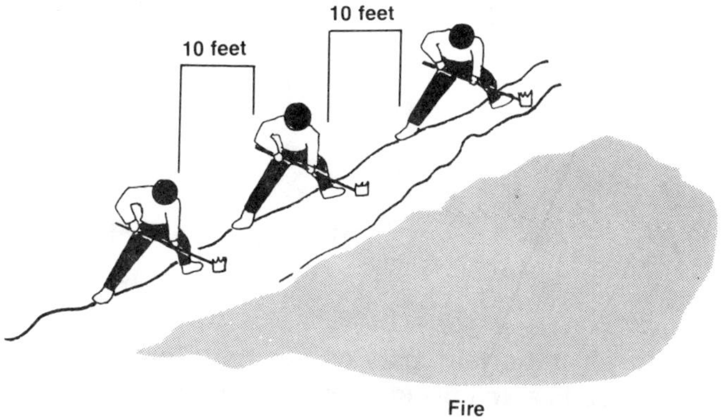

Tool spacing and good communications between crew persons are important. As assignment length increases, the risk of close tool swings increases. Crew members should alert one another to rolling rocks, footing hazards or messages bumped back by crew leader.

Figure 12d

have the appearance of clusters, instead of being spread out the minimum 10 feet. Individuals will get "tunnel vision" focusing on the fire instead of spacing, productivity and tool swings. You can also use these drills to watch how teamwork and stress affect the crew.

As a hand crew gains confidence and teamwork ability, the line quality and quantity will improve and production rates increase. As heavier fuel types and cutting tools are introduced, safety again must be closely monitored. Initially, in our academy, we put saw teams well in front of the lead Pulaski. This allows the saw team to concentrate on team work and coordination without having to worry about being pushed by the crew behind them. This again goes back to the principle of safety and quality first, before quantity. As the crew improves its tool usage and line quantity in heavier brush types, you can vary slope or topography to help reinforce pacing.

Up to this point, the crews have worked mostly in short, 10-to-15-minute scraping tool exercises on 15-to-20-minute initial-attack grass fires. Though they may have even worked in heavier brush mixes where they work up to three hours as a unit, it's important to reinforce early on that it's not uncommon for a hand crew to work a twelve-hour shift. This is why physical conditioning, teamwork and proper

Burnout is an important part of the hand crew's assignment. Burnout, like any firing operation must be coordinated and timed. Communication is the key.

HAND CREW LINE CONSTRUCTION AND BURNOUT AND HOLDING ESTIMATING CHART[1]

Number of personnel necessary to construct 100 chains (6,600 feet) in specified hours by fuel type.[2]

		Number of Personnel Required to Construct Line in Hours HOURS							
Fuel Type	Basic Rate Per Person Hour	1	2	3	4	5	6	7	8
1	4.0	25	14	10	9	8	7	6	6
2	3.6	28	16	12	9	8	7	7	7
3	4.7	21	12	9	7	6	6	5	5
4	3.7	27	15	11	9	8	7	7	6
5	2.7	37	21	15	13	11	10	9	9
6	1.4	71	41	30	24	21	19	18	17
7	2.7	37	21	15	13	11	10	9	9
8	1.4	71	41	30	24	21	19	18	17
9	1.2	83	48	35	28	25	22	21	20
10	1.1	91	52	38	31	27	24	23	22
11	.7	143	82	59	48	42	38	36	34
12	.7	143	82	59	48	42	38	36	34
13	.4	250	143	104	84	74	66	63	60
14	.3	333	190	139	113	98	88	84	80
15	.5	200	114	83	68	59	53	50	48
16	1.2	83	48	35	28	25	22	21	20
17	6.2	16	9	7	6	5	4	4	4

[1]*Fireline Handbook FSH 5109.17, United States Forest Service, Washington, DC, 1971*
[2]*Fatigue factors and rest breaks figured into estimates.*

tool usage are critical. At this point in the academy, the crew leader has a very good familiarity with individual crew members and their abilities. He/she carefully monitors attitudes and work performances as cutting time is increased. Stress and short tempers often arise and must be dealt with immediately, so morale and teamwork do not deteriorate. I have always believed that the handling and disposition of these early problems sets the tone for the whole fire season. If the crew leader displays good supervisory techniques, stability will result. If little or no counseling takes place and the crew is allowed to freelance and resolve its own conflicts, the stage is set for future problems.

It has been my experience that the first exercise in mixed brush and steep slopes will generally exceed the stress limits of one or two of the 15 persons. It's almost impossible to initially prepare the crew for this stress. You must try to quickly identify the limitations of the crew and take rest breaks frequently. Use this break time to critique work and discuss stress. I also like to discuss botany and weather in the surrounding area.

Photo by Keith Cullom

Crew persons must never get so involved with the tool action that they lose sight of fire behavior and adjacent personnel.

If you do not closely monitor stress, injuries are likely to occur, and/or there will be a serious loss of teamwork and morale. The academy goal is to work up to a point where the crew has worked eight hours in heavy mixed brush up to 40 tons per acre and on slopes of 70 percent, both in day and night conditions. The crew needs to be exposed to the heat and low humidity associated with actual fire conditions.

Line assignments should always include up to a mile of walking to get to the practice area. This allows crews to practice tool spacing and coordination.

A sampling of the 110-hour academy:

A. **One hour of physical fitness (two-mile run plus aerobics) each morning**
B. **Classroom sessions in the morning, field exercises in the afternoon**
C. **Fire shelter practice during first three days**
D. **Sixteen hours of fire safety and fatality review**
E. **Twenty-four hours of live fire training (grass fires)**
F. **Practice working in close coordination with bulldozers and brush trucks**
G. **Principles of first attack**

Hand Crew Use

Wildland fire agencies that do not employ hand crews may need to develop and train engine company personnel for this function. It is just as important for engine company personnel who may be utilized as a temporary hand crew to have proper training prior to the fire as it is for designated hot shot crews. Also, engine company personnel may be in less-than-optimum physical condition for this type of assignment, so safety and pacing become extremely important.

In order to accomplish necessary production, it's probably a good idea to have a minimum of five to six persons designated as a temporary hand crew. This allows for a crew leader plus four or five working members. Tool mix and assignment should be based on crew experience and physical condition, not just the line assignment requested by the operations chief or incident commander. Suppose you need a crew to work the hot flank of the fire, but crew members available are not skilled or haven't worked with hand tools in several years. Slopes are steep and the weather is hot and dry. It would be risking personnel and compromising safety to assign them to the hot flank of the fire. In this scenario, it would be best to use these individuals on the cold flank and caution them to pace themselves and aim for line quality, not quantity.

Another situation might be where the operations chief needs a hand crew in heavy brush to comprise one or more saw teams. If personnel are not trained and don't have appropriate safety gear (i.e., chaps), they shouldn't be using chain saws. Working a saw cutting firewood at home on your day off is a lot different than operating one on a steep slope in close coordination with a puller.

Crews should always start their line from an anchor point. They

The saw team is a key to high production in heavy fuel types. The saw team consists of a sawer and puller. Note ear, eye and leg protection.

must have full protective gear, including a fire shelter. The crew should always have radio communications. At all times, incident control objectives should be formulated around the crew's experience and capabilities (direct attack where possible).

If a wildland fire agency uses engine or brush company personnel as a hand crew more than once or twice a fire season, it's best to carry hand tools on the apparatus. Determining what tools to carry should be based on fuel types in the region. Grass fuel types will require more scraping tools (round-pointed shovels or McLeod tools).

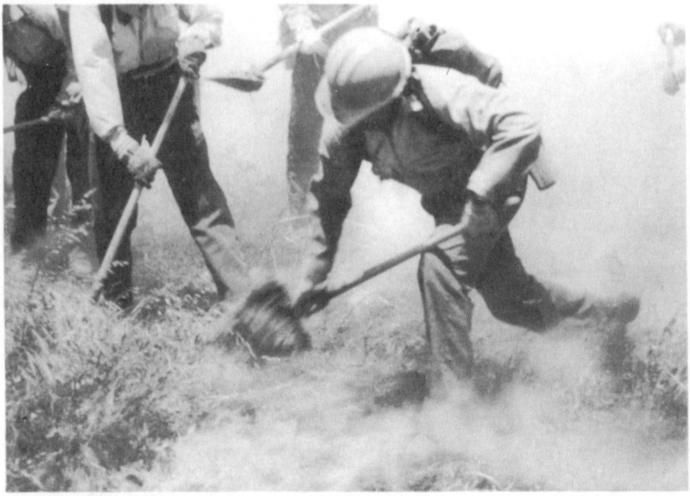

Shovel rotation requires firefighters to be in excellent condition. This technique is very useful in grass for knocking the heat out of the fire.

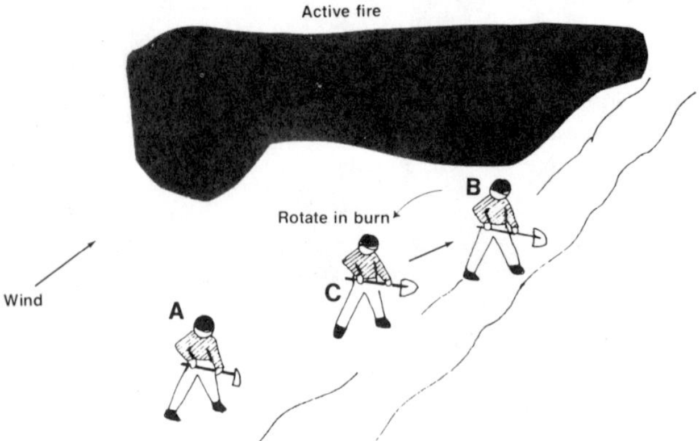

Shovel rotation is a good technique for cooling down a hot fire flank. The above illustration shows a three-person shovel rotation. Often a four- or five-person rotation reduces fatigue and exposure to heat. Person "A," with lead Pulaski, locates and loosens dirt for shovels. The Pulaski should set up out of the rotation zone, but close enough for the shovels to quickly use. Shovels (B, C) throw loose dirt on flames in a sweeping action. Shovels rotate into the burn (black).

Brush fuel types will require cutting tools (Pulaski tool, brush hook or chain saw). Timber understories with lots of duff and down-dead material might require a combination of the above.

A special caution on the use of chain saws: Personnel should practice with hand tools frequently to keep tool proficiency levels high. Monthly drills should be held in average fuel and weather conditions so that personnel must cut three to four chains of line per month using the various tools carried.

Remember, stress SQQT.

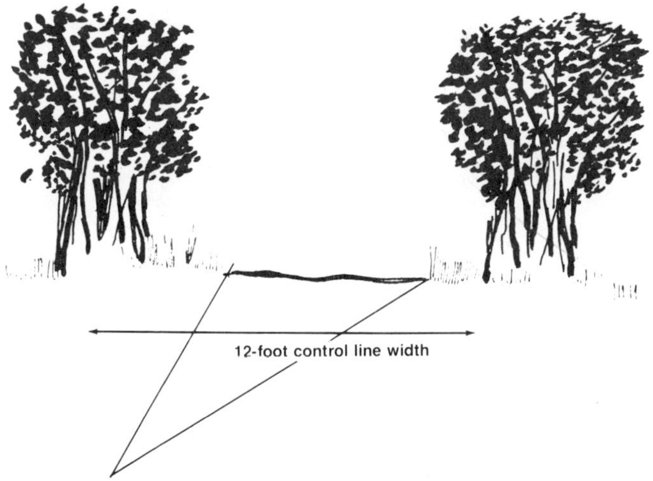

A field rule of thumb says, "Construct line 1.5 times the height of the fuel." It's important to brush fuel types to remove brush stobs down to surface levels in the middle 1/3.

Chapter 13

Protecting the Wildland/ Urban Interface

The 1985 and 1990 wildland fire seasons were two of this nation's most disastrous and costly. A large number of wildland/urban interface fires damaged or destroyed hundreds of structures. Municipal fire departments were crossing the traditional urban limit line to back up wildland firefighters and protect structures.

PROBLEMS ENDEMIC TO THE WILDLAND/URBAN INTERFACE

Providing structural protection during a wildland fire presents a myriad of problems for the incident commander and/or operations chief. The difficulties associated with protecting structures during a wildland fire really start with the homeowner. Most homeowners in the wildland/urban interface:

A. **Have not experienced, nor do they understand, the problems associated with a wildland/urban interface fire.**
B. **Moved into the wildland/urban interface wanting natural aesthetics; the "back to nature" syndrome.**
C. **Feel very secure and certain that the local fire department will be able to protect their homes should a fire occur.**
D. **Know little about how flammable vegetation will react during a fire — the "it all looks so green" syndrome.**
E. **Feel a major wildland/urban interface fire is a low probability.**
F. **Have read articles or heard how flammable wood shake and wood construction is, but still feel the beauty and natural appearance far outweigh the risks.**

G. **When asked the question, "Would you evacuate your home if a fire threatened?" most say no.**

Fire departments are going to have to spend a lot of time and energy educating architects, contractors, planning commissions and subdivision and review committees on the growing problems with expansion into the wildland/urban interface. These professionals, commissions and committees often convey the following messages to the public:

A. **Wood construction is visually more appealing.**
B. **Architects should blend the structure into the wildland setting without disturbing natural slope or vegetation.**
C. **A structure needs maximum wood, glass and decks to take full advantage of natural views, vegetation.**
D. **Subdivisions in the wildland/urban interface should be designed with lower density, larger parcel acreage, minimum roads into the subdivision and larger structures. (This had led to the birth of what I term the "horizontal highrise": large 3,000-square-foot structures built on steep slopes with lots of wood, glass and decks.)**
E. **Custom home designs and new building concepts allow development of parcels or lots once thought unbuildable because of steep slopes, poor soils and access or no utilities. Seclusion and privacy take precedence over emergency services access.**

The above statements and attitudes used to be attributed only to Southern California because of its high density and chaparral fuel types. However, 1985 and 1990 were a glaring example that the wildland/urban interface fire problem is a national one.

The problem must be addressed in two ways. First, education for homeowners, architects, contractors and elected officials on the hazards associated with development of the urban interface is a necessity. Second, fire departments must develop an aggressive pre-fire planning program including active involvement in the subdivision, planning and review processes.

Pre-fire planning can be an extremely useful tool for incident commanders or operations personnel who respond to these incidents. It is much easier during pre-fire planning to envision and solve problems concerning access, water systems, resource and personnel deployment, tactics, strategy and fallback positions.

A review of past wildland/urban interface fires will show that structures were lost or damaged for the following reasons:

A. **Wood shake roofs**
B. **Wood construction**
C. **Structure not separated from flammable vegetation**

D. Fire department had poor access to structure(s)
E. Subdivision located in a major fuel bed of heavy fuel types
F. Structures built on steep slopes covered with flammable vegetation
G. Limited water supply
H. Resources and personnel arrived too late
I. Critical fire behavior with wind models over 30 mph

PRE-FIRE PLANNING

Company or chief officers should review the above factors during the pre-fire planning process. To be effective, pre-fire planning should be ongoing. The spring months prior to declared fire season and the

Plan on the unexpected. Preplan your access routes. Here, a bridge collapses.

fall months near peak fire season are especially significant.

The spring review can be tied into weed or hazard abatement programs. Fuel types will look very different than they do in fall months.

Homeowners new to the area are often unaware of the fire hazards associated with not separating vegetation from structure. Hopefully, your fire department has an aggressive program of citing homeowners who do not comply with weed-abatement notices.

Additionally, the spring review should check on any winter damage to access or fire roads. Try to envision a fire starting in the fuel bed adjacent to the various structures. How would you provide access for resources/personnel deployed to the incident? Would they have adequate road widths and green belts to ensure personal safety as the fire moves through the area?

Evaluate likely fire behavior effects as the fire approaches the structures. You can be more aggressive in early fire season with its higher live fuel moisture levels than you can later in the year. Also, when structures do start to burn, they will add to and modify fire behavior. If structures that have wood shakes burn, plan for spot fires and additional roof fires downwind as convective heat currents carry wood shakes aloft in the convective column. Depending on wind speed and weather factors, spotting and new roof fires could start from one-fourth to two miles ahead of the fire front.

The fall pre-fire plan should be formulated just prior to peak fire season and lowest live-fuel moisture levels. This is the stage of the fire season when most wildland/urban interface structural losses occur.

As mentioned earlier, fuels will look very different than they did in spring. Note any remaining weed-abatement hazards. Evaluate any access and housekeeping problems in and around structures. For instance, a large wood scrap or corded firewood piled too close to a structure could add tremendous thermal output to a fire. Unprotected or weed-covered liquefied petroleum gas tanks near a structure could present a life-safety problem for firefighters and nearby homeowners. Abandoned vehicles in the fuel bed can also create problems – have them towed away.

If it appears on either pre-fire planning tour that the subdivision or area has many fire-related problems, the fire department should host a homeowner's meeting. At the meeting, openly share concerns about protecting structures should a fire start and, more importantly, discuss what homeowners themselves should do if a wildland fire threatens.

You should also cover evacuation procedures. Undoubtedly, there will be homeowners who will indicate they will refuse to leave their homes during a wildland fire. You might as well give self-help pointers to these individuals. If they decide to stay, take advantage of the extra help and have them assist you by securing their homes and surrounding area (close windows, doors, etc.).

Evacuation during a wildland fire is difficult, at best. One road system is expected to handle both fire department access and homeowner egress. Nighttime evacuation is even more difficult than daytime.

Best results are achieved by coordinating with local law enforcement agencies. Many communities have designated law enforcement as the lead agency in any evacuation. A pre-fire-season meeting with law enforcement officials to discuss urban interface fire evacuation problems is a must.

Develop common expectation levels and plans. A developing wildland/urban fire may tax even large fire and law enforcement agencies. You must mutually decide on priority access and egress routes. Additional personnel for manning closure points or house-to-house evacuations may have to come from other city or county staff (public works, road or health departments).

A developing wildland/urban interface fire will also require additional plans for media access and political involvement. Once structures start to burn, the incident will receive a high priority from all forms of media. You must have a policy on media access to the firegound.

A single public information officer will quickly become overloaded and unable to keep all the media on scene together. Plan for this problem. Keep the media well informed of the situation and any incident action plan updates. If the media senses you are not being aboveboard, they will freelance and get their stories from firefighters on the line. This is likely to result in less-than-satisfactory media releases.

A community's political structure will come into play once the fire involves structural loss or evacuations. The best way to prepare local government for this contingency is to educate officials prior to fire season. Use a field tour or slide show to illustrate fire problems. Educate them about the Incident Command System and how management of a major incident works. Explain how incident control objectives are developed. Ask how they see themselves getting involved if a major incident does happen. Answer any questions or concerns.

DEPLOYING RESOURCES

Historically, major wildland/urban interface fires occur during periods of critical live fuel moisture levels and critical fire weather (high wind models). It is imperative that all company and chief officers know when these components are about to unite and make their decisions based on fire-behavior potential. To repeat, *always think incident potential*. Underestimating a wildland fire near a subdivision or tract could mean that the additional resources needed to protect structures will not arrive in time to pre-position in and around buildings. This could mean loss of multiple structure and/or unduly exposing personnel to heat and smoke.

As new subdivisions encroach into the wildland areas, you must continually review your response cards. A wildland/urban interface fire calls for more resources and personnel than a wildland fire. To keep ahead of the power curve and forecast incident potential, you need resources for an aggressive initial attack. You must also preposition resources for potential structural protection.

Here's a question: Using your response cards for a wildland/urban interface fire, how many engines could you deploy for structural protection in the first hour of the incident? Why one hour? Because, generally, a fire department will declare an extended attack or major incident if the fire is not contained within an hour. By this time, more resources have probably been committed, and mutual aid requested.

If the incident commander has not forseen the potential for structural protection within the first hour and ordered it by then, it often

The running attack works well in light fuels. The engineer must watch the firefighter, fire and driving hazards all at once.

won't arrive in time. Mutual aid resources will require additional time to access the area, pre-position, and be apprised of incident objectives.

Review response cards. Resources ordered for a developing wildland/urban fire should be ordered by strike teams (five engine groupings), not single resource. A strike team and leader can accomplish multiple control objectives as well as assure strike-team safety.

Let's look at a Type 1 engine strike team (five engines), each with 500 gallons of water (2,500 gallons total). A strike-team leader can accomplish many control objectives with that much water – not to mention the 20 personnel and equipment accompanying it! However, a single Type 1 engine with 500 gallons of water and four personnel will obviously limit firefighting capabilities.

A single resource is likely to deploy to the first firefighting problem and lose focus of the overall incident. Once briefed, a strike team leader can keep resources mobile and move across a large area.

Remember: Think incident potential. If you see the need for two or three engines to protect structures, order a strike team. By the time it arrives, things may well have escalated. Plan for equipment breakdowns and personnel injuries. A strike team gives you a cushion.

How many engines do you need to protect a group of structures or a subdivision? Good question. Every wildland/urban interface fire will burn differently and engender any number of unplanned-for problems. Pre-planning, weather factors, the time required for pre-deployment, incident control objectives and past experience must equally be drawn upon to get the answer.

The incident commander should develop attainable incident objectives, taking into account available resources and personnel. The initial-attack incident commander will use pre-planning, knowledge of fuel types, weather and topography to forecast incident potential early on, maybe even before the first chief officer arrives.

Initial reactions and basic control objectives established by the first-arriving officer are critical in formulating an action plan that carries a high probability of success. Some examples of factors influencing succes:

LOW PROBABILITY OF SUCCESS

A. Resources not scheduled to arrive at structures *before* the fire does.
B. Wind speeds over 30 mph, critical fire behavior
C. Wood shake roof, wood construction
D. Structures built on slopes over 50 percent. Natural vegetation on slopes
E. Structures and vegetation not separated
F. Poor access to structures

Photo by Keith Cullor

Even on a small wildland fire, an anchor point is important prior to starting an attack.

G. Structures spaced less than 20 feet apart
H. Poor water supply
I. Isolated structures with narrow access, no green belts or protection for firefighters or resources
J. No incident action plan. Free-lance firefighting

K. Single-resource ordering, deployment
L. Resources focus on a hydrant or single structure

The direct attack. A running-attack wet line is followed up by a hand tool to secure any hot areas. An anchor point is important. The black serves as a safety zone.

HIGH PROBABILITY OF SUCCESS

A. Good pre-planning, pre-attack by fire department and used by first-arriving officer
B. Resources ordered early, pre-deployed in advance. Incident objectives known
C. Good incident action plan, control objectives. Expectation levels set with law enforcement.
D. Wind speeds under 15 mph. No critical fire behavior
E. Subdivision has fuel management plan. No vegetation in and around the structures
F. Slopes do not exceed 30 percent
G. Air attack and/or bulldozer, hand crews support operations
H. Good water supply
I. Building construction other than wood
J. Good wide-access roads with wide turnouts and green belts
K. Strike team deployment
L. Resources keep mobile, flow with the fire and changing conditions. Wise use of water

The wildland/urban interface fire will require firefighters to blend structure-fire and wildland-fire tactics and strategy. First, have confidence in the incident action plan and control objectives given your strike team. Second, keep mobile and don't let personal emotions or homeowner hysteria cause you to lose sight of control objectives and commit to a structure already too far gone to save. This jeopardizes the entire incident.

When should you let a structure burn or drive by it to one that is not yet burning? Experience will tell you that if a wood roof is starting to burn as you drive up, it's probably not salvageable. Wind is a very key factor in this premise. Two recent wildland/urban interface fires (Panorama and Paint) in California, both of which destroyed over 200 homes, totally consumed homes in three to 11 minutes' burning time. Both fires were wind driven. However, isolated rooms, decks or eaves burning may indicate an aggressive attack if discovered in time and you can quickly deploy attack lines.

Water is very important in a developing urban interface fire. Tank water and the wise use of it may save many homes. The use of ¾- or 1-inch booster line instead of 1½-inch cotton jacket hose will help conserve water. Do not depend on the water system, especially in a mountainous subdivision where loss of electrical power could knock out water or well pumps.

In areas or subdivisions where there is a low probability of successful suppression, the best protection may be forced evacuation of residents. Law enforcement is a very intrinsic part of this emotional issue. It is paramount that resources and personnel not be wasted on a low-probability situation or where their safety is compromised. The incident commander must be allowed to let structures burn when the risk to firefighters is grave.

In summary, the best way to evaluate potential structural protection success is through good pre-fire planning, early resource ordering, pre-deployment and a good incident action plan. Knowledge of these can make the difference between a successful effort and an unsuccessful one.

Chapter 14

Protection of Isolated Structures

In the previous chapter we discussed protecting multiple structures during a wildland fire, with emphasis on the importance of pre-fire planning. Planning is probably even more critical in wildland fire areas where you are protecting isolated structures or ranches.

There are numerous concerns associated with country roads, canyons and long driveways that must be evaluated prior to the start of fire season. These include:

A. **Road bed material**
B. **Road width**
C. **Road slope**
D. **Fuel canopy overhang**
E. **Adjacent fuel types**
F. **Canyon width, topography**

Rural roads can have very diverse road beds. Road beds made of gravel, rock base or sand should be evaluated closely. These can deteriorate with time to the point where large holes or washes could seriously impact access or egress during a fire. While the road surface and hazard may be easily avoided or traversed by a small sedan, large heavy equipment may have a problem. During extreme fire behavior or a firestorm, such roads may delay egress long enough to threaten your safety as well as that of the vehicle you are driving.

Road width is a closely-related problem. Narrow and/or windy roads create a real hazard during smoky situations. Many isolated structures and ranches will have one-lane access roads. During a fire, such roads should be secured and only fire equipment allowed to access or egress. Even then, a traffic plan should be formulated in case an unanticipated need occurs. You don't want equipment traveling to your location on a one-lane road just as you are egressing in a smoky, firestorm situation. This becomes even more critical when dealing with mutual aid resources that may not have common radio frequencies. Fire engineers or drivers should make mental notes of all wide spots or turnouts in case an emergency is encountered.

Road slope can also be an important consideration. Roads traversing a middle or upper slope (Figure 14a) may be subjected to con-

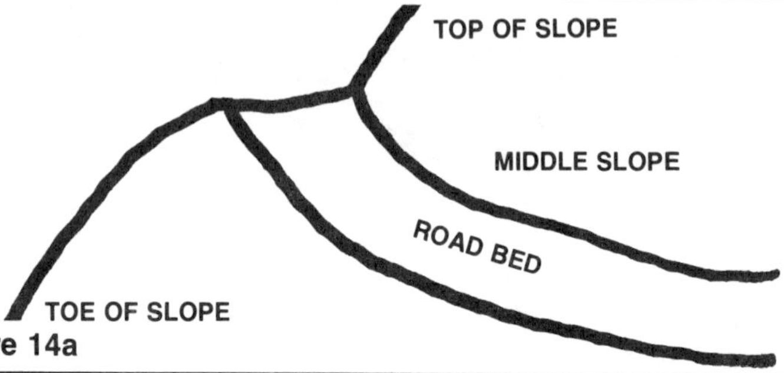

Figure 14a

vective and radiant heat in excess of human tolerances. Narrow roads that run through middle or upper slopes require slow driving speeds.

Fuel canopy overhang is another concern. (Figure 14b). Be very cautious about access roads where a good fuel ladder runs from grass to heavy fuel types as well as situations where large "jack pots" of down-dead fuels parallel the road. Flame lengths and thermal outputs in the above examples may exceed survivability and block your egress.

Company officers should be alert to grass along the road that may be used later to support a firing operation for safety or tactical needs (Figure 14c). This is preferable to firing in heavier fuel types where there is not sufficient light fuel to carry your fire away from the control line.

In canyons where isolated structures or ranches must be protected, these items should be evaluated:

A. Narrow canyon wind patterns
B. Fire behavior potential
C. Separation between toe of slope and structures

Figure 14b

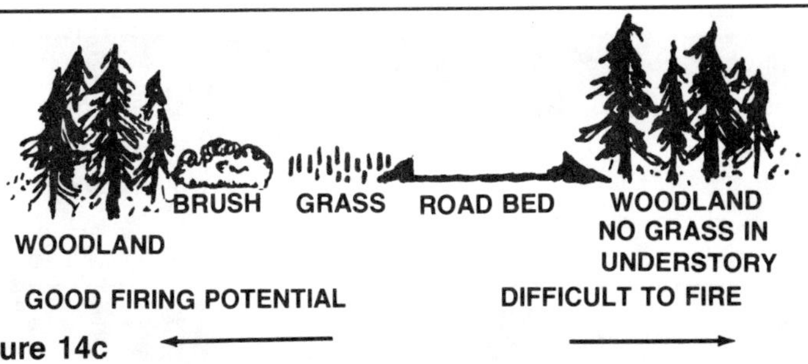

Figure 14c

D. Environment for personnel and resources

E. Rolling material

F. Spotting potential

Narrow canyons or drainages exhibit diverse wind patterns and eddy influences (Figure 14d). Depending on canyon width, topography, fuel types and wind speed, spotting may create problems. A fast-moving fire or extreme fire behavior will modify even Figure 14d examples. Canyon winds are an important factor in ability to protect a structure or carry a backfire away from the structure.

Often canyons will become involved with a backing fire (Figure 14e). Depending on a variety of factors and assuming the structure is sufficiently safe from heat radiated from the toe of the slope, this can be used to the firefighter's advantage. If sufficient light fuels are in place to carry a backfire, the slope wind and backing fire will pull flames away from the structure. Experience, timing and resource placement are very important in this scenario. If winds change or resources are not pre-positioned to protect the exposed structure, you may lose that exposure. Coordination and communications are essential. Many states have strict laws concerning backfiring. Company and chief officers should be well versed in how and when to use this important tool.

When protecting isolated structure(s), life safety of residents and personnel is the firefighter's number one control objective. Most residents living in the urban interface have not experienced a wildland

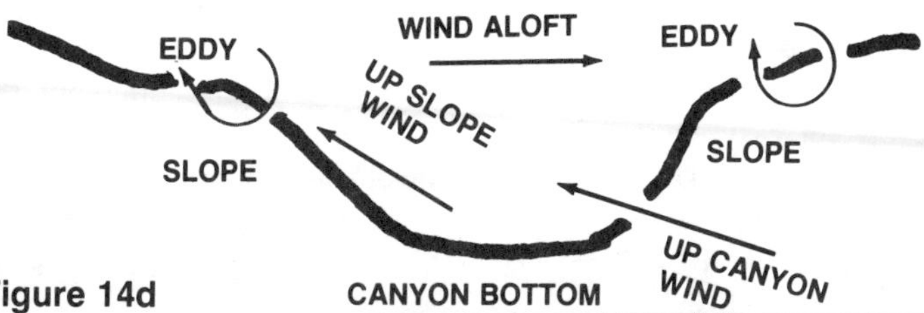

Figure 14d

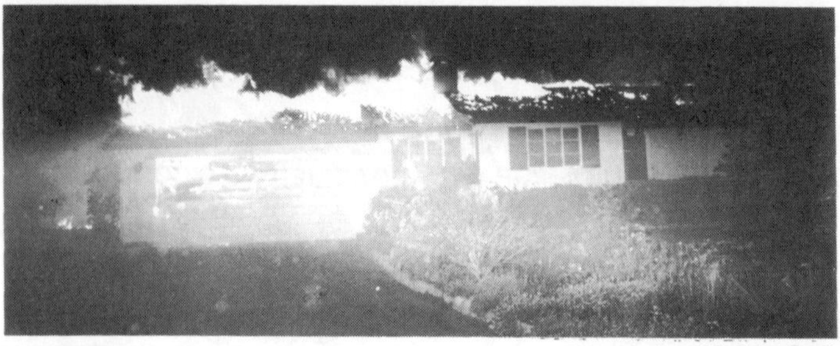

Photo by Keith Cullom

As a general rule, if a roof fire (wood shakes) is discovered on arrival in a wind-driven wildland fire, it's considered a write-off by tactical definition.

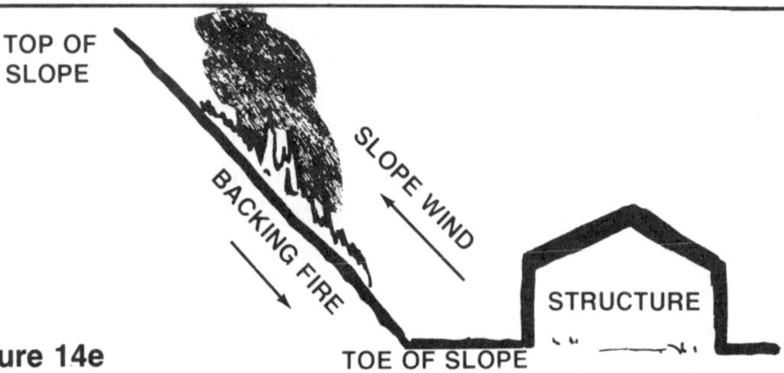

Figure 14e

fire before. Many will want to stay with their homes. This added "exposure" may create additional problems for the company officer and fire personnel. If at all possible, try and talk them into evacuating, if time and conditions permit. If not, discuss your expectations with the "hold outs." Keep names and address of those who remain at homes or ranches, so if you leave the area during the fire someone can check on them later.

Evaluate risks associated with protecting the structure and or resident(s). A quick tour around the exposure can be very helpful. Figure 14f illustrates key points to check.

The structure should have a minimum 30-foot separation from fuel. It should also have a green belt or lawn where a safety zone can be established. Pre-position engine(s) downhill or facing out the driveway for easy egress. Do not allow vehicles to block the egress lane. *Keep mobile:* Do not commit yourself to a fixed water source or ranch well. If you want to lay out/pre-position hose, do it dry. Instruct your crew to wait to charge lines in case you must quickly disconnect and leave.

Keep your crew together. Patrol around the structure. Watch

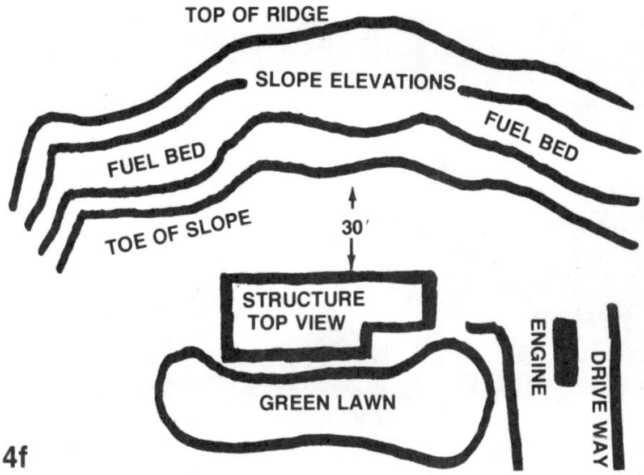

Figure 14f

eaves, roof, roof vents and decks. Locate, identify utility shut offs. Make sure either the resident or fire crews have secured all windows and doors and closed all blinds, shades and curtains. Remove combustible furniture from decks and place inside the structure.

Unfortunately, a common habit on ranches is stacking firewood under wood decks or next to the house. This can add tremendous heat to a fire, once involved.

Remember also that a high-thermal-output fire may reduce oxygen levels to a point where your fire apparatus may not start. Make sure vehicles are correctly and safely positioned ahead of the fire. (Think worse case.)

Be alert to wildlife running out of the fire area. Do not pick up animals or corner them.

Identify potential fire problems. Many ranches have liquefied petroleum gas (LPG) for heating. Check out the storage tank for this and make sure it's clear of flammable vegetation. Check barns and sheds for flammable liquid storage. Check flammable vegetation clearance.

Do not waste water. Even if you find a good source, plan your tactics wisely and don't wet down roofs or grounds well in advance of the fire front. A rule of thumb concerning the use of tank water is "One-half tank for the fire, one-half tank for you (safety)." This is important if water sources are scarce or limited.

Also, keep in constant communications with your division or group supervisor.

When should you "write off" a structure or ranch? Here are several examples of what I believe constitute too high a risk:

A. The structure or ranch has no separation from the fuel bed. Fuel bed is grass or medium/heavy brush. The structure has a wood roof

Photo by Joe Hughes, New Jersey Forestry

One of the nation's rapidly developing wildland/urban interface areas — the New Jersey Pine Barrens.

and wood construction. Weather model is very high or extreme. You have successfully evacuated residents.

B. The structure is at the top of a major slope and in a continuous fuel bed of brush (Figure 14g). The fire is running upslope. No one is at home.

C. The structure is located at the head of a box canyon in a continuous fuel bed. There are no safety zones or green belts for personnel. The structure has a wood roof and wood construction. There's no on-site water availability and residents have been safely evacuated (Figure 14h).

D. The structure is located on a narrow ridge line with a major drainage on either side of the ridge. The fuel bed is continuous. The structure is wood construction. Fire weather is extreme and no one is at home (Figure 14i).

E. The structure is in a major forested area, in a closed canopy stand. The road has a narrow access. The structure is wood construction and has no separation from fuel. Down-dead material abounds. The fire is running in the crowns. No one is at home (Figure 14j).

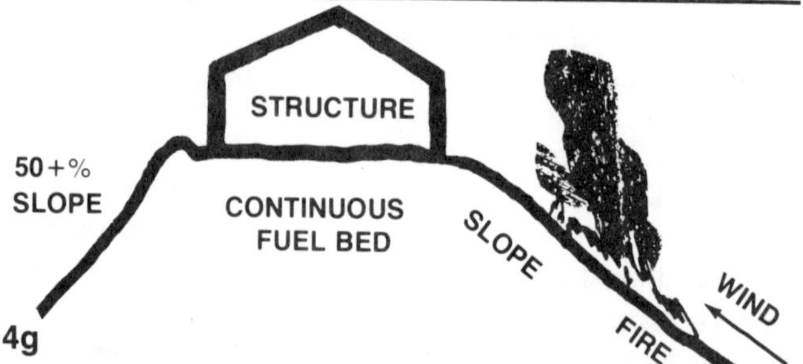

Figure 14g

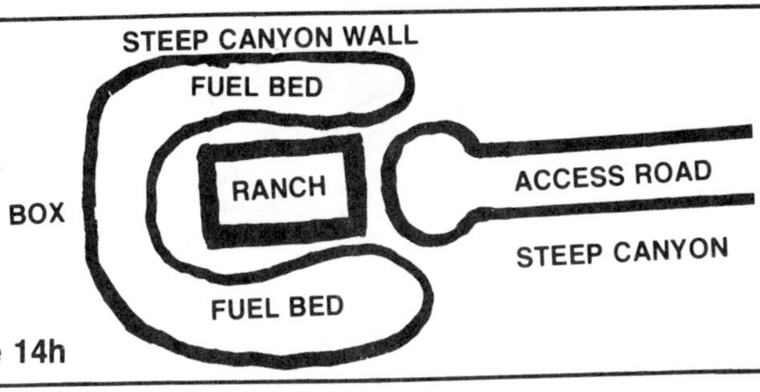

Figure 14h

F. Long narrow, steep canyon walls and a major fuel bed are present. Weather is extreme. You have mutual aid; however, no communications or clear control objectives arc given, and it appears no coordination of action is taking place. the area has been evacuated.

G. In your judgment as company or chief officer, the situation cannot be handled with the personnel and/or resources available. Every threatened resident has been safely evacuated.

I'm sure there are many additional scenarios where you will not feel comfortable protecting a structure in a given fuel bed, topography or weather situation. Using the above examples as a base, survey your urban interface or adjoining mutual-aid areas and locate potential problems. Discuss these and pre-plan how you might handle evacuation or structural protection in a worse-case situation. Make sure you consider both daytime and nighttime evacuations.

Several nighttime problems I have encountered:

A. You can't see overhead power lines.

B. Lots of hidden hazards for foot traffic (sprinkler heads, garden tools, etc.).

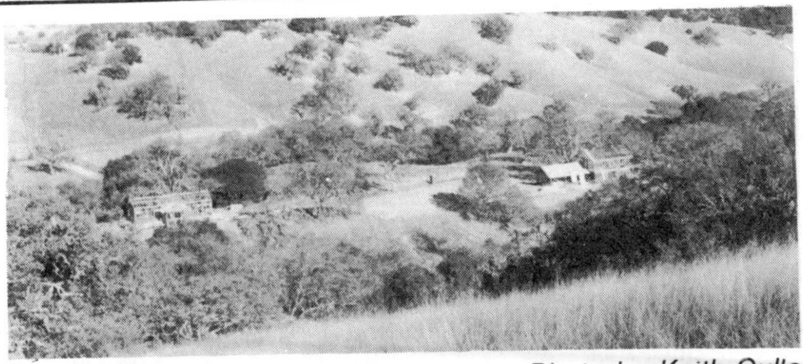

Photo by Keith Cullom

Preplanning new construction in the wildland/urban interface is critical to developing fire strategies. Access, construction and separation from fuels are key points.

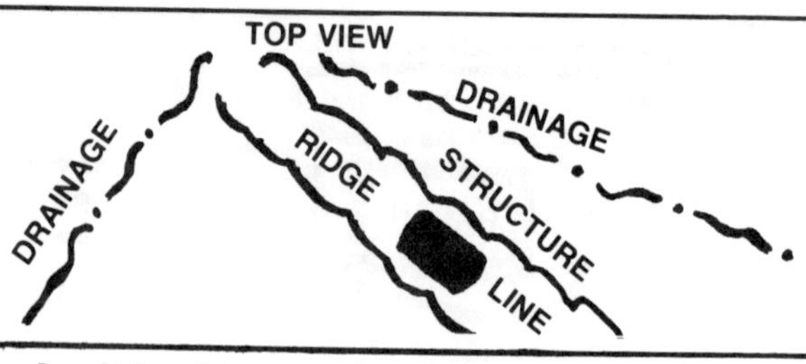

Figure 14i

C. **Set-up makes it hard to move hose lines.**
D. **Penned livestock must be moved.**
E. **Ranch gates are locked.**
F. **Explosives are stored in out buildings.**

Pre-planning isolated wildland areas should be a team effort. As an example:

A. **FIREFIGHTER**
   Check:
   1. **Fuel types, fuel loading as you drive the canyon area.**
   2. **Down-dead fuels.**
   3. **Fuel canopy overhangs.**

B. **FIRE ENGINEER** (Driver)
   Check:
   1. **Road conditions.**
   2. **Safety turnarounds.**
   3. **Run times at safe speeds to each structure.**
   4. **Driving hazards, road beds, bridges, wash outs, etc.**

C. **FIRE CAPTAIN** (Officer)
   Evaluate:
   1. **Wildland fire potential**
   2. **Structure construction**
   3. **Wildland fire tactics that could be used**
   4. **Safety zones**
   5. **Hazards**
   6. **Evacuation problems (non-ambulatory residents, children etc.)**

Figure 14j

Chapter 15

Up-grading from Initial Attack

Most fire departments, in their manual of operations, include a statement from the fire chief or operations chief on attack philosophy. In wildland fire agencies, this statement should include, but not be limited to:

A. **Firefighters shall be in good physical condition and take an annual pre-fire season fitness test.**
B. **Firefighters shall wear full wildland fire protective gear.**
C. **Firefighters are not a renewable resource. However, most brush and timber species *do* recover after a wildland fire, so don't utilize an attack method that will jeopardize personnel safety.**
D. **Homes and/or valued timber or watershed should be protected next, after life safety.**
E. **Initial-attack incident commanders should make a direct attack when possible, in a cost-effective and safe manner.**
F. **Attack methods should be based on the following variables:**
    1. **Life safety of fire personnel**
    2. **Life safety of residents in the fire area**
    3. **Resources available for initial attack**
    4. **Ability to deploy resources at the scene**
    5. **Experience and past success of the incident commander**
    6. **Fire behavior factor (weather, fuels and topography)**
    7. **Physical condition of firefighters**
    8. **Ability to control fire before it escapes initial attack**
    9. **Ability to cover exposures first, then attack the fire**

In most cases, the first-in company officer is also the initial-attack incident commander. Company officers and chief officers must understand the above priorities so they will make attacks consistent with the safety of personnel as first priority.

A department should have operating levels for the fireground. Most departments stress trying to control a fire with initial attack resources. An example of how such a policy might look is as follows:

FIREGROUND OPERATIONS/COMMAND FLOW/UPGRADE
Initial Attack

A. Communications
Size-up from first-arriving company officer.

B. Action

1. **Keep responding chief updated on your operation.**
   a. Attack – If you have sufficient resources/personnel and can formulate an action plan (tactical assignments).
   b. Stage – Can you assign resources/manpower yet formulate an action plan?
   c. Command – Incident has spread rapidly, upgrading its status. Establish command post, name incident, evaluate need for staging. Starting incident action plan.

The first-in company officer must assume responsibility for a good size-up on arrival at the incident. This size-up should include the important factors of *weather, fuel burning, slope, size of fire, access, exact location,* and *incident potential*. These are important considerations for other responding resources and dispatch, as well as the chief officer.

This size-up does not have to take up much air time if you include a few key words to indicate your intentions. An example might be as follows: "5713 arrived, 2315 San Marcos Pass Road, fire burning in grass, brush; winds are moderate, steep slopes, limited access, fire has burned two to three acres, potential for extended attack with homes threatened: We're in the attack mode." The responding resources dispatched and chief officer will be able to visualize the incident and 5713's actions.

A key part of 5713's size-up was given as *"potential for extended attack"* and *"We're in the attack mode."* This will alert resources not yet onscene that 5713 is starting an attack, probably structural protection. This should also be the signal for the next arriving company or chief officer to assume command of the developing incident because 5713 felt it was important to make an attack to start fire control, protection of immediately-threatened structures or evacuation. The term *attack mode* should also alert incoming resources not to call 5713 for an assignment because he/she is starting an attack. The next-in company or chief officer will assume command and assignments.

When the next company and/or chief officer arrive, they should update the size-up and formally assume command. This is an integral part of developing the incident action plan and control objectives. When assuming command:

A. **Get a good overview of the incident** (drive, fly or walk). I like to get the overview prior to announcing I have arrived onscene. This allows you to prepare for the transition of command without being overwhelmed by radio traffic.

B. **Formally advise the dispatch center you are assuming command.**
As part of that statement include:
1. **Incident name (e.g. "San Marcos")**
2. **Command post location**
3. **Staging area location**

C. **Update size-up of incident** (acreage burned, weather factors, control problems).

D. **Start the incident action plan and control objectives.** This should begin with the first-arriving company officer filling out a basic four-part ICS 201 form or using a command kit including field operations guide (FOG). Initially, these points should appear on the ICS 201:
1. **Confirmed location** (address, road, canyon, ranch, etc.)
2. **Basic map — access road(s). North Pointer. Any useful landmarks** (ridge, mountain, canyon names)
3. **Responding resources, personnel**
4. **A few broad, basic control objectives**
5. **Weather observations** (taken with belt weather kit)

There is no magical method or a clear-cut definition to determine when an incident should be upgraded from initial attack to extended attack, however, here are some examples:

A. **The incident escapes the first-arriving engine's control capabilities.**

B. **The incident is not controlled by the arrival of the first chief officer.**

C. **It is over five acres in size.**

D. **Burning index is over 61.**

E. **Specialized resources are required** (dozers, aircraft, hand crews).

F. **The incident cannot be controlled by the first-alarm assignment.**

I would like to stress example "F" because it gives the first-in company officer a chance to learn how to tactically deploy and manage an incident. It also allows upgrading of the incident, should conditions warrant.

Two additional terms used at the initial-attack level are *staging* and *command*. If the first-in company officer has a problem accessing the incident or getting a good vantage point from which to make assignments, he/she can establish a staging area near the incident, where resources can be held prior to responding to the incident.

Staging can also be useful when the fire is spreading under extreme fire-behavior conditions, making it unsafe to attack until it burns further from the point of origin. The term *command* indicates that the incident is developing so rapidly that it is classified as an extended-attack incident even before first-in officers arrive. This usually occurs when extreme weather models are present. Command indicates that you are not going to "initial attack the fire to death," but rather deploy resources based upon broad control objectives and divisional assignments.

The thought process for a command-size incident says, "Let's estimate the potential acreage this fire can burn and base our actions on that potential." Based on incident priorities and a span of control of five resources to one supervisor, resources will be geographically assigned to a division. If it is a functional assignment, they will be assigned to a group.

The initial-attack incident commander is responsible for developing initial broad-control objectives and incident action plan. This includes filling the need for command and general staff.

LEVEL

Extended Attack

A. Communications

1. **Size-up from first arriving company officer.**
2. **Start developing control objectives.**
3. **Apply resources to accomplish control objectives.**
4. **Start developing resources/personnel needs for control objectives.**

B. Action

1. **Advise responding chief officer.**
2. **Establish command post/staging area.**

The term *extended attack* indicates that, either as the first-in officer arrived or during the initial attack, the incident continued to grow, requiring more resources. Any incident that continues to burn out of control after all first-alarm resources have been deployed, requiring additional resources, should be upgraded at the next size-up update to an extended attack.

Generally, the first-in chief officer, once onscene and briefed by the initial-attack incident commander, will formally assume command. After this formal change of command, the initial-attack incident commander, will formally assume command. After this formal change of command, the initial-attack incident commander generally assumes the role of Operations. This makes sense because the first-in company officer should be most familiar with his/her area, surrounding resources and personnel.

At this point, the initial-attack incident commander has briefed the first-arriving chief officer using the ICS 201 or a command pak. They have reviewed the following:

A. **Confirmed location. Access road(s). Identified key roads, canyons and ranches surrounding the incident.**
B. **The basic map and key roads, ranches and landmarks for reference. North pointer.**
C. **Responding/assigned resources and personnel accounted for and identified.**
D. **Broad control objectives from the initial-attack incident commander to the first-in-chief officer.** (These, hopefully, are based on past experience and familiarity of the incident area.)
E. **A brief summary of incident weather.**

The control objectives should be crisp and clear, using a few key words such as:

- "*Hold* **fire north of San Marcos Road."**
- "*Contain* **fire in Tepusquet drainage."**
- "*Keep* **fire west of Highway 37."**
- "*Fire* **and** *hold* **Jackson Ridge Road."**
- "*Protect* **structures along Mission Ridge Road."**
- "*Ensure* **firefighter safety as the top priority."**
- "*Limit* **fire to smallest acreage consistent with cost effectiveness."**
- "*Minimize* **damage to San Raphael watershed."**

Once an agreement is reached on these basics, the chief officer who has assumed command shares with the operations chief some basic concerns or ideas as a background. These may be based on:

A. **Past experience**
B. **Comfort level with operations chief**
C. **Resource values or structures threatened**
D. **Fire behavior**
E. **Success of initial-attack resources and personnel**
F. **Incident potential**
G. **"Political" interest in this incident**

I feel "E" is very important. It is often extremely helpful to chief officers as they enter a developing wildland incident.

If the first-arriving chief officer rolls up to the incident and observes the following, the comfort level (confidence) increases:

A. **First-arriving company officer is ready with size-up, action mode, location of first-arriving unit.**

B. **If first-arriving company officer announced the command mode, then an appropriate command post location was selected and used.** (Appropriate equates to: out of heat and smoke.)

C. **First-arriving company officer named the incident, assumed command and now identifies the command post location.**

D. **Filling out the ICS 201 form has begun** (basic map, resources and personnel listings).

E. **Some basic thoughts on control objectives have been written down.**

F. **Basic tactical objectives are given to arriving resources and personnel.**

If the first-arriving company officer opted for an aggressive attack mode, then the following is evaluated:

A. **Size-up should give incoming resources, personnel and chief(s) an idea of incident complexity and potential.**

B. **First-arriving company officer should formally transition command to next-in company officer or chief officer.**

C. **Personnel safety should have been carefully evaluated prior to tactical deployment.**

Confusion and problems arise when the first-arriving company officer who visualizes a developing wildland fire:

A. **Gives little or no size-up**

B. **Gives no tactical assignment to additional arriving resources and personnel** (in other words, allows free-lance firefighting)

C. **Goes into an attack mode, but will not answer radio communications from dispatch or chief**

D. **Forces first-arriving chief officer to go into smoke and heat to find him/her**

E. **Has started no planning and the incident is developing rapidly**

F. **On an urban-interface fire with homes threatened, continues to attack burning grass and brush. Does not set up for structure protection or order additional resources to cover exposures**

LEVEL

Major Incident

A. **Communications**

1. **Size-up from incident commander**

2. **Whether incident will require command team**
3. **Order major resources**

B. **Actions**
1. **Evaluate incident action plan**
2. **Expand command post to handle developing needs**
3. **Increase command/general staff**

A *major incident* is the highest-level upgrade. Once an incident reaches the point where it requires more than two geographical divisions, covers over 300 acres in size, is still burning after one burn period or requires mutual aid or a command team (or a combination of the above), the chief officer may want to upgrade to a major incident. Additional staff, including Plans, Logistics and Finance, are added to tactical divisions support operations.

Prior to selecting any attack method, be aware that:

A. **The first-in company officer is responsible for assuming command for initial attack. This should include a good size-up of incident level and potential.**

B. **The department must have a good policy statement outlining its wildland fire attack philosophy.**

C. **Company and chief officers should pre-plan key fuel beds and identify possible command post and base locations.**

D. **The importance of personnel safety on any attack method should be stressed.**

Over 90 percent of all wildland incidents are controlled by initial-attack and minimal command personnel. Most initial-attack incidents are held under 10 acres. Management for these incidents lies chiefly with the first-arriving company officer. In such cases, the experienced company officer must evaluate a multitude of factors in a relatively short span of time. The decisions he/she makes cover the same basic areas of incident management that a command team evaluates, only the depth is different.

In Figure 15a, the company officer is the incident commander, responsible for managing the incident. This means that decisions associated with *Planning, Operations, Finance* and *Command* are made by this officer. Generally, this is accomplished with little hesitation and few problems, as most initial-attack incidents are not complex enough to require additional Planning, Logistics or Finances. Most initial-attack incidents also stay within the recommended span of control of five to one (one supervisor for every five firefighters).

Most experienced company officers will accomplish the process shown in Figure 15a in a few minutes. The important thing to remember is to allow for Planning, Logistics and Finance.

Once the initial-attack incident commander has applied resources

Initial Attack Incident

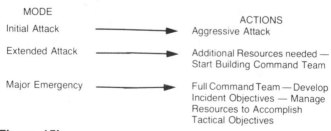

Assesses Situation (Planning)

Plots Incident on Map (Planning)

Develops Strategy (Planning)

Lists Resources Responding (Planning)

Adjust Resources to incident to accomplish tactical objectives (Operations)

Evaluates Operations (Command)

Makes Decisions (Command)

Evaluates Logistical Needs (Command)

Evaluates Cost Effectiveness (Command)

Evaluates Public Relations (Command)

Monitors Safety (Command)

Figure 15a

to accomplish incident objectives, he/she must begin the important process of obtaining feedback from these resources as to the likelihood of success. This feedback is very important because it can "tip off" the incident commander as to possible needs for additional personnel and resources in advance.

The incident commander must remain flexible and be able to adjust tactics should incident conditions change (weather, equipment failure, fuel type, etc.). If, after feedback is obtained, the incident remains out of control, the incident commander must reevaluate the plan and incident objectives. The key phrase is, "Don't initial attack the fire to death." If it continues to burn over the hill, and feedback confirms this same, pull back and start the planning process. For the time being, allow resources to continue the attack. Stress quality work and safety (a key point here is to secure and reinforce all control lines put in to this point), but do advise resources that you may adjust their

MODE		ACTIONS
Initial Attack	→	Aggressive Attack
Extended Attack	→	Additional Resources needed — Start Building Command Team
Major Emergency	→	Full Command Team — Develop Incident Objectives — Manage Resources to Accomplish Tactical Objectives

Figure 15b

assignments. *Stay flexible.*

An example of a typical system of progressive levels for operations and management is shown in Figure 15b. In the transition from initial attack to major emergency, an important given is that the incident commander is responsible for expanding the command team. This means that, as the incident shifts away from an aggressive attack with minimal formal planning, the incident commander must take responsibility for devising a method to accomplish the incident objectives, as shown in Figures 15c, d and e.

While the initial-attack incident requires only one manager to perform incident command, operations, planning, logistical and finance processes, if incident complexity changes and additional resources and personnel will change the span of control, the incident commander must formally initiate the functions listed above. This would probably follow such a progression:

A. Initial-attack incident commander receives feedback indicating fire is still escaping initial attack. ("We're having problems on

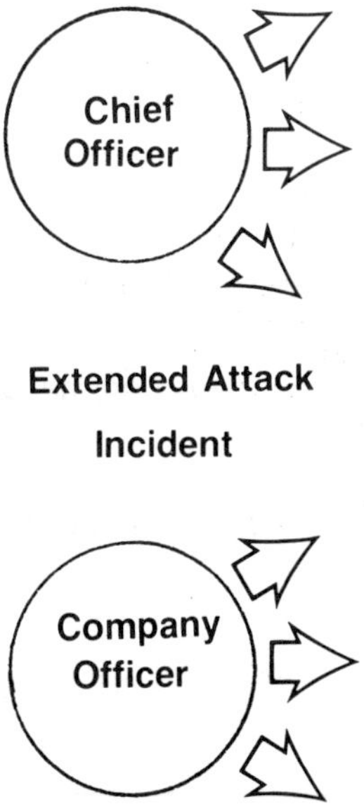

Receives briefing from initial attack incident commander. (Command)

Reviews initial attack strategy incident tactics with new operations chief. (Command)

Establish new incident strategy — incident objectives — review with operations chief. (Command)

Agree on time to review incident with operations chief. (Command)

Manage the incident, evaluate needs for planning, logistics. (Command)

Start role as operations chief after briefing chief officer and turning incident over. (Operations)

Review situation plot intelligence on map. (Operations)

Review resource status, plot divisional or group boundaries or functions. (Operations)

Order staff as necessary to meet divisional or group functions. (Operations)

Adjust assignments as necessary to accomplish incident objectives. (Operations)

Evaluate new request for resources, manpower. (Operations)

Manage tactics for incident. (Operations)

Figure 15c

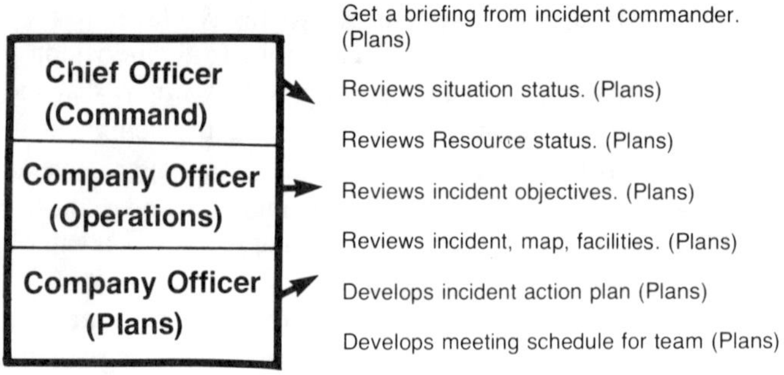

Figure 15d

the hot flank, we're getting some spot fires.'')

B. He/she advises dispatch that incident is being upgraded. Incident is named, formal command post set up. Initial-attack IC assumes command, announces command post location.

C. Situation, resource status is assessed and plotted on map (if not already done).

D. Initial-attack IC requests operations chief. This can be another company officer on scene *or* self. If a chief officer is responding but not yet on the scene, he/she may assume command after a formal briefing and appoint first-in officer to handle operations, as he/she is up-to-date on the incident.

In Figure 15c, the first-arriving chief officer has been briefed by the initial-attack incident commander (company officer), and, because of the developing situation and upgrade, the chief officer

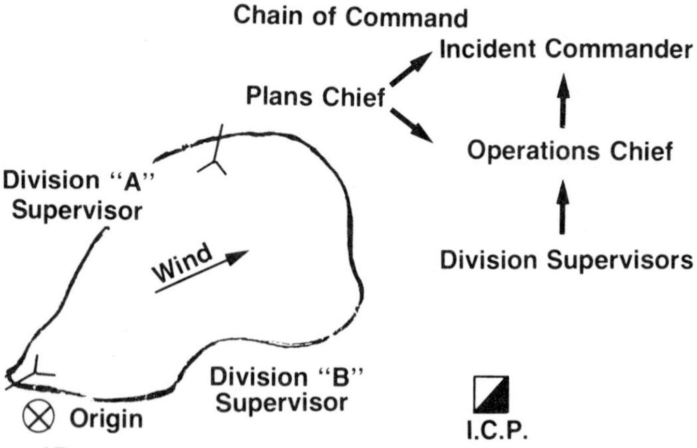

Figure 15e

assumes command. Since the initial-attack incident commander possesses a great deal of knowledge about the incident, he/she is a good choice to handle the operations chief position, once both agree on new incident objectives and a basic framework for expanding incident management.

Obviously, at this point, both will retain shared responsibilities for planning, logistics and finance. The primary necessities for this incident are still Management and Operations (tactical); however, Planning will require full considerations as the incident Logistics, Finance and Operations needs grow. A key to safe, cost-effective operations is having an incident action plan (IAP) – a framework coordinated by a plans chief.

During this point in an extended attack, it is quite possible that the incident command team will include the three functions listed above and probably two divisions (or maybe one group). Division supervisors provide basic supervision of resources.

The need to fill support positions under Command, Operations or Plans will quickly be addressed as the plans chief tries to bring all incident functions together to establish the IAP. Depending on incident complexity and duration, logistical needs must be addressed next.

If the incident continues to grow in complexity and duration, the incident commander should consider filling the Finance position to evaluate cost effectiveness and respond to equipment-rental or time-keeping needs.

THE COMMAND TEAM

As the incident continues in duration, it will become necessary to fill other support positions:

A. **Safety** – Safety officer (Command Staff)
B. **Situation** – Situation status (Plans)
C. **Fire Behavior** – Fire behavior technical specialists (Plans)
D. **Branch Director** – After five divisions are established (Operations)
E. **Air Operations** – If two or more air resources are used (Operations)
F. **Service Branch** – (Logistics)
G. **Support Branch** – (Logistics)

SUMMARY

Key points to remember when developing a management team for an incident include:

A. **Incident commander is responsible for activating other staff** (Operations, Plans, Logistics and Finance).

B. Plan early in an incident. Remember span of control.
C. If a fire continues to escape initial attack, pull back and start planning.
D. Set broad incident objectives.
E. Brief staff as they are activated.
F. Manage your staff. Stay out of specific task work.
G. Stress safety, cost effectiveness.
H. Remain flexible at all times.

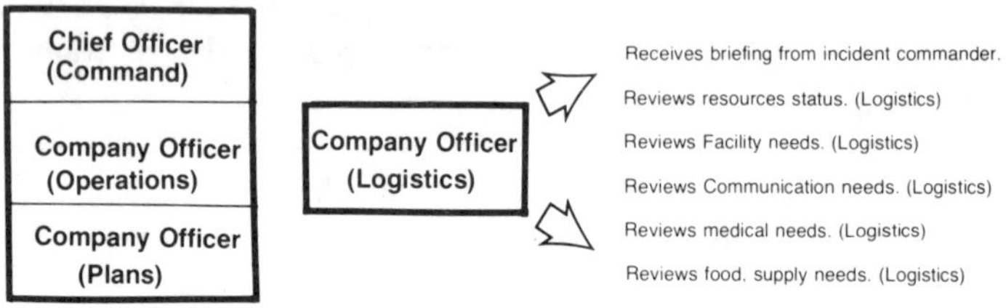

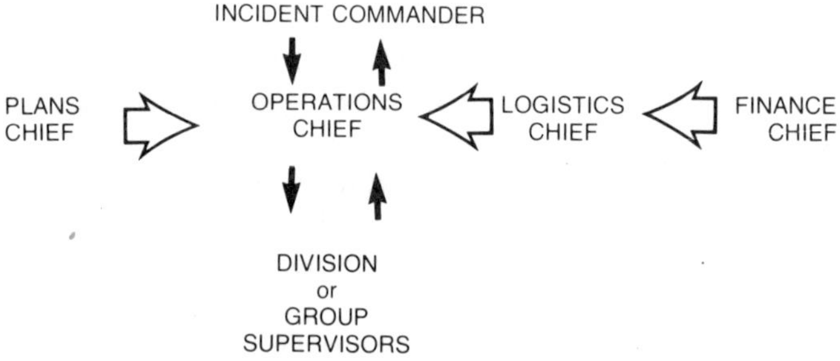

Chapter 16

Incident Planning and Activating the Incident Command System

As mentioned earlier in the book, command teams are an important part of the basic transition from initial attack to a major incident. The primary functions of a command team include:

A. **Command** – Overall incident management

B. **Operations** – Manages tactical plan to accomplish incident objectives

C. **Plans** – Gathers intelligence, formulates incident action plan

D. **Logistics** – Provides service and support functions

E. **Finance** – Monitors all aspects of the incident for cost effectiveness

THE PLANS CHIEF

The *plans chief* is often the catalyst for a command team. He/she brings together reports from all the functions and formulates them into an incident action plan (IAP). This is no easy accomplishment, and is often a major reason why the transition from attack to command takes so long and sometimes never is fully completed.

An important duty of the plans chief is keeping up with the status of an incident. This includes fire behavior, fireline organization and resources. Since the initial-attack incident commander is responsible for initiating all incident functions, many times, the plans function falls behind the "power curve." If the incident commander or operations chief has not plotted the incident on a map and listed resources – allocated, assigned and en route – then he/she will have to spend some time obtaining this intelligence from division or group supervisors.

Incident Command System Form 201 is an excellent aid to assist the incident commander in recording the necessary situation and resource data for the plans chief. It is a four-part form consisting of pages for organization, summary of current actions, an incident map and resource summary. If this form is completed prior to the arrival of the plans chief (and is up to date) it's possible to start developing the incident action plan and the planning process as soon as the plans chief arrives.

INCIDENT PLANNING

Most incidents will not require a formal written plan, but most need to have a formal process to assure that the following basic functions are performed:

A. **Review incident intelligence, brief staff** (information sharing)
B. **Set meeting schedule**
C. **Conduct planning meeting**
D. **Collect incident documents**
E. **Coordinate incident activities**

The plans chief must be able to clearly "take charge" and serve as a moderator during the planning process. It should be noted here that some incident commanders will want to manage the planning meeting. However, even though the incident commander is responsible for overall incident management, the plans chief must bring the team together and coordinate information exchanges. This will facilitate the planning meeting, because a trained plans chief knows how to ask the right questions at the appropriate time.

Some overall keys to planning include:

A. **Have only necessary staff attend briefings, exchanges and meetings.**
B. **Set time for meetings and hold to that time.**
C. **Establish a "rotation" for information sharing.**
D. **Document comments. Use Incident Command System forms when possible.**
E. **Keep staff focused on objectives.**
F. **End meeting on time. Announce next meeting.**

During the information-sharing process, where, again, the plans chief serves as moderator, the following areas should be reviewed:

A. **Overview of incident** (plans or incident commander)
B. **Incident map** (plans)
C. **Incident topography** (plans)
D. **Incident fuel type(s)** (plans)
E. **Current situation** (operations)
F. **Resources involved** (operations, plans)

G. **Overhead personnel on incident** (plans)
H. **Communication needs** (plans, logistics)
I. **Transportation needs** (logistics)
J. **Facility needs** (logistics)
K. **Service-supply needs** (logistics)
L. **Fiscal considerations** (finance)
M. **Contracts** (finance)

Additionally, the command team will want to exchange information of interest to all team members. This includes:

A. **Problems** (e.g. "We have some crews that need relief, but they're a key part of today's assignment.")
B. **Special equipment needs** (such as heli-torch for firing operations)
C. **Manpower**
D. **Special supervision considerations** (e.g. "We will be using two strike teams of inmates on Division D today.")
E. **Safety concerns** (e.g. "We will be using dozers on Division F; remind their hand crews to be alert.")
F. **Political aspects** (e.g. "Be aware that the governor will be here between 1000 and 1100 hours.")
G. **Environmental problems** (e.g. "Let's make sure we water-bar all dozer lines once the incident is controlled.")
H. **Mutual aid** (i.e. "It's especially important that all agency representatives get a good update this morning.")
I. **Cooperating agencies** (law, Red Cross, highways) (e.g. "Are our new traffic and road block plans approved by law enforcement?")

Most planning meetings will take only 30 to 45 minutes if managed correctly. This is important to remember, because, often, the operations chief may only be available for that long a period. Keep it on time and to the point. Remind all staff in advance to come prepared to planning meetings.

FORMULATING THE INCIDENT ACTION PLAN

The majority of extended-attack or major emergencies will require some sort of written incident action plan. This may only consist of the previously-described ICS Form 201, but more likely will also contain the following:

A. **Incident objectives** (developed by incident commander)
B. **Incident organization** (plans, operations)
C. **Divisional assignments** (plans, operations)
D. **Safety message** (safety officer or incident commander)
E. **Incident map** (plans)
F. **Traffic plan** (logistics)

G. Medical plan (logistics)
H. Weather forecast (plans)
I. Fire-behavior forecast (plans)
J. Communications plan (logistics)
K. Air attack summary (operations)
L. Time of next meeting or briefing (plans, incident commander)

As you can see, it is extremely important to start incident planning *early*. All personnel should understand that, for plans to function best, the situation status must be current, and the resource status must accurately reflect allocated, assigned, staged and out-of-service resources. An incident map should be drawn, complete with landmarks,

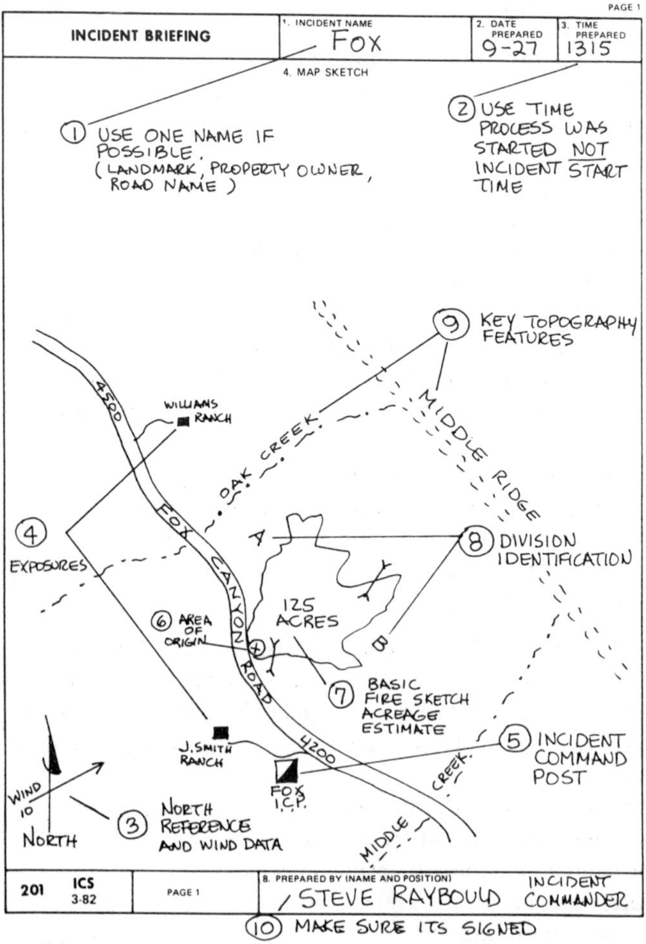

Figure 16a

roads, incident name, divisional assignments and a "north" reference. If possible, the fire sketch should include an acreage estimate and open line. Remember, the plans chief will be responsible for using this data to form an incident action plan.

Be on time to planning meetings and briefings. Come prepared to exchange information and listen. Take notes and think out your questions. Don't waste the team's time.

Once completed and signed, the incident action plan provides a contract between the incident commander and agency administration, emergency services coordinator and board of supervisors or chief executive officer. By "contract," I mean the incident commander has

PAGE 2

7. SUMMARY OF CURRENT ACTIONS

A BASIC REVIEW OF INITIAL ATTACK ASSIGNMENTS. THIS INCIDENT IS ESTIMATED TO BE 125 ACRES. TWO DIVISIONS HAVE BEEN ASSIGNED.

DIVISION A PROTECT STRUCTURES AT WILLIAMS RANCH. ANCHOR TO FOX CANYON ROAD, FLANK FIRE. PROTECT ORIGIN AREA

DIVISION B PROTECT J. SMITH RANCH STRUCTURES. ANCHOR TO FOX CANYON ROAD, FLANK FIRE, USE AIRCRAFT AND BULLDOZERS TO ASSIST AS THEY ARRIVE.

AIRCRAFT PRIORITIES

(1) SAFETY OF PERSONNEL ON GROUND
(2) SLOW HEAD OF FIRE
(3) DIVISION B TARGETS
(4) DIVISION A TARGETS

201 ICS 3-82 | PAGE 2

Figure 16a

set a level of expectation for personnel while addressing the interests and limitations of the officials listed above (who have authority for policy, fiscal and jurisdictional issues). See Figure 16a for ICS Form 201.

The incident action plan establishes upfront current actions, resources and personnel on scene, incident objectives and related data. Even on a smaller incident, where the incident action plan consists only of the four-part ICS 201, a contract is still developed between the incident commander (captain or battalion chief) and the next level of supervision (battalion chief or operations chief). Simply stated, this contract says:

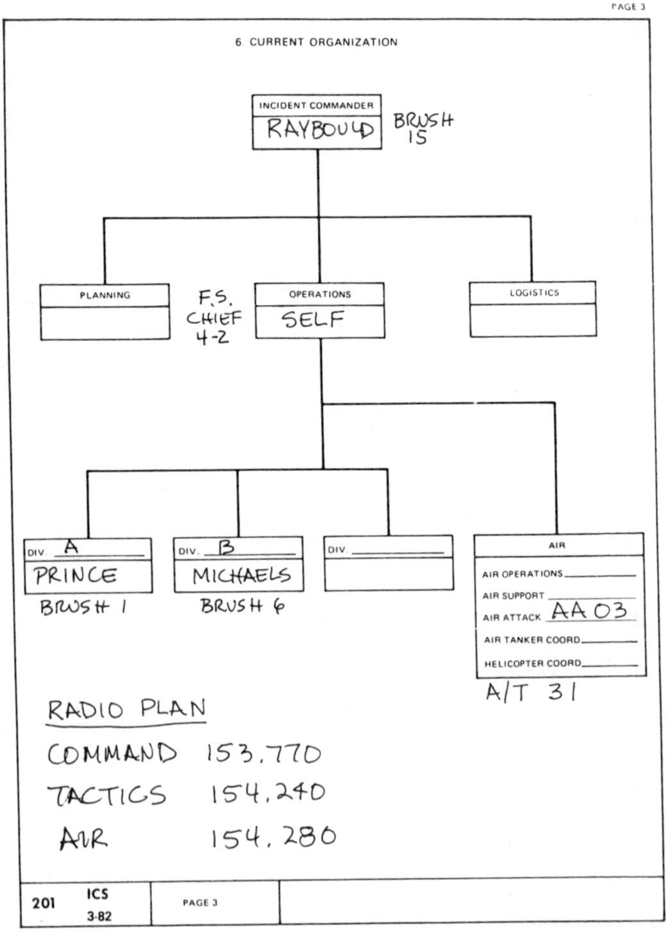

Figure 16a

A. *"I, the incident commander, have given a size-up of the incident, which I used to develop the incident map, ICS 201, page 1."*
B. *"I have named the incident and established a basic transportation plan, included on the incident map."*
C. *"I have used my size-up and pre-planning knowledge of fuel types, fuel bed, fuel age class and topography to develop a basic overview of incident potential."*
D. *"Based on my pre-planning knowledge and current weather conditions, I have formulated some basic control objectives. I realize my attack should be flexible and able to expand if the incident escapes initial-attack efforts." (ICS 201, page 2.)*

PAGE 4

5. RESOURCES SUMMARY

RESOURCES ORDERED	RESOURCE IDENTIFICATION	ETA	ON SCENE ✓	LOCATION/ASSIGNMENT
INITIAL	BRUSH 1		1312	DIVISION A WILLIAMS RANCH
ATTACK	ENGINE 1		1314	DIVISION A WILLIAMS RANCH
RESPONSE				
	BRUSH 4		1317	DIVISION A HOSE LAY
	ENGINE 4		1318	DIVISION A HOSE LAY
	DOZER 1	1340		DIVISION A FLANK ATTACK
	BRUSH 6		1321	DIVISION B SMITH RANCH
	ENGINE 6		1323	DIVISION B SMITH RANCH
	FS BRUSH 41		1320	DIVISION B HOSE LAY
	FS CREW 1		1322	DIVISION B LINE CONSTRUCTION
	FS BRUSH 46	1400		DIVISION B HOSE LAY
	AIR ATTACK 03	1341		COORDINATE AIR TANKER (S)
	AIR TANKER 31	1350		
	BRUSH 15		1300	COMMAND
	FS CHIEF 4-2		1331	OPERATIONS

201 ICS 3-82	PAGE 4	

Figure 16a

At this point (initial attack), the only name on the plan may be yours. You, as incident commander, are responsible for activating support functions (plans, logistics, finance) or tactical function (operations). It is possible, however, that the initial-attack response activated some outside mutual aid or automatic aid such as air attack. In this case, fill in the appropriate name(s). (ICS 201, page 3.)

The last page of ICS 201, page 4, may be the most important if the incident develops. It is imperative that all resources and personnel assigned to an incident are accounted for and tracked. The planning section chief must have accurate data to start the T-card process. It is also important, from the safety and assignment standpoint, to have all resources and personnel accounted for. Though this sounds like an extensive and time-consuming job, an experienced company officer should be able to complete it in minutes.

I often hear company and chief officers grumble, "If we spen more time fighting fires and less time filling out forms, we could pu out fires before they escaped initial attack." In some cases, it's harc to argue with that logic, except that it assumes every incident will reac the same, fire weather will always be predictable, no resource break downs will occur, no old-age fuels will burn and above all, we wil always be lucky. The problem is that there are far too many variable: at a wildland incident.

To be effective, the Incident Command System must start eve before the incident does. The system's terminology and processe must be in place and familiar *prior* to the incident. The forms and thei intent must be clearly recognized as more than a paper process. Every one must be aware that having a systematic checklist for the inciden commander to follow ensures maximum personnel safety, tactica options and cost effectiveness. Luckily, most initial-attack incident can be managed without the addition of any more forms than this.

As previously mentioned, to be effective, the first-arriving com pany officer (incident commander) needs to decide if he/she is goin to aggressively attack the incident or command the incident. If th incident is developing too rapidly for the first-arriving resource to b effective, then command should be instituted. Obviously, you can't b in the attack mode and mental attitude and at the same time be a incident commander.

One can't expect a company or chief officer to command witho the tools to accomplish the job. A simple command kit can be put tc gether quite inexpensively. This kit is carried in the turnout jack pocket, apparatus or glove box. It contains:

A. An up-to-date field operations guide (FOG)

B. Two sets of ICS 201 four-part forms (One set may go to Pla or another chief officer.)

C. Three to four pencils or three to four multi-colored felt tip pens

D. A plastic seal lock freezer bag to hold items A. through C.
(keeps them clean and dry)

This is a basic kit and can be expanded to meet agency-specific needs. The important point is that each company and chief officer should carry and be familiar with the field operations guide.

Now let's take a sample incident and apply Incident Command System four-part 201 (ICS 201).

The incident starts on September 27 at 1245 hours. Location is the 4200 block of Fox Canyon Road, just north of the J. Smith Ranch. Area of origin has been identified. The fire is burning in grass/brush and has quickly spread northeast toward Middle Ridge. Two major drainages are identified (Middle Creek and Oak Creek). An estimated 125 acres have burned at this point.

Incident Commander Wilmore arrives in Brush 15 and sets up his command post at the J. Smith Ranch. A size-up is given and Incident Commander Wilmore names the incident "Fox" and dubs himself "Fox Command." He also announces that the Fox Command Post is located at the J. Smith Ranch, 4200 Fox Canyon Road.

At this point, we have a map with good detail and key topography features noted. Major drainages and exposures are identified. North reference, wind direction and wind speed have been estimated. (If you have a belt weather kit it's also a good idea to list air temperature and humidity in future briefings.)

Incident Commander Wilmore has developed a basic two-division layout. (Divisions are formed from area of origin clockwise, using letters: A, B, C, etc.) Divisions (geographical assignments) should be established using span-of-control or difficulty-of-assignment criteria. The Incident Command System uses a 5:1 span of control: one supervisor for every five personnel, a maximum of 25 personnel per strike team leader, five strike teams per division supervisor, five divisions per branch director, five branch directors per operations chief.

The difficulty of the assignment may also dictate the necessary level of supervision or resource commitment. A line-construction assignment in steep, broken topography and heavy brush may require multiple hand crews and extra supervision because of safety concerns.

The Fox Incident was initially projected at two divisions. This takes into account that basic division breaks (X) can be changed and expanded. We could, if span of control allowed, make a division run from Fox Canyon Road to Middle Ridge. We could also assign a group supervisor to coordinate functional responsibility for structural protection. A group supervisor is designated to carry out assignments not clearly tied to the geography of an incident. We could establish a group C supervisor and assign him/her to protect the Smith and Williams ranches.

An often-asked question is, "What happens if we want to add more divisions and stick with the clockwise assignment of letters?" This is a good question. There are two basic ways to handle this:

A. Using the "Fox," two-division example, you can easily add Division C by realigning the A-B division break as follows. New Division A, Fox Canyon Road to Oak Creek Drainage; new Division B, Oak Creek Drainage to Middle Ridge; new Division C, Middle Ridge to Fox Canyon Road.

For the purposes of incident planning, divisional boundaries do *not* have to conform to the black line. Back off and allow for initial fire growth. It's more important to project growth, use defined boundaries and "grow into the division" as the fire develops.

B. Let's say the Fox Incident now requires two additional divisions, and Division A and B are well established and working. No official incident action plan has been developed and no published incident action plan has been distributed. In this case, I favor re-lettering so that you stay in clockwise rotation. Relettering is initially confusing for radio traffic and supervision, but if the incident is still developing, it has advantages if instituted early enough (ICS 201 stage).

Some officers and plans chiefs prefer to leave well enough alone. If Division A and B are active and functioning, C and D divisions can be added out of sequence. This may be least disruptive on the short term for a one-burn-period incident, but it creates a problem if additional divisions are needed.

Remember, don't be rigid about initial divisional breaks. Let the incident grow and the organization grow into the assignment. Keep span of control and difficulty of assignment in mind. Remember also the distinction between a division and a group. A division is a geographical assignment, while a group is a functional assignment such as structural protection.

On page 2 of ICS 201, the incident commander develops some broad assignments for initial-attack resources and personnel. Most agencies utilize a basic mission statment of (in priority):

A. Protect life first.

B. Protect valued resource next (structures, timber, dedicated watershed).

C. Extinguish brush and grass with lowest acreage loss possible.

In the case of the Fox Incident, the first mission of protecting life is accomplished by providing structural protection. Now, if the wind shifts, the mission may change to include evacuation of ranches in the area. Some important points to remember when formulating a mission:

A. Use a few key words.

B. Protect area of origin.

C. Give basic directions *only* for attack method. Be flexible. Let division supervisor report back with recommendations for attack and priorities.

D. Make best use of specialized equipment. Prioritize by incident potential:

1. Hand crews

2. Aircraft

3. Dozers

Page 3 of ICS 201 is a basic organizational chart for the incident at this point. Note that the incident commander is already starting a radio plan. He has listed radio frequencies for command, tactics and air. It is important to set good radio discipline early in a developing incident.

As mentioned earlier, page 4 may be the most important part of ICS 201 and the initial development of an incident action plan. The plans chief must have accurate, up-to-date personnel and resource information. The initial-attack incident commander must take the responsibility of getting this information and recording it until the plans chief position is filled. This page is also useful to establish basic tactical assignments and forecast logistical needs (food, fuel, etc.).

If, at this point, the incident is still developing and will need upgrading within several hours, several key processes must be accomplished in a timely manner:

A. Brief the incoming chief officer, using the just-completed ICS 201.

B. Stress to the operations chief that he/she must not over-order during the transition period between initial attack and upgrading to an extended attack or major incident. (Hopefully you have briefed both the operations chief and division supervisor by now, and they understand your basic control objectives.)

The transition period requires some serious "quiet time" for planning. This planning must start from an accurate current ICS 201.

During initial planning, you should give the operations chief full latitude to take appropriate steps to accomplish life safety, structural protection or resource protection, but stress that, unless the situation is life-threatening, large-scale ordering of resources and personnel should wait until after the initial planning meeting.

An example of a reasonable request:

A. *"Two additional brush engines, one additional dozer, one additional Type 1 air tanker."*

An unreasonable request:

B. *"One Type 3 engine strike team, one Type 1 hand-crew strike team, three additional Type 1 air tankers."*

Initial planning should only take 15 to 20 minutes, but it's important to take this time so that the incident commander can evaluate the need for staff support. I personally feel you should activate staff support as a team early on if the incident is a developing one.

Key positions and their role in developing the incident action plan include:

A. Safety Officer

Monitors incident safety, develops safety message. Part of the command staff.

B. Information Officer

Develops initial/updated media releases based on ICS 201. Assigned to command staff. You can't activate this function too early.

C. Planning Chief

The key command team member, in my opinion. Responsible for bringing all aspects of the incident together in the form of an incident action plan (IAP). Responsible for coordinating planning meetings. *A good plans chief is essential for a developing incident.*

A good plans chief will probably bring along a person for RESTAT and SITSTAT functions. How do you know a good plans chief from a bad one? Good question. A good plans chief comes prepared to start work (forms, pencils, etc.). A good plans chief asks lots of questions and reviews the ICS 201 in good detail. A good plans chief is also an apt listener and knows when and where to give input but, above all, he/she gets things done on time.

D. Logistics Chief

Responsible for activating necessary service and supply functions. Early activation is essential to secure meals, fuel, base and camp needs. Logistics can also help establish a formal incident command post and staging area. Approves the traffic plan and communications plan. Develops layout for base, camp.

E. Liaison

I list this support position because it is an important link between assisting and cooperating agencies. It is part of the command staff.

The above support staff will be working with you to plan for the next burn period and develop the essential parts of the incident action plan (contract). Prior to formalizing the plan, start with a good briefing for your staff. A planning meeting should be held at the inciden command post. This will help you select a command post that has plenty of work spaces, adequate telephone communications and no discomfort caused by heat and smoke. The command post does not need to be at the area of origin, and, in fact, should not be unless the fire is not going to exceed initial attack size.

Such facilities as schools, parks, National Guard armories, fire stations and camp grounds can be used if *prior* approval is obtained. Pre-approval should be secured during the annual pre-fire planning process.

The necessary elements of an incident action plan include:

A. Incident objectives (ICS form 202)
B. Organization chart (ICS form 203)
C. Incident map
D. Incident safety message (Figure 16b)

SAFETY MESSAGE
FOX INCIDENT
9-27
NIGHTSHIFT

(1) WATCH FOOTING AND TOOL SPACING

(2) PLAN FOR DOWNSLOPE WIND CHANGE

(3) WATCH OUT FOR DOZERS WORKING AND ROLLING MATERIALS

(4) BE ALERT FOR SNAKES

(5) MONITOR FATIGUE IN PERSONNEL

(6) ALWAYS BE THINKING SAFETY ZONES AND ESCAPE ROUTES

CURTIS VINCENT
SAFETY OFFICER

Figure 16b

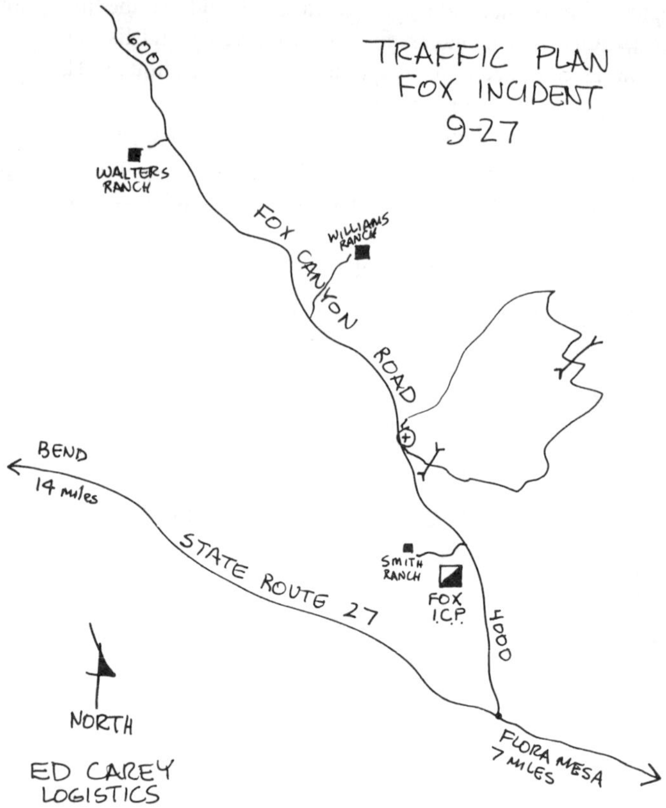

Figure 16c

E. **Divisional/group assignments** (ICS form 204)
F. **Radio communications plan** (ICS form 205)
G. **Incident traffic plan** (Figure 16c)
H. **Incident medical plan** (ICS form 206)

Let's review the basic components of each form and look at some suggestions for developing a quality product. Remember, the incident commander is responsible for approving the final incident action plan and attachments. Besides being a contract, the plan serves as an important post-fire permanent record and basis for critique. It should contain accurate, factual information presented in legible form. You should be proud of the product, or don't sign it.

Control objectives should be broad and flexible. Remember, if you are too specific, the incident may "outgrow" the incident action plan, causing many problems and precipitating the need for additional planning meetings. Control objectives should be attainable and cost effective. Firefighter safety, as always, should be the top priority. Keep in mind that it makes no sense to develop and list an objective if resources can't accomplish it in the time frame allotted. The acreage you save is just not worth the cost.

Earlier, I recommended some personnel for activating a management team. I did not list a finance chief. This was not to denigrate the importance of the position, but more based on the reality that most departments or agencies don't have or train finance chiefs. And, as with any position not filled under the Incident Command System, it

ORGANIZATION ASSIGNMENT LIST ICS-203 1/82	1. INCIDENT NAME	2. DATE PREPARED	3. TIME PREPARED
	FOX	9-27	1900
	4. OPERATIONAL PERIOD (DATE/TIME)		

POSITION	NAME
5. INCIDENT COMMANDER AND STAFF	
INCIDENT COMMANDER	RAYBOULD
DEPUTY	
SAFETY OFFICER	VINCENT
INFORMATION OFFICER	JOHNSON
LIAISON OFFICER	SIMMONS

6. AGENCY REPRESENTATIVES	
AGENCY	NAME
FS	GOLDENBEE
CHP	SGT. JONES
SHERIFF	SGT. WOODS

7. PLANNING SECTION	
CHIEF	EDDY
DEPUTY	
RESOURCES UNIT	
SITUATION UNIT	
DOCUMENTATION UNIT	
DEMOBILIZATION UNIT	
TECHNICAL SPECIALISTS	

8. LOGISTICS SECTION	
CHIEF	CAREY
DEPUTY	
a. SUPPORT BRANCH	
DIRECTOR	
SUPPLY UNIT	
FACILITIES UNIT	
GROUND SUPPORT UNIT	
b. SERVICE BRANCH	
DIRECTOR	
COMMUNICATIONS UNIT	
MEDICAL UNIT	
FOOD UNIT	

9. OPERATIONS SECTION		
CHIEF		SELF
DEPUTY		
a. BRANCH I — DIVISIONS/GROUPS		
BRANCH DIRECTOR		
DEPUTY		
DIVISION/GROUP (DIVISION circled)	A	PRINCE
DIVISION/GROUP (DIVISION circled)	B	MICHEALS
DIVISION/GROUP		
DIVISION/GROUP		
DIVISION/GROUP		
b. BRANCH II — DIVISIONS/GROUPS		
BRANCH DIRECTOR		
DEPUTY		
DIVISION/GROUP		
DIVISION/GROUP		
DIVISION/GROUP		
DIVISION/GROUP		
DIVISION/GROUP		
c. BRANCH III — DIVISIONS/GROUPS		
BRANCH DIRECTOR		
DEPUTY		
DIVISION/GROUP		
DIVISION/GROUP		
DIVISION/GROUP		
DIVISION/GROUP		
DIVISION/GROUP		
d. AIR OPERATIONS BRANCH		
AIR OPERATIONS BR. DIR.		
AIR ATTACK SUPERVISOR		PADILLA
AIR SUPPORT SUPERVISOR		
HELICOPTER COORDINATOR		
AIR TANKER COORDINATOR		

10. FINANCE SECTION	
CHIEF	
DEPUTY	
TIME UNIT	
PROCUREMENT UNIT	
COMPENSATION/CLAIMS UNIT	
COST UNIT	

203	ICS	PREPARED BY (RESOURCES UNIT)

Figure 16d

falls under the incident commander's responsibility. I, personally, approve of this.

As the incident commander, operations chief and plans chief are working on the control objectives they should be thinking cost effectiveness. Questions to ask:

A. *"Is there a cheaper way to accomplish our goals?"*

B. *"Are we using contract resources* (air tankers, helicopters, dozers) *in a cost-effective manner?"*

C. *"Have we looked at all the alternatives? What if we burned more acres and allowed the fire to advance into an old burn or fuel break instead of using aircraft retardant drops?"*

D. *"What is the most cost-effective way to feed personnel?"* (a logistics chief question)

1. BRANCH | 2. DIVISION/GROUP A | **DIVISION ASSIGNMENT LIST** ICS 204 (1-82)

3. INCIDENT NAME FOX | 4. OPERATIONAL PERIOD DATE 9-27 TIME NIGHT SHIFT

5. OPERATIONS PERSONNEL

OPERATIONS CHIEF SELF | DIVISION/GROUP SUPERVISOR PRINCE

BRANCH DIRECTOR | AIR ATTACK SUPERVISOR PADILLA

6. RESOURCES ASSIGNED THIS PERIOD

STRIKE TEAM/TASK FORCE/ RESOURCE DESIGNATOR	LEADER	NUMBER PERSONS	TRANS. NEEDED	DROP OFF PT./TIME	PICK UP PT./TIME
BRUSH 1	WILLIAMS	3			
ENGINE 1	PONCE	3			
BRUSH 4	LISS	3			
ENGINE 4	BIELITZER	3			
DOZER 1	ECKERT	1			

7. CONTROL OPERATIONS

(1) PROTECT WILLIAM RANCH STRUCTURES
(2) DIRECT ATTACK - HOSE LAYS UP FLANK FROM FOX CANYON ROAD
(3) UTILIZE DOZER TO FINALIZE CONTROL LINE
(4) BURNOUT ALL ISLANDS OF FUEL WITHIN 30' OF CONTROL LINE

8. SPECIAL INSTRUCTIONS

(1) THINK ABOUT REHAB, WATER BARS WHERE DOZER LINES ARE USED

9. DIVISION/GROUP COMMUNICATION SUMMARY

FUNCTION		FREQ.	SYSTEM	CHAN.	FUNCTION		FREQ.	SYSTEM	CHAN.
COMMAND	LOCAL				SUPPORT	LOCAL			
	REPEAT	153.770				REPEAT			
DIV./GROUP TACTICAL		154.240			GROUND TO AIR		154.280		

PREPARED BY (RESOURCE UNIT LDR.)	APPROVED BY (PLANNING SECT. CH.)	DATE	TIME
PETE SALETTI	WAYNE EDDY	9-27	1900

Figure 16e

OTHER ICS FORMS

ICS Form 203, an organization chart, is as basic and straightforward as it seems (Figure 16d). However, it's often not used to its full advantage. It should list agency representatives from all cooperating agencies. If possible, make sure the liaison officer makes direct contact with each one to give a good initial briefing and an idea of:

A. **Incident potential**
B. **Projected incident duration**
C. **Safety concerns for their personnel**
D. **What personal needs will be covered** (food, fuel, etc.)
E. **Next official briefing** (where and when)

ICS Form 204 consists of the basic division/group assignment lists initially taken from ICS 201. The 204 fleshes out initial broad

1. BRANCH	2. DIVISION/GROUP B	DIVISION ASSIGNMENT LIST	ICS 204 (1-82)

3. INCIDENT NAME FOX

4. OPERATIONAL PERIOD DATE 9-27 TIME NIGHT TIME

5. OPERATIONS PERSONNEL

OPERATIONS CHIEF SELF — DIVISION/GROUP SUPERVISOR MICHEALS

BRANCH DIRECTOR ______ — AIR ATTACK SUPERVISOR PADILLA

6. RESOURCES ASSIGNED THIS PERIOD

STRIKE TEAM/TASK FORCE/ RESOURCE DESIGNATOR	LEADER	NUMBER PERSONS	TRANS. NEEDED	DROP OFF PT./TIME	PICK UP PT./TIME
ENGINE 6	HOBBS	3			
BRUSH 6	VITTUM	3			
FS BRUSH 41	CARLSON	5			
FS CREW 1	LINANE	15+1			
FS BRUSH 46	ODELL	5			

7. CONTROL OPERATIONS

(1) PROTECT SMITH RANCH STRUCTURES
(2) UTILIZE HAND CREW FOR LINE CONSTRUCTION
(3) UTILIZE HOSE LAYS

8. SPECIAL INSTRUCTIONS

THE OPERATION CHIEF HAS ESTABLISHED DIVISION "B" AS HIGH PRIORITY FOR AIR ATTACK.

9. DIVISION/GROUP COMMUNICATION SUMMARY

FUNCTION		FREQ.	SYSTEM	CHAN.	FUNCTION		FREQ.	SYSTEM	CHAN.
COMMAND	LOCAL				SUPPORT	LOCAL			
	REPEAT	153.770				REPEAT			
DIV./GROUP TACTICAL		154.240			GROUND TO AIR		154.280		

PREPARED BY (RESOURCE UNIT LDR.)	APPROVED BY (PLANNING SECT. CH.)	DATE	TIME
PETE SALETTI	WAYNE EDDY	9-27	1900

Figure 16e

objectives to more specific detail and depth. It allows specific instructions, such as burn-out or air attack, to be listed. It's also very important to list radio frequencies on this form, because, at this point, it has probably become "*our* radio plan" (Figure 16e).

ICS 205 is the incident communications plan. In our example, the logistics chief is responsible for completing this form because the communications unit, under Logistics, was not activated (Figure 16f).

ICS 206 is a very important part of the incident action plan and goes hand in hand with the safety officer's message. It is essential that supervisors know the command team is committed to safety first and what will be done if an accident or injury occurs. Some stipulations you should consider (see also Figure 16g):

A. List the best, closest hospitals with full service and 24-hour emergency medical staffing.

B. Insist on a burn center, when possible, to treat burns over first degree.

C. Use helicopter service for critical injuries or serious burns so paramedics can stabilize victims.

D. Have all injuries (even minor ones) documented and reported to the safety officer.

E. I feel it's cost effective to have a paramedic ambulance at the base or command post at a developing incident.

INCIDENT RADIO COMMUNICATIONS PLAN		1. INCIDENT NAME FOX		2. DATE/TIME PREPARED 9-27	3. OPERATIONAL PERIOD DATE/TIME NIGHT SHIFT
4. BASIC RADIO CHANNEL UTILIZATION					
SYSTEM/CACHE	CHANNEL	FUNCTION	FREQUENCY	ASSIGNMENT	REMARKS
COUNTY FIRE	1	COMMAND	153.770	COMMAND OPERATIONS DIVISION SUPERVISORS	
FOREST SERVICE	3	TACTICS	154.240	DIVISION SUPERVISORS RESOURCES	
AIR	5	AIR TO GROUND	154.280	AIR ATTACK	
COUNTY FIRE	2	EMERGENCY MEDICAL	151.250	SAFETY PARAMEDICS	
205 ICS 8-78	5. PREPARED BY (COMMUNICATIONS UNIT) JIM PETERSON				

Figure 16f

MEDICAL PLAN	1. INCIDENT NAME	2. DATE PREPARED	3. TIME PREPARED	4. OPERATIONAL PERIOD
	FOX	9-27	1900	NIGHT SHIFT

5. INCIDENT MEDICAL AID STATIONS

MEDICAL AID STATIONS	LOCATION	PARAMEDICS YES	PARAMEDICS NO

6. TRANSPORTATION

A. AMBULANCE SERVICES

NAME	ADDRESS	PHONE	PARAMEDICS YES	PARAMEDICS NO
SPEED AMBULANCE	1400 TULE DR., FLORA MESA	627-1313	X	
MEDIC-STAR HELICOPTER	FLORA MESA HOSPITAL	627-8300	X	

B. INCIDENT AMBULANCES

NAME	LOCATION	PARAMEDICS YES	PARAMEDICS NO
SPEED AMBULANCE	COMMAND POST	X	

7. HOSPITALS

NAME	ADDRESS	TRAVEL TIME AIR	TRAVEL TIME GRND	PHONE	HELIPAD YES	HELIPAD NO	BURN CENTER YES	BURN CENTER NO
FLORA MESA	1400 TULE DRIVE, FLORA MESA	:10	:25	627-1000	X			X
BURN INSTITUTE	1326 FIRST ST, BEND	:40	2 HOURS	621-3111	X		X	

8. MEDICAL EMERGENCY PROCEDURES

1. NOTIFY SAFETY OFFICER IMMEDIATELY
2. ALL MINOR INJURIES TO PARAMEDICS AT COMMAND POST
3. ALL MAJOR INJURIES TO FLORA MESA HOSPITAL VIA AMBULANCE
4. ALL CRITICAL INJURIES TO FLORA MESA HOSPITAL VIA HELICOPTER
5. ALL BURN INJURIES TO BURN INSTITUTE VIA HELICOPTER

206 ICS 8-78	9. PREPARED BY (MEDICAL UNIT LEADER)	10. REVIEWED BY (SAFETY OFFICER)
		CURTIS VINCENT

Figure 16g

STATEMENTS OF INTENT

The traffic plan is developed by Logistics and can be based on the incident map on the ICS 201. The traffic plan should list attack routes, staging areas, base, camp and command post locations. It should also note any drop points.

The safety message should build on the initial overview listed on ICS 202. All supervisors should review the message and respond with a serious effort to stress safety. If supervisors show a commitment to safety, it will be taken seriously by personnel (Figure 16h).

The fire behavior forecast is prepared by the plans chief, as no

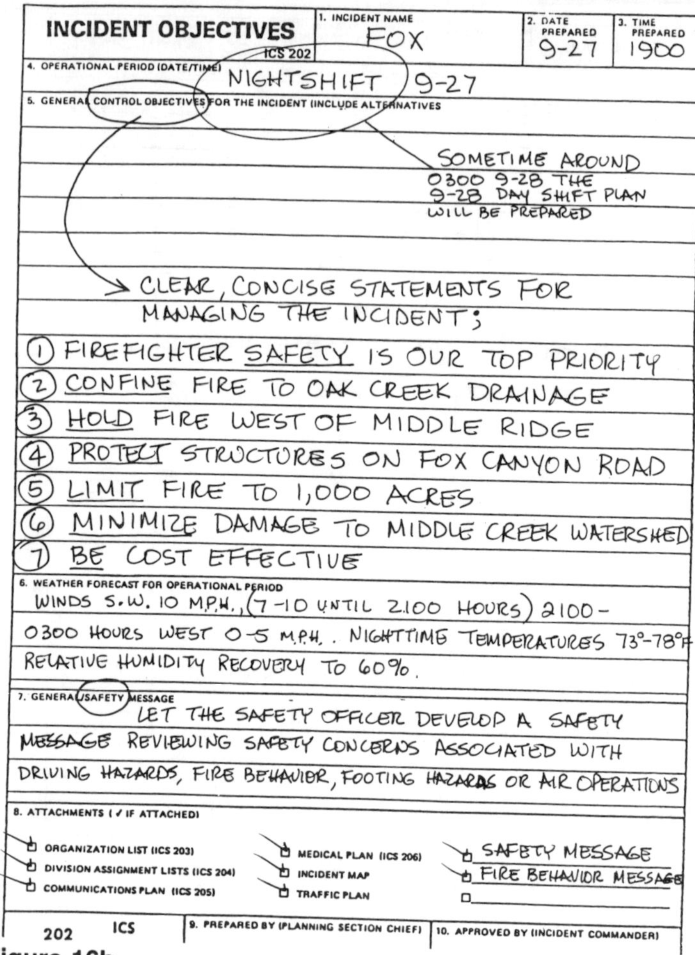

INCIDENT OBJECTIVES ICS 202

1. INCIDENT NAME: FOX

2. DATE PREPARED: 9-27

3. TIME PREPARED: 1900

4. OPERATIONAL PERIOD (DATE/TIME): NIGHTSHIFT 9-27

5. GENERAL CONTROL OBJECTIVES FOR THE INCIDENT (INCLUDE ALTERNATIVES)

SOMETIME AROUND 0300 9-28 THE 9-28 DAY SHIFT PLAN WILL BE PREPARED

CLEAR, CONCISE STATEMENTS FOR MANAGING THE INCIDENT;

(1) FIREFIGHTER SAFETY IS OUR TOP PRIORITY
(2) CONFINE FIRE TO OAK CREEK DRAINAGE
(3) HOLD FIRE WEST OF MIDDLE RIDGE
(4) PROTECT STRUCTURES ON FOX CANYON ROAD
(5) LIMIT FIRE TO 1,000 ACRES
(6) MINIMIZE DAMAGE TO MIDDLE CREEK WATERSHED
(7) BE COST EFFECTIVE

6. WEATHER FORECAST FOR OPERATIONAL PERIOD

WINDS S.W. 10 M.P.H., (7-10 UNTIL 2100 HOURS) 2100-0300 HOURS WEST 0-5 M.P.H. NIGHTTIME TEMPERATURES 73°-78°F RELATIVE HUMIDITY RECOVERY TO 60%.

7. GENERAL SAFETY MESSAGE

LET THE SAFETY OFFICER DEVELOP A SAFETY MESSAGE REVIEWING SAFETY CONCERNS ASSOCIATED WITH DRIVING HAZARDS, FIRE BEHAVIOR, FOOTING HAZARDS OR AIR OPERATIONS

8. ATTACHMENTS (✓ IF ATTACHED)

- ☑ ORGANIZATION LIST (ICS 203)
- ☑ DIVISION ASSIGNMENT LISTS (ICS 204)
- ☑ COMMUNICATIONS PLAN (ICS 205)
- ☑ MEDICAL PLAN (ICS 206)
- ☑ INCIDENT MAP
- ☑ TRAFFIC PLAN
- ☑ SAFETY MESSAGE
- ☑ FIRE BEHAVIOR MESSAGE
- ☐

202 ICS | 9. PREPARED BY (PLANNING SECTION CHIEF) | 10. APPROVED BY (INCIDENT COMMANDER)

Figure 16h

fire behavior technical specialist has been activated yet. This is an important addition if firing or air operations are an operational goal (Figure 16i).

It's important all staff come prepared to work. They should have:

A. A current field operations guide (FOG)

B. Working materials for their position

C. A briefing

D. Jointly reviewed the FOG

E. Jointly reviewed their ICS position checklist found in the FOG (pages 1-3)

F. An awareness of your expectations

FIRE BEHAVIOR FORECAST

NAME OF FIRE FOX PREDICTION FOR NIGHT SHIFT

DATE AND TIME OF FORECAST 9-27 2000 SHIFT DATE NIGHT

SIGNED: WAYNE EDDY FIRE BEHAVIOR OFFICER
PLANS CHIEF

WEATHER SUMMARY: NIGHTTIME TEMPERATURES 73°-78°F RELATIVE HUMIDITY RECOVERY TO 60% BY 2300 HOURS. MILD DOWNSLOPE WINDS AT 2200 0-5 M.P.H.

FIRE BEHAVIOR(GENERAL): THERMAL BELT ACTIVE TONIGHT. GOOD CHANCE FOR SMOKE INVERSIONS.

FIRE BEHAVIOR (SPECIFIC):

- NO ERRATIC WINDS IN EITHER DIVISION
- NO FRONTAL ACTIVITY NEXT 24 HOURS
- NO CHANGE IN WEATHER NEXT 24 HOURS.
  TOMORROW: 90°F HIGH, RELATIVE HUMIDITY 15-20%, WINDS 7-10 M.P.H. (WEST).

AIR OPERATIONS: SMOKE INVERSION WILL LIMIT

- AIRCRAFT IN DIVISIONS A, B UNTIL 0900.

SAFETY:

- WATCH FOR THERMAL BELT ACTIVITY

unicomm2

Figure 16i

ESCAPE FIRE SITUATION ANALYSIS

A subject I feel is worth mentioning in this book is the process used by federal fire agencies called the *Escape Fire Situation Analysis (EFSA).*[1] I am a strong advocate of this process and decision-making system. I utilized it indepth during a 14-day period during the 1985 Wheeler Fire. My reaction was, what a tool!

The Forest Service has used this system for many years for fires that develop to an extended attack. The process is really a way to blend and involve the layer of supervision or political structure above the incident commander with the command staff. It really allows the two levels of management (incident and political) to combine decision-making expertise for cost-effective and safe incident management.

Escape Fire Situational Analysis – Blaine Cornell, Forest Service, Marana, AZ, I-520, February, 1985.

IMPORTANT AREAS REQUIRING PROTECTION FROM L.PNF

LAND RESOURCE MANAGEMENT PLAN. (Draft) APRIL 1985

(1) Recommended Wilderness Areas (Roadless Areas)

(a) Matilija (#129) Map designation 64
(b) Sespe-Frazier (#002)

(2) Wildlife

(a) Sespe Condor Sanctuary - Map designation 65

(3) Botanical Areas

(a) Dry Lakes Ridge - Map designation 67d

(4) Special Emphasis Areas

(a) Sespe Creek Wild and Scenic River - Map designation 70

Currently don't have location of identified Cultural Resources and Developed Recreation Sites.

Also, mining claims, range improvements, powerlines, waterlines, etc.

USDA - FOREST SERVICE

ESCAPED FIRE SITUATION ANALYSIS

REGION: PACIFIC SOUTHWEST REGIONS	FOREST: LOS PADRES NATIONAL FOREST OJAI RANGER DISTRICT
DATE: JULY 3, 1985 / TIME: 1000 hours	EFSA NUMBER: 3 OF

I. FIRE SITUATION

FIRE NAME: WHEELER	CURRENT SIZE: 24,000
FUEL: Grass, chamise, ceonuthus, oak woodland	FIRE BEHAVIOR: Daytime moderate spread behavior Nightime critical spread behavior

NARRATIVE *(attach description of the existing local and regional fire situation)*: Fire started from possible incendiary device near Wheeler Springs off Highway 33 about 1500 hours; July 1, 1985. Weather model was extreme, temperature at ignition was 100° F, R/H 10%, fine fuel moisture 3.0%, winds SW 08 but gusty to 12. Fire spread quickly upslope to Nordhoff Ridge. The fire jumped northside of Highway 33 towards Dry Lake Ridge. The fire was active on southslopes all night. Major fire runs took place on the east side of Matalija Canyon and into the Ortega Drainage and Howard Canyon areas. Fire estimated at 1,500 acres by 1400 July 2nd. Extreme fire behavior pushed by sundowner influence. Pushed the fire into the Ojai wildland/urban interface by 1900 hours July 2. Matalija drainage Gridley drainage, and Dry Lakes Ridge. By July 2, 2400 the major fire runs push fire to 6,000 acres. The sundowner influence along with continued hot, dry weather created major fire runs on east, west fronts into the Santa Ana, Matalija, Senior, and Tule drainages. By 0600 July 3rd the fire pushing on two fronts exceeded 20,000 acres. The fire is pushing into wildland areas in daylight hours and into the wildland/urban interface during nightime hours. Major subdivisions in Ojai, Meiners Oaks, Matalija Ranch, Wheeler Springs and Casitas are threatened. The fire is being managed by a command team as of July 2, 0800. Many varied attack methods and management alternatives are being utilized.

II. FOLLOW UP

The selected alternative shall be reviewed prior to each shift change to determine if it is still valid. If not, new EFSA will be developed.

1. SHIFT REVIEW:

BY	DATE	TIME

DECISION TO MAKE A NEW EFSA

BY	DATE	TIME
Dave Haney - Ojai District Ranger	July 3, 1985	1000

2. EVALUATION OF SELECTED ALTERNATIVE:

IMMEDIATELY AFTER THE FIRE IS CONTROLLED, THE ACTUAL FIRE SHOULD BE EVALUATED AGAINST WHAT WAS PLANNED AND APPROVED.

FINAL SIZE*	ESTIMATED SUPPRESSION COSTS*	NET RESOURCE VALUE CHANGE*
	$	$

EVALUATION CRITERIA COMPLIANCE:

ALTERNATIVE APPROVED FOR IMPLEMENTATION:

SIGNATURE	LINE OFFICER TITLE	DATE	TIME
David Haney	District Ranger	3 July 85	1315

*Must agree with Form FS 5100-29 (1) R5-5100-221 (Iss. 4/82)

III. EVALUATION CRITERIA

For each category, develop the line officer's decisions on specific objectives, expressed as measurable criteria, to be used in the selection of the preferred alternatives.

CRITERIA (Check those criteria which MUST be met	MUST
ECONOMIC: As of July 3, 1985 1000 this fire is a major wildland/urban interface fire with threat to environmental sensitive areas, major watersheds and urban areas. This is requiring the command team to utilize large quantities of mutual aid manpower, resources, and support services. The incident is being managed by a regional fire team which has placed cost effectiveness a high priority and an important consideration in control objective selections. This incident involves multi-agencies who are working jointly on cost effectiveness and fiscal planning.	X
ENVIRONMENTAL: This major wildland/urban interface fire has moved into several environmentally sensitive areas and concerns. The command team is commited to resource protection, habitat improvement, sanctuary protection, air quality, and soils protection while evaluating all control objectives/strategies. We are also evaluating stream impacts, water resevior damage, lake siltation concerns, and riparian damage. The Condor Sanctuary is receiving special consideration because of Land Resource Management Plan concerns. (April 1985 document). All control lines constructed by hand crews, dozers or retardant are being evaluated during the EFSA process and rehab efforts. A rehab team is working the incident.	X
SOCIAL: Protection of structures in wildland/urban interface is a key concern. The safety and wellbeing of firefighters is our critical priority. This long term incident will require special efforts to maintain interagency cooperation, quality food, quality rest, and some sense of home in base/camp. A major goal of the command team is interagency, intercity, intergovernment involvement in planning, briefings, and control review.	
OTHER: The fire/law enforcement agencies are utilizing many varied aircraft, equipment, and tools on this incident. As this incident continues fatigue and incident size will dictate special safety, management evaluations, fire conditions, topography, fire behavior, and fuel types make this incident a "100 Year" fire.	X
APPROVED BY: (LINE OFFICER TITLE) Darrell Haney District Ranger	

(2)

Obviously, there are many factors to evaluate under the umbrella of cost effectiveness. I feel these include, but are not limited to, evaluating incident data and situation with sociological, environmental, resource and fiscal elements. Some considerations:

A. Not all wildland fire effects are negative.

In some areas, land-use or fuel-management plans may call for prescribed burns. Under the right weather window and live-fuel moisture level, the fire may naturally accomplish that goal.

B. Rare, endangered fauna and flora

The identification and acknowledgement of key habitat areas may play an important role in selecting an attack strategy. You may have no choice but to protect, at all costs, rare flora or specie near an incident. Conversely, fire in such an area may prove beneficial to some habitats.

C. Dedicated watersheds

Some wildland/urban interfaces have lakes and water reservoirs that depend on grass-, brush-, and timber-covered slopes to keep siltation or erosion from reducing storage capacity. These slopes also assist in reducing turbidity. A fire across a watershed may create problems years after the fire.

D. Urban interfaces

Many areas in the nation are experiencing rapid growth and encroachment into forests and wildland areas. To homeowners, the tragic loss of a home far exceeds the monetary cost of rebuilding the structure. Priceless keepsakes can never be replaced. Many times, the owner will move out of the area after the fire. This impacts economic and sociological elements of the town and community. Multi-

IV. ALTERNATIVES (See instructions on back)

	ALTERNATIVES			
	A	B	C	D
GENERAL PLAN OF CONTROL (STRATEGIC)	DIRECT ATTACK *Keep fire north of Ojai front fuel break-Shell Road, Fairview Ave *Some direct attack possible along Hwy 33 *Hold fire east of Matalija drainage *Hold fire west of Worn Canyon LOW PROBABILITY OF SUCCESS 20%	INDIRECT ATTACK *Utilize Dry Lake Road to north *Utilize Senior drainage to halt eastern spread *Utilize Ortega drainage to halt northern spread *Utilize Maple drainage to halt western fire spread *Keep fire north ~~of Ojai front~~ fuel bed LOW-MODERATE PROBABILITY OF SUCCESS 30%	COMBINATION ATTACK *Keep fire north of Ojai front fuel bed *Utilize Wilsie drainage to stop eastern fire spread *Utilize Superior and Coyote drainages to halt western fire spread *Hold fire west of Murietta Canyon drainage *~~Protect structures~~ along urban/interface MODERATE PROBABILITY OF SUCCESS 40%	CONTENGENCY PLAN (24 HOURS) *Protect structures wildland/urban interface *Halt western spread of fire in Laguna drainage to Chismahoo Mtn. *Halt eastern spread of fire Bear Canyon to Topotopah Bluffs *Keep fire south of Lions drainage MODERATE-HIGH PROBABILITY OF SUCCESS 70%
SPECIFIC PLAN OF CONTROL (TACTICAL)	*Engines protect structures along Ojai front fuel break, Shell, Fairview Roads. *Direct attack crews, dozers along Hwys 150,33 *Direct attack burn out along Dry Lake Road *Direct attack with crews along ~~Worn Canyon.~~ Backfiring	*Engines protect sturctures along Ojai front, Santa Ana drainage *Indirect attack engines, crews, dozers Tule drainage ~~*Utilize crews,~~ dozers,backfiring to halt fire in Senior drainage *Utilize crews, dozers to halt western fire spread	*Engines protect along Ojai front, Santa Ana drainage *Indirect attack engines, crews, dozers, Tule drainage *Utilize crews, dozers, ~~to halt~~ fire in Superior, Laguna drainages	*Engines protect sturctures *Crews, dozers construct, back-fire of fuelbreak, old burn *Crews, dozers, air support construct, backfire ~~off Bear Canyon~~ *Utilize crews to hold fire along Topotah Bluffs *Dozers, crews construct, backing south of Lyons ~~Canyon~~
PROBABILITY OF SUCCESS	20%	30%	40%	70%
ESTIMATED CONTROL TIME	2400 July 6	2400 July 7	2400 July 8	2400 July 10
STIMATED FINAL ACREAGE	19,000	15,000	13,000	99,200

ATTACH MAPS OF ALTERNATIVES

(3)

ply a single example by 50, 100 or 200, and you can see how this can devastate an area. The simple truth is that major wildland/urban interface fires will occur with more and more frequency. An incident commander must address this potential early on and allocate maximum personnel and resources to protect life and property.

E. Resource values

Timber is a major industry and the life blood of many towns and communities. A major timber fire can wipe out an area's economy and cause mass relocation of residents due to loss of jobs. Rehab and harvesting of a fire area require technical expertise and quick reaction once a fire is over.

F. Natural aesthetic beauty

Subdivisions and communities are designed around mature, aged

IV. ALTERNATIVES (See instructions on back)

	ALTERNATIVES			
	E			
GENERAL PLAN OF CONTROL (STRATEGIC)	CONTENGENCY PLAN B (48 HOUR) *Protect structures in Ojai front *Halt western fire spread at Rincon fuel break *Halt fire south of Potrero Seco fuelbreak *Halt fire west of Sespe Sanctuary Topotopah Bluffs			
SPECIFIC PLAN OF CONTROL (TACTICAL)	*Protect structures in Ojai front with engines *Utilize crews, dozers to construct hold Rincon fuelbreak, backfire *Utilize crews, dozers, air attack to hold fire south of Potrero Seco *Utilize crews, dozers, air attack to halt fire west of Sespe Sanctuary			
PROBABILITY OF SUCCESS	80%			
ESTIMATED CONTROL TIME	2400 July 12			
ESTIMATED FINAL ACREAGE	122,000			

ATTACH MAPS OF ALTERNATIVES

(3)

stands of trees, brush and other flora. People become attached to the natural setting and its character. In Southern California, homeowners frequently lose their residences as a wildland fire burning in chaparral sweeps into an urban interface. Yet they will rebuild and plant more flammable vegetation nearby. The residents of Northern California do not experience frequent wildland/urban interface fires, but build in and around that same chaparral plant community. They choose to risk living in close proximity with flammable natural vegetation and its aesthetics while hoping the fire service will suppress any fire before it burns their homes.

G. Fauna

Protection and considerations associated with fish and animals are very important. A serious fire can force migration of a species out of the region, creating imbalance for other plant and animal commu-

V. EFFECTS (See instructions on back)

	ALTERNATIVES			
	A	B	C	D
1. SIZE (Predicted final size in acres)	19,000	15,000	13,000	99,200
2. MARKET ELEMENTS				
Timber	N/A	N/A	N/A	N/A
Improvements 4 homes @105,000 per	420,000	420,000	420,000	Potential loss 1,000,000
Recreation	Unknown	Unknown	Unknown	Unknown
Wilderness	Unknown	Unknown	Unknown	Unknown
Wildlife	Unknown	Unknown	Unknown	Unknown
Fish	Unknown	Unknown	Unknown	Unknown
Water	Unknown	Unknown	Unknown	Unknown
Forage	Unknown	Unknown	Unknown	Unknown
SUM OF NET VALUE CHANGE	$ 420,000	$420,000	$420,000	$ 1,000,000
3. NON-MARKET ELEMENTS				
Air	Short term degradation	Same	Same	Same
Visual	Moderate term degradation	Same	Same	Same
Fuels	Good type conversion	Same	Same	Same
Threatened & Endangered Species	Threat to Dry Lake, Sespe Sanctuary	Moderate threat to Dry Lake, Sespe	High threat to Dry Lake, Sespe areas	High threat to Dry Lake, Sespe areas
	-3	-3	-4	-4
SUM OF NET VALUE CHANGE	$ -3	$ -3	$ -4	$ -5
4. SOCIAL ELEMENTS				
Firefighter Safety	-3	-1	-1	-1
Employment	+1	+1	+2	+3
Public Concern	-3	-3	-3	-3
Public Safety	-2	-1	-1	-1
Cultural	0	0	0	0
Other	0	0	0	0
SUM OF NET VALUE CHANGE	$ -10	$ -7	$ -7	$ -7
5. SUPPRESSION COSTS	$ 7,600,000	$ 3,750,000	$3,250,000	$ 24,000,000
6. COST PLUS NET VALUE CHANGE	$ 8,020,000	$ 4,170,000	$ 3,670,000	$ 25,000,000

nities. In, addition, the flora in an area serves not only as food, but also a protection from predators and a nesting area.

The loss of a major grass fuel bed might impact a rancher's ability to feed his/her cattle. I remember an example that occurred at a fast-moving grass and sage fire that was rapidly developing into a major incident. The fire burned all day and into the evening. The area was used extensively for grazing cattle, however, everyone, including myself, *assumed* the ranchers would move the cattle before the fire reached them. At least, we figured, they would cut fences and allow the cattle to go for it on their own.

Evening set in, and the opportunity presented itself for a major backfiring operation. It proved successful, effecting full control of

V. EFFECTS (See instructions on back)				
	ALTERNATIVES			
	E			
1. SIZE (Predicted final size in acres)	122,000			
2. MARKET ELEMENTS				
Timber	N/A			
Improvements	Potential loss 1,000,000			
Recreation	Unknown			
Wilderness	Potential loss 1,000,000			
Wildlife	Unknown			
Fish	Unknown			
Water	Unknown			
Forage	Unknown			
SUM OF NET VALUE CHANGE	$ 2,000,000	$	$	$
3. NON-MARKET ELEMENTS				
Air	Short term degradation			
Visual	Moderate term degradation			
Fuels	Good type conversion			
Threatened & Endangered Species	HIGH threat to Sespe Sanctuary			
SUM OF NET VALUE CHANGE	$ -5	$	$	$
4. SOCIAL ELEMENTS				
Firefighter Safety	-1			
Employment	+5			
Public Concern	-2			
Public Safety	-1			
Cultural	0			
Other	0			
SUM OF NET VALUE CHANGE	$ -4	$	$	$
5. SUPPRESSION COSTS	$ 24,400,000	$	$	$
6. COST PLUS NET VALUE CHANGE	$ 26,400,000	$	$	$

(4)

the fire. Tragically, it was a short-lived victory for firefighters. It was soon discovered that the cattle had not been evacuated or moved. Instead, they moved into steep canyons and got boxed in with only one way in and out. It was estimated that nearly 2,000 cattle were trapped and burned. Those that did not die had to be shot. This was a terrible economic loss for the ranchers and a sad public relations situation for us.

Also, a fire moving across a watershed may cause siltation and turbidity in a lake or stream, seriously harming fish and reproduction of future fish life.

H. Recreation value

Many forest and wilderness areas are established by law to remain wilderness, roadless and in their natural setting. The intent is to pro-

VI. EVALUATION

Each alternative is evaluated against the same criteria developed in Section II.
Review all pertinent data previously developed which relate to the criteria.

CRITERIA	ALTERNATIVE			
	A	B	C	D
ECONOMIC	2	2	1	1
ENVIRONMENTAL	2	2	2	1
SOCIAL	1	1	1	2
OTHER	2	2	2	2

KEY

0 = Does not meet criteria | 1 = Partially meets criteria | 2 = Fully meets criteria

(5)

vide future generations with a chance to view mother nature's splendor. While a fire may be devastating to such an area, as mentioned earlier, not all fire effects are negative. The Wheeler fire opened up over 80,000 acres of previously-restricted areas to recreational use. This summertime restriction was because of the old-age-class fuel and potential for a conflagration. The fire took care of the fuels problem, so the Forest Service opened up the area.

I. Fragile soils

Some soils are very shallow and cannot withstand surface temperatures over 400 degrees F. This temperature creates a condition called *hydrophobic soil,* which affects the topsoil horizon's ability to absorb and pass moisture (rainfall). As a fire moves through a fuel bed, the resins and waxes it does not consume are deposited on understory

VI. EVALUATION

Each alternative is evaluated against the same criteria developed in Section II.
Review all pertinent data previously developed which relate to the criteria.

CRITERIA	ALTERNATIVE E			
ECONOMIC	1			
ENVIRONMENTAL	1			
SOCIAL	2			
OTHER	2			

KEY

0 = Does not meet criteria   1 = Partially meets criteria   2 = Fully meets criteria

VII. SELECTED ALTERNATIVE

SELECTED ALTERNATIVE: CONTENGENCY PLAN B (48 HOURS)

Explanation (document the rationale, criteria, value change, available resources, etc., for selection of this alternative):

We recommend the selection of Contengency Plan "B" based on:

1. Wheeler Fire History (July 1-3)
2. Fuel age class (50-70 year)
3. Adverse weather model - temperatures 95 - 100°F, R/H 10-15%, downslope sundowner winds
4. Firefighter safety/fatigue
5. Lack of sufficient personnel, resources for aggressive attack
6. Poor access
7. Adverse topography model
8. Weather projections (July 3-7)

We feel that the Contengency Plan B is our best alternative and based on above factors and potential threat to the wildland/urban interface, the threat to environmental senstive areas of Dry Lake and Sespe Sanctuary.

Public information direction (for keeping public informed of situation) shall be developed as appropriate:

All media contacts and releases shall be taken off the incident 209 and approved by Wheeler Command or Wheeler Information Officer.

(6)

leaves, needles and organic layer to be further leached into the first three soil horizons. This resin layer forms a non-permeable water barrier, promoting erosion and loss of valuable topsoil. Topsoil takes many, many years to re-establish itself; sometimes it never does. The lack of valuable nutrients for plant growth means that rehab efforts by man or mother nature take years. This consideration becomes very important in determining the potential for a fire/flood sequence.

J. Air quality

Degredation of air quality, even for a few hours, causes concern in the public. The decision to allow extra tons of airborne particulate matter to move into an air basin may just be plain unacceptable to the public and hard to justify to the forest supervisor, county administrator or region chief. Even though firefighters and fuel managers understand that smoke from a wildland fire is less toxic and hazardous than most smoke and airborne pollution, the "man on the street" is not convinced.

The direction in which drift smoke will travel and the likelihood of a stable air mass subsiding smoke into an urban area must receive serious consideration. During the Wheeler Fire, numerous people called the dispatch center and wanted to know if the fire department was going to pay to have their swimming pools cleaned of ash deposits.

An escape fire analysis allows the incident commander and plans chief to clearly identify needs for resource advisors and technical specialists. The real benefit here is get these experts involved in the

The Incident Command System must start early with control objectives and a completed ICS-201 Form.

			STRIKE TEAM TYPES AND MINIMUM EQUIPMENT				
STRIKE TEAM TYPES		NUMBER/TYPE	PUMP CAPAC.	WATER CAPAC.	2½″ HOSE	1½″ HOSE	1″ HOSE
KIND ENGINES	A	5 - Type 1	1,000 GPM	400 Gal.	1,200 Ft.	400 Ft.	200 Ft.
	B	5 - Type 2	500 GPM	400 Gal.	1,000 Ft.	500 Ft.	300 Ft.
	C	5 - Type 3	120 GPM	300 Gal.	N/A	1,000 Ft.	800 Ft.
	D	5 - Type 4	50 GPM	200 Gal.	N/A	300 Ft.	800 Ft.
KIND CREWS	G	Hand crew combinations consisting of a minimum of 35 persons (Do not mix Type 1 and Type 2 crews)	Type 1 handcrews have no				
	H		Type 2 handcrews may have				
KIND DOZER	K	2 - Type 1 1 - Dozer Tender	Heavy dozer (i.e., D-7, D-8 or				
	L	2 - Type 2 1 - Dozer Tender	Medium dozer (i.e., D-5, D-6				
	M	2 - Type 3 1 - Dozer Tender	Light dozer (i.e., D-4 or				

mobilization phase of the incident, and not leave them waiting until full control of the fire has been effected. Some key personnel that should be identified in advance of a major incident are:

A. **Soils technician** – hydrophobic soil identification
B. **Fire-behavior technical specialist** – fire effects
C. **Flood-control technician** – likelihood of siltation in streams and lakes, fire/flood sequence
D. **Archaeologist** – to identify sensitive artifacts, monuments, and relics (cultural concerns)
E. **Botanist/fuels management technical specialist** – sensitive flora identification, fuel management plan
F. **Wildlife biologist** – to evaluate impacts on wildlife and habitat

The escape fire situation analysis form is straightforward and easy to use. Much like the incident action plan, it is used to the extent of need. It can be simple or detailed. The basis is plus (+), minus (−) and zero (0) symbology. A plus indicates a positive change; a

MINIMUM STANDARDS

STANDARDS	MINIMUM MANNING				
	LADDER	HEAVY STREAM	S/T LEADER	PER SINGLE RESOURCE	TOTAL PERSONNEL
	20 Ft Ext.	500 GPM	1	4	21
	20 Ft. Ext.	N/A	1	3	16
	N/A	N/A	1	3	16
	N/A	N/A	1	3	16
restrictions on use			1	N/A	36
use restrictions			1	N/A	36
equivalent)			1	2 1	6
or equivalent)			1	2 1	6
equivalent)			1	2 1	6

minus impact, negative change. Zero is no effect.

As the incident commander and command staff start formulating alternatives as the fire develops, the EFSA helps formulate a strategy matrix. Depending on incident size, complexity and duration, you should develop one to three alternate strategies. Each should include:

A. **Basic strategy** (direct-indirect attack)
B. **Personnel/resources needed**
C. **Estimated control date/time**
D. **Estimated final acreage**
E. **Estimated suppression costs**
F. **Estimated rehab costs**
G. **Probability of success** (very important)

The EFSA also has a checklist for analysis of effects. As forementioned, these include sociological, environmental, cultural and economic.

Based on a careful evaluation of these factors, a sound, safe and cost-effective decision can be made. By involving the next level of management and technical specialists in this decision process, a foundation of expertise is established should post-fire problems arise such as public criticism or a law suit. It looks very professional if the command team can display a decision-making process such as the EFSA to the public if that process includes input from upper management and technical specialists.

INCIDENT MANAGEMENT TIME CYCLE

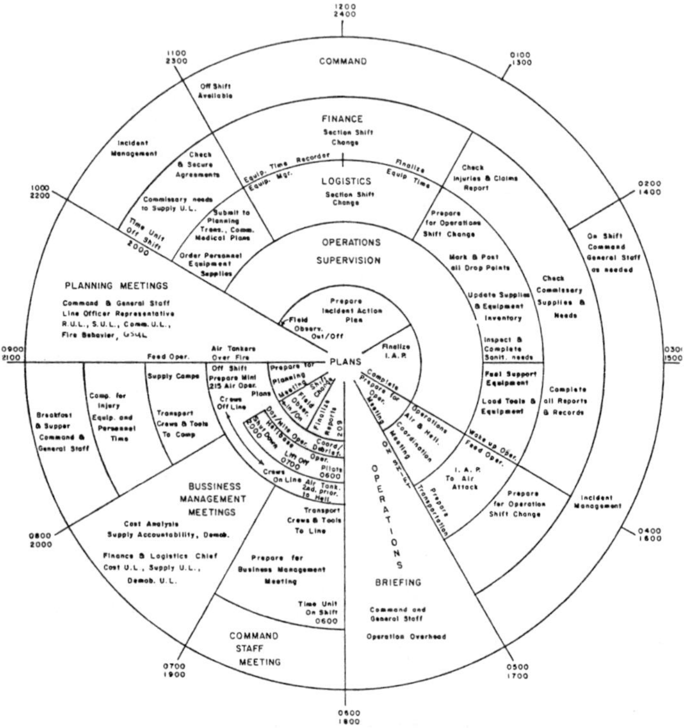

I am including a sample EFSA for review in this chapter. Fit th EFSA or other decision-making model into your plans. If the inciden is simple and no adverse impacts are envisioned, just review the forn orally with key staff. If the incident is developing, then start imple menting the model early in the mobilization phase. A trained plan chief knows the EFSA process and staff requirements for completion It looks far more complex than it has to be; use it and you will appre ciate its advantages.

Like the incident action plan, the EFSA must be kept curren

COMMAND TIME CYCLE

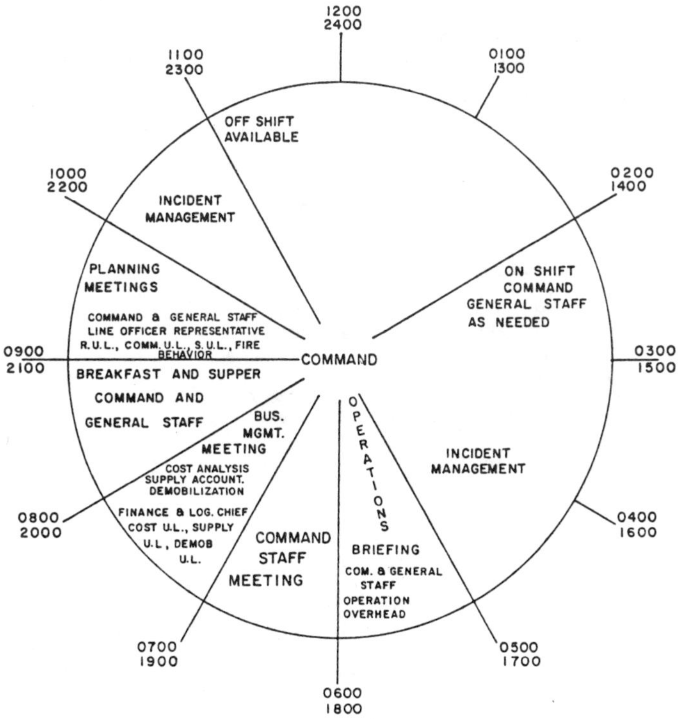

In addition, always retain it as part of the final incident documentation package.

ICS ORGANIZATION GUIDE

C
O
M
M
A
N
D

1. **Incident Commander — one per incident. Unless incident is multi-jurisdictional.**
2. **Multi-jurisdictional incidents establish Unified Command with each jurisdiction supplying individual to represent agency in Unified Command Structure.**
3. **Incident Commander may have Deputy.**
4. **Command Staff Officers — one per function per incident.**
5. **Command Staff may have assistants as needed.**
6. **Agency Representatives report to Liaison Officer on Command Staff.**

INCIDENT BASE RECOMMENDED MINIMUM PERSONNEL REQUIREMENTS (PER 12 HOUR OPERATIONAL PERIOD)

(If camps are established, the minimum personnel requirements for the Base may be modified or additionl personnel may be added to support camps.

	UNIT POSITION	SIZE OF INCIDENT (NUMBER OF DIVISIONS)				
		2	5	10	15	25
O	Operations Section Chief	One Per Operational Period				
P	Branch Director		2	3	4	6
E	Division/Group Supervisor	2	5	10	15	25
R	Strike Team Leaders	As Needed				
A	Task Force Leaders	As Needed				
T	Air Operations Director		1	1	1	1
I	Air Attack Group Supervisor	1	1	1	1	1
O	Air Tanker Coordinator	As Needed				
N	Helicopter Coordinator	As Needed				
S	Air Support Group Supervisor	1	1	1	1	1
	Helibase Manager	One Per Helibase				
	Helispot Manager	One Per Helispot				
	Fixed Wing Support Leader	One Per Airport				
	Staging Area Manager	One Per Staging Area				
	Planning Section Chief	One Per Incident				
	Resources Unit Leader	1	1	1	1	1
	Status Recorders	1	2	3	3	3
	Check-in Recorders	As Needed				
	Technical Specialists	As Needed				
	Situation Unit Leader	1	1	1	1	1
	Field Observer		1	2	2	3
P	Weather Observer	As Needed				
L	Aerial/Ortho Photo Analyst	As Needed				
A	Display/Report Processor		1	1	1	2
N	IR Equipment Operators	Two If Needed				
S	Computer Terminal Operator		1	1	1	2
	Photographer			1	1	1
	Documentation Unit Leader		1	1	1	1
	Demobilization Unit Leader			1	1	1
	(Demob Recorders from Resources)					

	UNIT POSITION	SIZE OF INCIDENT (NUMBER OF DIVISIONS)				
		2	5	10	15	25
L	Logistics Section Chief	One Per Incident				
O	Service Branch Director	As Needed				
G	Communications Unit Leader	1	1	1	1	1
I	Head Dispatcher	1	1	1	1	1
S	Incident Dispatcher	1	2	3	3	4
T	Message Center Operator		1	1	2	2
I	Messenger		1	2	2	2
C	Communications Technician		1	2	4	4
S	Medical Unit Leader	1	1	1	1	1
	Medical Unit Leader Assistant	As Needed				
	Food Unit Leader		1	1	1	1
	Food Unit Assistant (each camp)	As Needed				
	Cook		1	1	2	2
	Assistant Cook		2	2	6	12
	Helper		8	8	16	24
	Support Branch Director	As Needed				
	Supply Unit Leader		1	1	1	1
	Camp Supply Assistant (each camp)	As Needed				
	Ordering Manager			1	1	1
	Rec/Distribution Manager		1	1	1	1
	Tool/Equipment Specialist			1	1	1
	Recorders		1	1	2	2
	Helpers		2	2	2	2
	Facility Unit Leader		1	1	1	1
	Base Manager		1	1	1	1

	Camp Manager (each camp)	As Needed				
	Facility Maintenance Specialist		1	1	1	1
	Security Manager		1	1	1	1
	Helpers		6	6	12	12
	Ground Support Unit Leader	1	1	1	1	1
	Equipment Manager		1	1	1	1
	Assistants	As Needed				
	Equipment Timekeeper		1	1	1	1
	Mechanics	1	1	3	5	7
	Drivers	As Needed				
	Operators	As Needed				
FINANCE	Finance Section Chief	One Per Incident				
	Time Unit Leader		1	1	1	1
	Time Recorder,Personnel		1	3	3	5
	Procurement Unit Leader		1	1	1	1
	Compensation/Claims Unit Leader		1	1	1	
	Compensation Soecialists	As Needed				
	Claims Specialists	As Needed				
	Cost Unit Leader		1	1	1	1
	Cost Analysts			1	1	1

OPERATIONS TIME CYCLE

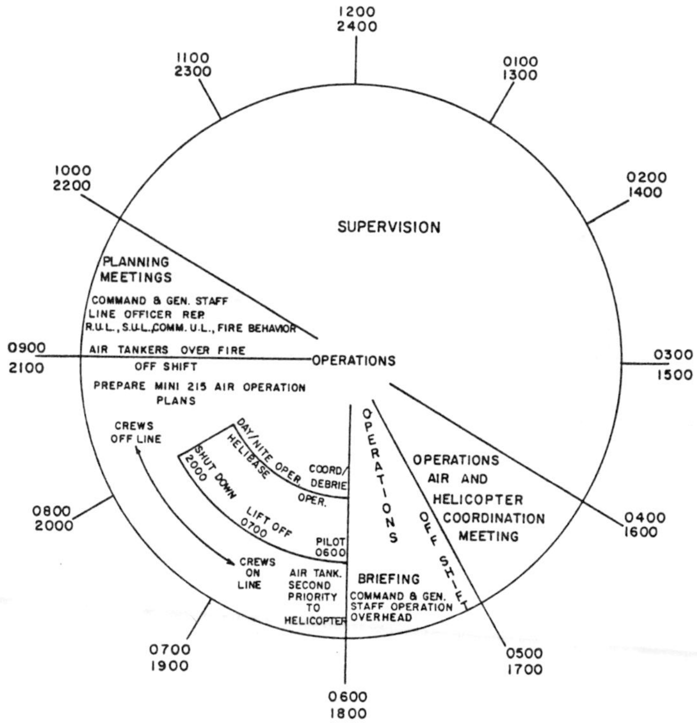

T-CARD COLORS AND USES

Eight different color resource cards (T-Cards) are used to denote kind of resources. The card colors and resources they represent are:

KIND RESOURCE	CARD COLOR	FORM NUMBER (219)
Engines	Rose	3
Handcrews	Green	2
Dozers	Yellow	7
Aircraft	Orange	6
Helicopter	Blue	4
Misc. Equip/ Task Forces	Tan	8
Personnel	White	5
Location Labels	Gray	1
Property	White/red	9

PLANS TIME CYCLE

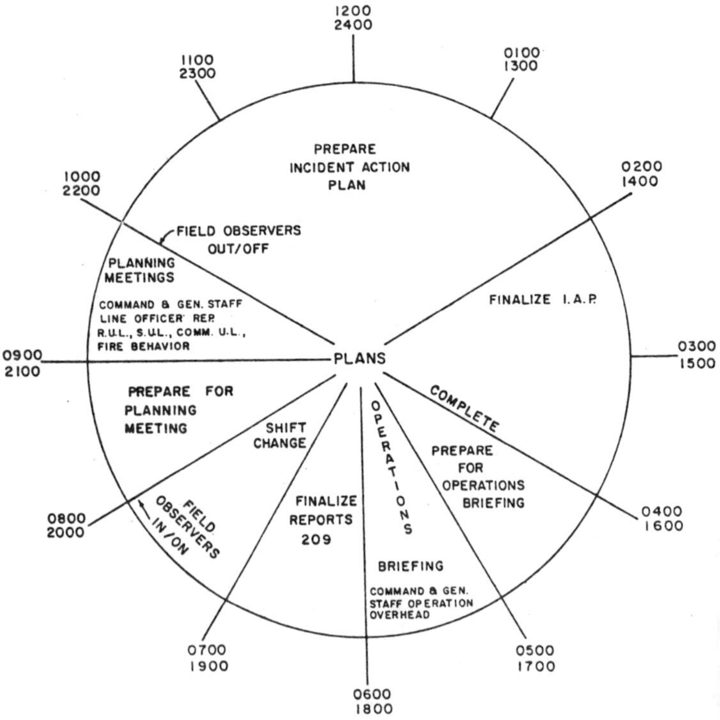

INCIDENT COMMAND SYSTEM FORMS

Forms and records which are routinely used in the ICS are listed below. Those marked with an (*) are commonly used in written Incident Action Plans.

Incident Briefing	ICS Form 201
*Incident Objectives	ICS Form 202
*Organization Assignment List	ICS Form 203
*Division Assignment List	ICS Form 204
*Incident Radio Communications Plan	ICS Form 205
*Medical Plan	ICS Form 206
Incident Organization Chart	ICS Form 207
Incident Status Summary	ICS Form 209
Status Change Card	ICS Form 210
Check-In List	ICS Form 211
General Message	ICS Form 213
Unit Log	ICS Form 214
Operational Planning Worksheet	ICS Form 215
Radio Requirements Worksheet	ICS Form 216
Radio Frequency Assignment Worksheet	ICS Form 217
Support Vehicle Inventory	ICS Form 218
Resource Status Card (1-8)	ICS Form 219
Air Operations Summary Worksheet	ICS Form 220
Demobilization Checkout	ICS Form 221

LOGISTICS TIME CYCLE

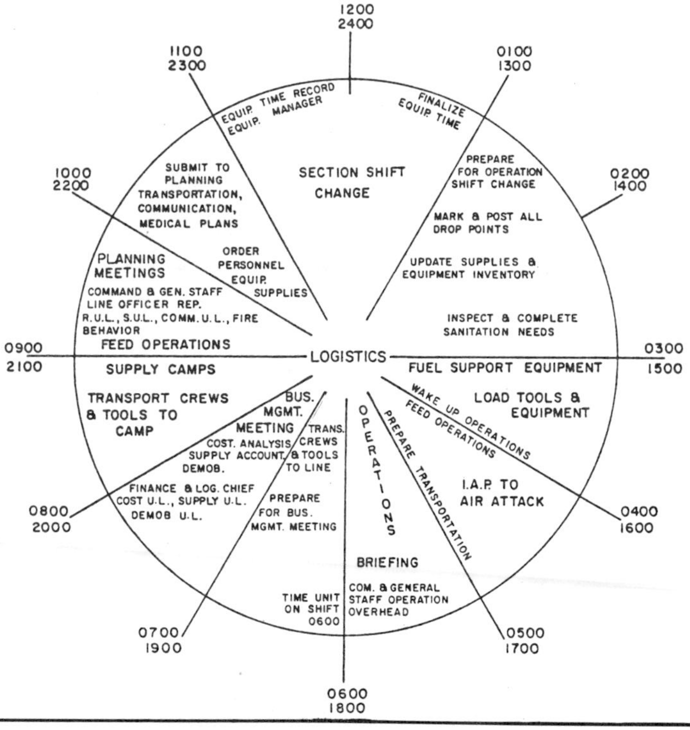

FINANCE TIME CYCLE

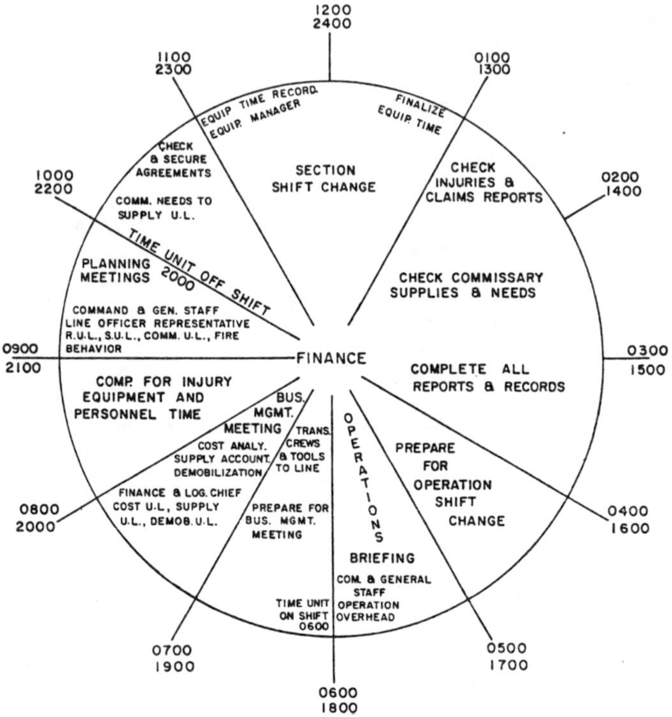

Chapter 17

Basic Investigation and Scene Preservation

Most arson investigators will group company officers into one of two basic categories – awfully good or awfully bad. To the investigator, either the point of origin was properly preserved and taped or the point of origin was totally destroyed.

It is true that the company officer is generally first to arrive on scene and is therefore often the key to making or losing a possible arson conviction. The company officer, as well as all other personnel, must realize the importance of scene preservation and providing the arson investigator with an uncontaminated area of origin.

Scene preservation really starts with a basic understanding of the arsonist's thought processes. These include easy access, fuel to burn and easy egress. If treated as a part of pre-fire planning preparation this becomes easy to visualize.

Factors to evaluate include:

.. **All access routes into fuel beds.** Which routes have easy access? gress? *Visibility* is a key issue here. The public has been made aware f the Secret Witness, Stop Crime and Crime Watch programs, and e arsonist knows that if his/her vehicle looks suspicious or is seen aving a fire scene he/she runs a high risk of apprehension.

Access routes with few houses or intersection roads are likely rgets. Roads that loop or return to the general area should be noted ecause often arsonists want to "see their work" after the set.

Roads with a lot of turnouts and pull-offs should also be evalued. When looking at these access routes, note fuel types and possible se of ignition. Many state and county road departments mow roadsides prior to fire season in high-arson risk areas. If, during pre-fire planning, the company officer feels an area is an easy target or has had a lot of sets, the mowing idea has merit.

B. Fuels. In most cases, the arsonist will not spend much time outside his/her vehicle trying to get a set to take. Grass or light fuels are an easy target because most ignition devices used by the arsonist generate sufficient temperature to ignite light fuels. In preplanning fuel beds and first-in districts, evaluate access roads that have light fuels off the shoulders.

C. Other variable factors including:

1. Map/plot on district maps. Know arson fire locations (especially unsolved fires).
2. Schools in/near fuels beds. Travel routes to/from area schools.
3. Subdivisions/housing tracts with lots of children.

D. Visual identifications (practice)

This can be a team effort for the company. Vehicle or suspect identification while responding to a wildland fire – or any fire – is difficult. Many times, the company officer is busy evaluating size-up factors while the engineer is busy driving. However, it can be done with a little practice and team work.

For instance, the engineer can remember color(s) and the first half of the license plate of a suspicious vehicle. The company officer can count vehicle occupants and memorize the second half of the

Photo by Keith Cullo

Engine companies should protect the area of origin from foot and vehicle traffic.

license plate and the state. This procedure can also work for suspects on foot in the fire area. The engineer can estimate size, height and facial characteristics. The company officer should note clothing details, shoes, etc. In both cases, make a note of date and time. Practice these techniques year around and they become a valuable tool.

Some of the specific problems associated with ineffective scene preservation include:

A. Poor vehicle placement at scene
B. Hand crew anchor point
C. Bulldozer anchor point/unloading area
D. Hoseline placement/water damage
E. Excessive foot traffic
F. Fire personnel smoking in area — discarded butts
G. Did not flag off large enough area

Engineers/company officers should always consider point of origin when placing resources. Many times, the area within a 30-to-50-foot radius of the point of origin may reveal key evidence. In most cases, that first-arriving resource placement sets the attitude for other resources that arrive later.

Keep in mind that it is not at all uncommon to find multiple devices at an incident. Footprints, cigarette butts, wrappers, trash, bottles, etc. may reveal key bits of information.

The company officer, during the size-up process, must quickly *evaluate* and *identify* the area of origin. This area should be quickly flagged or secured prior to any initial-attack actions. Most fire departments use brightly-colored engineering tape or police crime-scene tape to identify the area of origin. Once the investigation concludes, remove the tape – for esthetics and public relations.

Many times the company officer will be able to identify the area of origin before arrival. Key fire behavior factors include wind direction, speed, slope and topography. In most wildland fires involving wind speed, a clear head and origin area can be quickly identified. Roadside fires can be an exception, as traffic can create eddies and modify fire spread.

BURN INDICATORS

Part of identifying the area of origin is using burn pattern indicators. These assist in narrowing the area of origin down to the point of origin. Each fuel category (slash, grass, brush and timber) has burning characteristics that can be used to point the company officer or investigator in the right direction.

A. Slash (down dead)

1. Stems, twigs and leaves between one-fourth and one-half inch diameter may produce sufficient heat and white ash to destroy any paper products that were part of the ignition device (paper matchbook, cigarette, etc.). White ash must be closely inspected if near area of origin.

2. Evergreen slash may produce more white ash than deciduous leaves, twigs and stems.

B. Grass

1. Short grass is hard to evaluate – it produces a very erratic spread if it is windy, and primarily black ash. Evaluate all areas of white ash found in the area of origin.

2. Grass over 12 inches. The heads will generally "fall" pointing to the area of origin. This is accurate only on cured grass.

3. A backing fire in grass may produce fingers of unburned or partially-burned fuel. This is due to upslope runs, which may occur once the fire burns to the lowest point of slope and runs back upslope.

4. A rapidly-developing grass fire pushed by a wind may produce sufficient indrafts of air along flanks to push grass heads towards the burned area.

C. Brush

1. Expect a lot of white ash, especially in areas with lots of down-dead leaves, stems and twigs. This may make it difficult to locate an ignition device (if there is one).

2. The char on brush main stock will be higher on the upslope side of the brush (See Figure 17a).

3. Brush canopy will display more heat damage or burnout on the upslope side than the area of origin (see Figure 17b).

4. Brush stobs left over after an intense fire will be cupped into points towards the direction of spread.

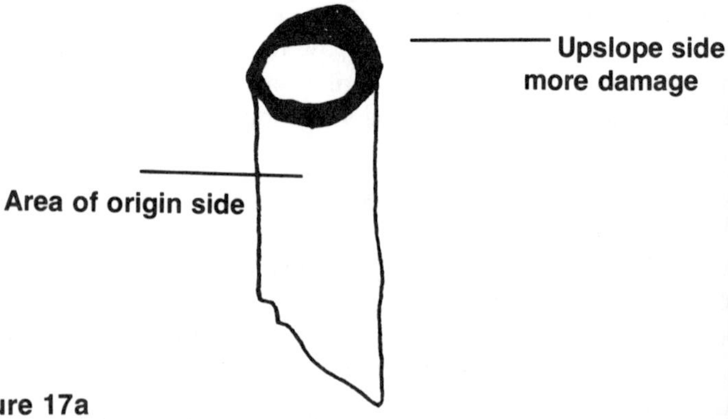

Figure 17a
Cross section of brush stock.

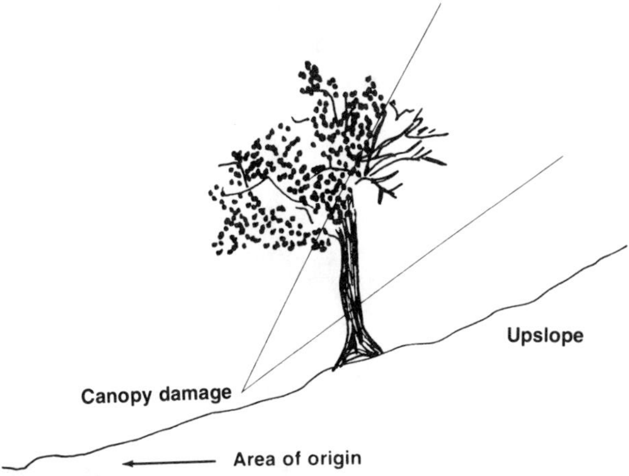

Figure 17b

Damage to canopy foliage will be higher and more severe on upslope.

D. Trees

1. The char on tree bark will be high on the upslope side and lower towards the area of origin.

2. The depth of char on tree bark is greater where heat has been sustained (see Figure 17c).

3. A crown fire may also reveal some indication of direction of travel. The canopy will generally reveal more damage in the direction of spread, less in the direction of area of origin.

E. Ground Litter, Rocks and Roadside Fires

1. Cigarette cartons and wrappers in the area of origin may be damaged only on the flame-exposed side. This side will be more damaged in the direction of the area of origin.

2. Beer bottles and glass on the ground will sustain heat damage and may exhibit a brown stain on side (exposure) pointing to area of origin.

3. Exposure to oncoming flames will cause rocks on the ground to suffer heat damage and possibly exhibit a brown stain on the side pointing to area of origin. Grass around the base of a rock will be burned on the side facing area of origin.

4. Large down-dead logs with grass around their bases will show grass burned on the side pointing to area of origin.

5. Downed pine needles or leaves on the ground will exhibit

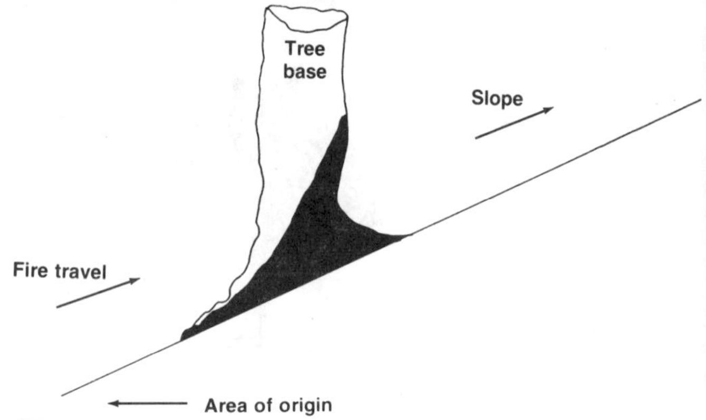

Figure 17c
Figure illustrates that, as a fire moves upslope, depth and degree of char will be higher on the upslope side of the tree base.

more heat damage on the side pointing to the area of origin.

6. Fence posts or power poles will sustain more damage on upwind side.

7. Roadside fires can exhibit erratic burn indicators. Depending on winds, traffic volume and roadside cuts, wind eddies can affect the fall of burned grass, ground litter and burned-over debris. Take traffic patterns, wind speeds and roadside cuts into consideration in these areas.

When deploying resources such as bulldozers, hand crews or engine-company hoselines, consider area of origin when establishing an anchor point. Many times, the area of origin and anchor point are established in conflict. This means the anchor point is often the area of origin. Since this area usually exhibits low fire behavior, care should be taken to minimize suppression activities.

Engine company or staff personnel at the scene but not directly involved in firefighting activities can also contaminate the area of origin. Footprints, discarded cigarette butts or tire patterns can confuse investigators.

Be observant. Look for out-of-place objects, vehicles, people. Document your observations. Until the investigator arrives, the first-arriving company officer can do much to assist the investigation. This really begins with understanding how the area of origin can be contaminated or destroyed.

Many communities/states have law enforcement officers respond with fire personnel to assist in traffic control and evacuation. They too, should be trained in wildland fire scene preservation and how to flag the area of origin.

Wildland arson is on the rise. Assist your arson investigator by remembering to:

A. **Identify area of origin prior to resource deployment, if possible and fire conditions allow.**
B. **Flag the area of origin. Be liberal in identifying area of origin.**
C. **Maintain security in area of origin.**
D. **Document your situation — date, time, suspicious vehicles, personnel and your initial actions.**
E. **Be cautious in your public information news releases. It's much safer to use words like "under investigation," or "undetermined" at this point rather than, "It was arson."**
F. **Ask your arson investigator to give your company a basic investigation class prior to the wildland fire season.**
G. **Remember your travel route in area of origin. This will help eliminate footsteps/prints.**
H. **Train your personnel to keep from making statements to the public prior to investigators' arrival.**

Chapter 18

The Wheeler Incident and Long-Range Planning Concepts

The Wheeler fire, near Ojai, CA, burned 15 homes and 118,000 acres of wildland area during the period of July 1 through 15, 1985. This incident was unique from several aspects, including adverse fire behavior, application of the Incident Command System and interagency cooperation.

Several important factors set the stage for this fire. Of primary concern to most fuel managers was the fact that the 1983 and 1984 rainy seasons were characterized by below-average rainfall. This, coupled with the old age class and decadency of the fuels, accounted for the adverse fire behavior.

Another prime factor was a lack of fire history in this fuel bed, the last major fire being the Matilija incident, which burned over 219,000 acres in 1932. The weather in May/June assisted the lack of rainfall in drying the fuels to a critical state (53 percent at the time of the incident). Preceding the Wheeler fire, the burning index had been critical.

Another important component was that surrounding counties had been experiencing several initial-attack wildland incidents prior to Wheeler, as was the whole western United States, initially reducing the availability of additional overhead personnel, support staff and critical resources. These factors, coupled with a fuel bed of steep, broken topography and limited access, curtailed the effectiveness of initial-attack resources.

The Wheeler conflagration started on July 1, at approximately

1515 hours, amid extreme weather conditions. The dry bulb was 102, relative humidity 16 percent, fuel stick 3.0 and the burning index 153. A wind was blowing southeast at four miles per hour over the point of origin near Wheeler Springs in the Los Padres National Forest. The cause of the fire: arson.

The first unit onscene was a district fire management officer, who arrived within minutes to find two acres of grass and brush moving into heavy chaparral and steep topography. Approximately two minutes after arrival of the first officer, the first Los Padres engine module arrived.

Within 10 to 15 minutes after arrival of this first engine, the incident was 30 acres in size, burning with two heads on a steep, inaccessible slope. Then the fire spotted across Highway 33, burning on both sides of the highway. Highway 33 is a primary two-lane road between Ojai and the Bakersfield area that normally has a moderate traffic load.

Within the next 30 minutes, mutual aid in the form of a five-engine strike team from the Ventura County Fire Department arrived. A number of problems faced this initial-attack force, including the need to evacuate residences as well as a campground in Wheeler Springs. Traffic on Highway 33 also had to be managed until closure could be requested from law enforcement personnel.

Fire behavior continued to be adverse, with extreme rates of spread. Approximately one hour into the incident, the fire was 1,000 acres in size and continuing to burn into the steep, hard-to-access rocky slopes.

The initial-attack incident commander established his control objectives as life safety, then property values, choosing an aggressive initial attack. The evacuation of the surrounding area complemented these initial control objectives. Being familiar with this area, the IC recognized a threat to firefighters in the critical fuelbed and adverse conditions. For the duration of this incident, safety of public and firefighting personnel continued to be the top priority.

Pre-fire planning done by Ojai District personnel and command staff helped a great deal. It is this author's opinion that this planning can be credited for successfully minimizing risk to firefighting personnel and damage to residences throughout the incident.

Based upon fire behavior during the first several hours of Wheeler, the initial-attack incident commander and forest officials quickly determined a need to organize a command team and prepare for a major incident. This was important from the standpoint of ordering additional overhead personnel and critical resources based on the potential of this fire. Had forest officials continued to initial attack or increment order for the incident over the next 24 hours, they might not have received the resources and support necessary to manage an incident of this size and complexity, because within the next 48 hours over 280 fires would burn in California.

At about 1830 hours on July 1, the initial-attack incident commander and forest officials on the Wheeler incident requested a regional command team. At 1930 hours, members of this team began to transition and work with local district personnel. By 0500 hours the next day, the original command team had arrived and been briefed by the incident commander, the district ranger and the deputy forest supervisor.

These briefings included a review of suppression actions so far, basic control objectives, current personnel and resources assignments and a fire-behavior assignment. The district ranger went over the district fuels plan and environmental and life safety concerns and the deputy forest supervisor reviewed the escape fire situation analysis, including environmental, sociological, safety and economic concerns. The deputy supervisor also gave the regional command team a delegation of authority. After these briefings and a question/answer period at the district ranger office in Ojai, the regional command team took over management of the incident at 0800 on July 2.

The initial attack overhead blended into the regional command team and provided liaison and technical support. Challenges for the command team included multiple wildland/urban interfaces, several declared environmental wilderness areas, a scenic river area, a botanical area, a condor sanctuary and several key watersheds surrounding large lakes and reservoirs providing drinking water to urban areas.

As previously mentioned, old-age-class fuel types and heavy fuel loading with down-dead fuels aided continuity. The topography in the fire area and surrounding fuel beds was, for the most part, steep and inaccessible. These factors, coupled with the Fourth-of-July influx of tourists into recreational areas, demanded that extensive coordination and planning go into establishing incident objectives.

The regional command team incident commander, working closely with the district ranger and deputy forest supervisor, saw a critical need based on the incident facts and weather trends to establish early-on coordination with surrounding communities, cities and other cooperators. This group was to include mayors, city councilmen, water districts, road departments, public works, law enforcement and fire district agencies. What started out as an initial briefing on incident potential turned into frequent daily meetings with this group as the incident grew in size and complexity and threatened urban interfaces.

The effort and priority placed on key informational exchanges and briefing sessions proved to be beneficial in helping reduce rumors and engendering community support for suppression efforts.

Another key area was long-range planning. Resources were ordered by strike team rather than increment, as the operations chief tried to keep control objectives broad and flexible. During the first week of Wheeler, these objectives were more defensive than offensive. Because of the fire behavior, risk to firefighters and poor access, major emphasis was placed on structural protection and backfiring away from critical wildland/urban interfaces.

The operations staff continually evaluated control objectives and firefighter safety during the first week as the fire continued to burn day and night, at times burning in five different directions. As critical weather conditions continued, firefighter fatigue became a major concern.

Operations were designed to shift from traditional divisional assignments, enabling better span of control. Because of the regional fire problem and multiple major fires burning in California over the July 4th weekend, many of the ground personnel ordered for Wheeler came from other incidents, and many of these crews had worked two weeks without a day off.

Obviously, this had some impact on line-construction rates and caused the Operations Division much concern about safety. Incident safety officers worked closely with operations personnel to evaluate work shifts, line operations and injuries, and, as was mentioned earlier, safety was the highest priority.

All personnel assigned to the Wheeler fire should be commended for maintaining an excellent safety record, considering all the factors involved and complexity of the incident. Only one serious – and 54 minor – injuries took place among the over 3,000 personnel participating in the incident.

On the 6th of July, another important concept was initiated: the 24-hour workshift. Previously, many personnel had been working 16-20 hour shifts before reaching the base camp.

The benefits of the 24-hour work cycle were:

A. Shift changes were made during low fire activity, resulting in better continuity of fire suppression during afternoon and early-evening high-fire activity.

B. Planning and intelligence improved because they were handled over longer time frames.

C. Rest cycles could be implemented (as previously discussed, many ground personnel came to the incident from other fires and thus had not had a day off over a long period of time).

The 24-hour rest cycle gave crews going off shift a chance to relax, do laundry, maintain equipment and pursue leisure activities. In addition, the incident commander realized that, given the likely duration of the incident, quality meals with sufficient supplemental fruits, juices and condiments were critical to morale and rejuvenation of personnel.

At the height of the fire, more than 3,000 personnel, over 200 engines, 40 bulldozers and 68 handcrews were on scene, all requiring extensive logistical support. This included establishment of a base and camp complete with trailer space for the command team function, a major supply depot for tools and equipment, a vehicle maintenance and mechanic operator, a medical team and evaluation center, a major communications center, a rest and relaxation area and a fire information center.

The logistics chief on the original team evaluated the incident potential and worked with local resources and personnel to find an existing park that would meet all of the above needs. An agreement was reached and signed with the county parks department for use of Seoul Park, east of Ojai.

Cost effectiveness was another positive aspect of this incident. The suppression costs for the Wheeler incident were $9 million, or about $473 per acre. Of this, approximately $4.2 million was spent on personnel-related items. Approximately $100,000 a day was spent on food and supplies. Air operations, including helicopter and fixed wing, accounted for $1.1 million of the overall costs. The finance chief and her staff did an outstanding job in daily crew hours accountability and monitoring expenses for the incident. Additionally, accounts were quickly evaluated and settled when possible, minimizing the long-range impact. Three public information centers and a cadre of fire information officers also did an excellent job in keeping all forms of media updated and current with fire activities. This included tours of the incident command post.

At most wildland incidents, a key concern is staying consistent and within National Inter-Agency Incident Management System (NIIMS) organizational guidelines (Figure 18a). The Wheeler incident was very diverse and complex (seven branches), requiring the command team to create a special long-range planning section.

Unusual incident conditions at Wheeler included:

A. Fire Behavior Characteristics

Erratic and extreme rates of spread. The fire was 30 acres in size after ten minutes of burning and 1,000 acres after one hour. Additionally, days after its start, a six-hour burning period consumed

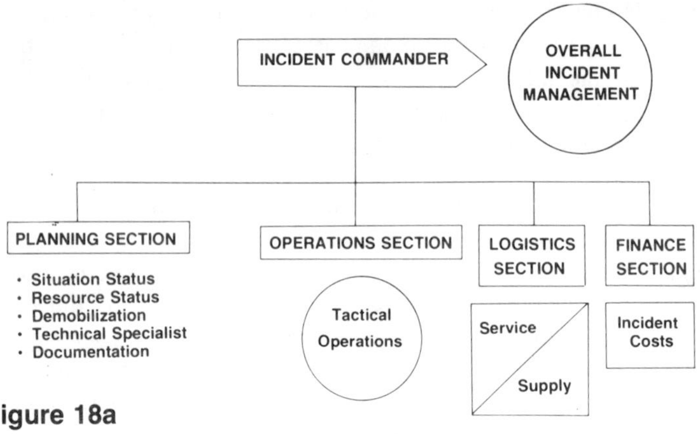

Figure 18a

20,000 acres. At one point, the fire had five separate heads and directions of spread.

B. Wildland/Urban Interfaces

The fire threatened several urban areas including Ojai, Matalija, Meiners Oaks and Carpinteria.

C. Critical Dedicated Watersheds

The fire burned into three watersheds surrounding key water storage reservoirs and a lake. These areas provide primary or secondary water for the above-listed communities.

D. Continuous Old-Age-Class Fuel Beds

The last fire was in 1932, and it covered 219,000 acres.

E. Steep Topography, Poor Access

Limited ability to use direct attack methods over most of the fire area.

F. Environmentally-Sensitive Areas

Two major dedicated preserves plus another proposed scenic river area, all near the fire.

G. Rapidly-Changing Weather

Weather modeling and forecasts changed every few hours. The fire was creating its own microclimatic conditions.

H. Multiple Major Fire Burning in California During Same Time Frame

Manpower and resources were limited, requiring advance planning for resources and personnel ordering. At one point, 196 overhead personnel ordered for Wheeler took 48 hours to arrive.

The Wheeler incident was managed by California Regional Fire Team five. The team structure was as outlined in Figure 18b.

Realizing the potential size and complexity of the incident, in

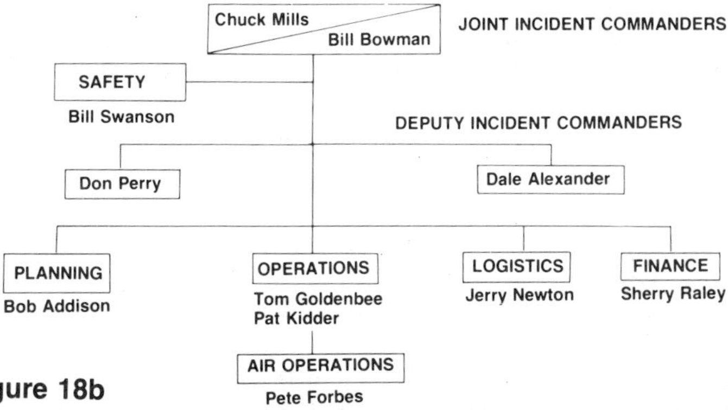

Figure 18b

cident commanders divided functional responsibilities along with the multi-jurisdictional involvement. Chuck Mills handled incident operational issues while Bill Bowman coordinated cooperating and assisting agency involvement. This included daily briefings for law enforcement, utility companies, water districts, political interests, city and county officials and mutual aid participants. This briefing, held each morning, had 15 to 20 persons in attendance. They were briefed on the current situation and incident needs. This briefing concept was a valuable tool that enabled local agencies to get involved and keep current on the situation and get reassurances that the command team was managing the incident taking everyone's concerns into consideration.

The fire grew so quickly in size and complexity, that a need was seen for advance planning exclusive of this incident. The responsibility of long-range planning was given to this author. A staff was assigned as outlined in Figure 18c.

The second deputy incident commander (Alexander) assisted in

Donald Perry	DEPUTY COMMAND
Jerry Gelock	PLANS CHIEF
Tom Harbour	PLANS CHIEF
Dave Freeland	ENVIRONMENTAL TECHNICAL SPECIALIST

Figure 18c

incident management and demobilization. The primary objectives of long-range planning included:

A. **Develop long-range strategies for 24-, 48-, and 72-hour increments**
B. **Forecast fire behavior and incident potential**
C. **Evaluate threats to dedicated watersheds**
D. **Evaluate impact to water storage reservoirs and lake**
E. **Review pre-attack plans for existing access, fuel breaks and dozer lines**
F. **Develop, review and update escape fire situation analysis**
G. **Develop, post and keep current large visual display of current 24-, 48- and 72-hour strategies and fire's edge**
H. **Brief the command team and visiting officials as need arises**
I. **Develop and write up long-range plans. Provide input to incident planning for inclusion into incident action plan (IAP)**

There are benefits from implementing a long-range planning concept. It will:

A. **Complement incident planning**
B. **Enable long-range 24-, 48- and 72-hour resource and personnel ordering**
C. **Lend more operational flexibility**
D. **Enable command team to better meet environmental concerns as escape fire situation analysis is reviewed and updated**
E. **Enable better utilization of pre-attack plans**
F. **Assist in maintaining cost effectiveness**
G. **Help develop a final documentation package for the incident**
H. **Assist rehabilitation team in initial assessment of burned area and post-fire effects**

The long-range planning team worked in a separate trailer but met frequently with the incident planning chief to keep him current with activities. There were many reasons why the Wheeler incident was managed cost effectively and safely, and long range planning was one of those.

SUMMARY

It would be hard to list all the positive support given during the Wheeler conflagration because there was so much. Forest officials and the over 300 overhead personnel who backed up the command team deserve a tremendous amount of credit for minimizing the loss of life and property and limiting the fire's size.

I believe it is important that readers examine the potential for a conflagration in a wildland area in or around their own jurisdictions. Ask yourself how you would "host" such an event. Could you ade quately staff a major incident? Could you set up an ICP/base that could hold a 1,000-plus people? Do you have the ability to feed 500 to 1,000 people? Do you have authority to purchase meals, food stuff and supplies for 500 to 1,000 people?

Communities must evaluate their preparation, pre-planning capabilities and potential for a large incident such as the Wheeler fire. Discussion should take place with city and county politicians in advance, since they are generally involved in a declaration of any local emergency. Hopefully, these steps will assure that everyone is prepared should a large wildland incident occur.

Chapter 19

Principles of Unified Command

Wildland fires frequently burn across areas where two or more fire agencies have jurisdictional responsibility. The Incident Command System operates under the principle of one incident commander *per incident*. In situations where a fire does burn into a fuel bed where two or more agencies have jurisdictional responsibility, the unified command concept is utilized. Simply stated, unified command means that the agencies having jurisdictional responsibility agree to have *one* common set of control objectives, *one* ordering process, *one* incident command post and *one* planning process. All of the above is agreed upon without loss of individual jurisdictional authority (Figure 19a). Each agency retains full control and authority over its jurisdiction.

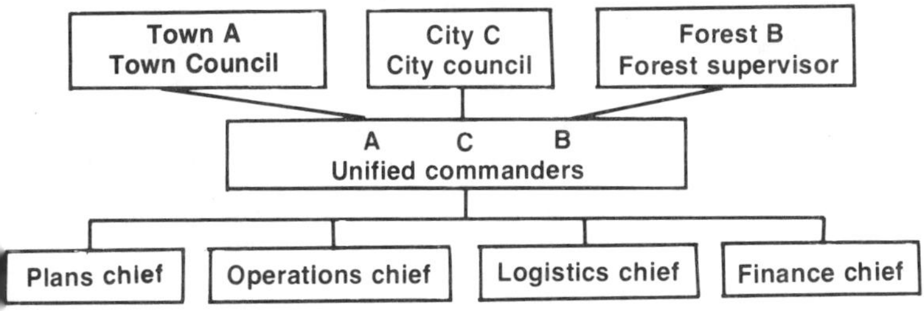

Unified Command. Each agency with jurisdiction of the incident reports to a political governing body or supervisor. This level of government expects that the agency's policies will not be compromised nor authority delegated to another agency. Unified command allows this without violating the Incident Command System management principle of one incident commander per incident.

Figure 19a

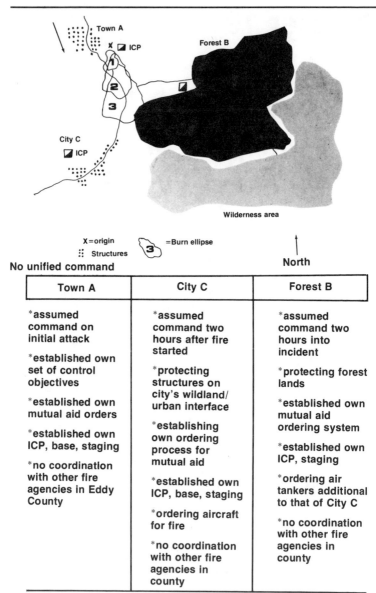

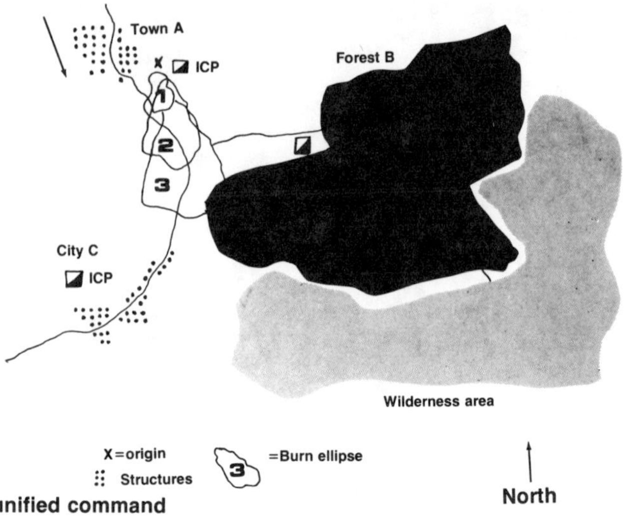

No unified command

Town A	City C	Forest B
*assumed command on initial attack *established own set of control objectives *established own mutual aid orders *established own ICP, base, staging *no coordination with other fire agencies in Eddy County	*assumed command two hours after fire started *protecting structures on city's wildland/urban interface *establishing own ordering process for mutual aid *established own ICP, base, staging *ordering aircraft for fire *no coordination with other fire agencies in county	*assumed command two hours into incident *protecting forest lands *established own mutual aid ordering system *established own ICP, staging *ordering air tankers additional to that of City C *no coordination with other fire agencies in county

Figure 19b

Figure 19a illustrates the unified command concept at a multi-jurisdictional wildland incident. In this example, three fire agencies are involved in a developing wildland fire in Eddy County. The fire started in "Town A" and spread to "Forest B" and "City C." Town

A has made an initial attack and has assumed command of the incident. Town A is utilizing its own personnel and resources and calling for mutual aid from Eddy County.

By the third hour of the incident, both City C and Forest B have lands involved. Both the city and forest service initiate initial attack to protect structures and forest lands. Both order mutual aid from Eddy County. City C and Forest B establish incident command posts and assume command in their respective jurisdictions.

Figure 19b represents the above situation three hours into the incident. It graphically points out that *each* agency has become autonomous from the others. Each has set up its own command post; each has made separate mutual aid orders. All of the agencies have their own control objectives and, obviously, no joint planning has taken place. This lack of coordination may negatively affect each agency by preventing resources and personnel from being deployed in an effective and timely manner. All control objectives may not be accomplished.

Using the above scenario and data, let's now apply the unified command concept (Figure 19c). In this case, let's say that, one hour into the incident, Town A's incident commander recognizes the fire has escaped initial attack and has the potential to become a major incident. The incident commander asks the dispatcher in Town A to have an agency representative from both City C and Forest B respond to the incident command post in Town A. The incident commander recognizes that, for unified command to be effective, it must be started early.

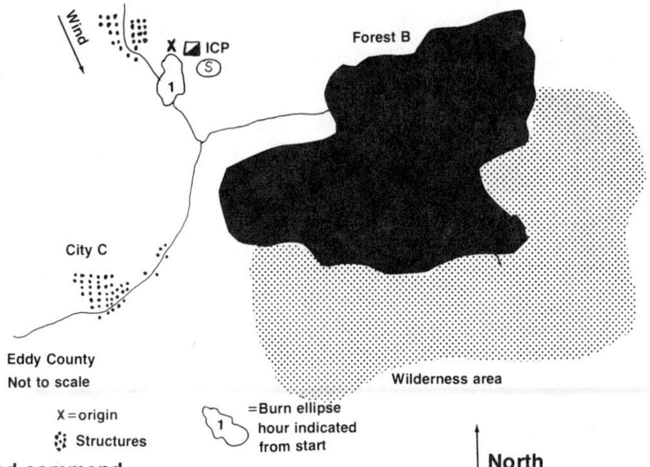

Unified command
Figure 19c

The Town A incident commander briefs the City C and Forest B agency representatives on the developing incident. Because it's clear that all three agencies will be involved, they agree to manage the incident as unified commanders. Each agency representative informs his/her agency of the agreement.

The principle of unified command is one of co-location for command, operations, planning, logistics and finance. Co-location means that there is *one* incident command post (ICP). The three agencies involved will truly become "unified commanders."

The "unified commanders" declaration does *not* violate the one-incident-commander-per-incident rule. It is not a violation, because, as they are co-located together, incident commanders can jointly make decisions and establish one common set of control objectives. However, only one of the three is the spokesperson at any given time. For instance, in the Figure 19c scenario, the unified commanders might agree that Town A has a high-priority problem to be solved, i.e. structural protection. Until this is accomplished, City C and Forest B agree that the Town A incident commander is the spokesperson. Now, as the incident develops or Town A's structures are no longer threatened, the responsibility can, and probably will, shift to Forest B or City C. Ranking and priority of the listed control objectives often influence the decision of who is the spokesperson for the unified commanders.

Because, in most developing wildland fire situations, personnel and resources are not unlimited, it's important to establish incident control objectives (incident action plan – Form 202). These serve as a basis for establishing priorities for such important resources as air tankers, hand crews and dozers. In addition, control objectives provide guidance for the operation chief.

The unified commanders will also utilize the control objectives to adapt personnel, resources and facilities to the needs of the incident. This list will also provide the basis for discussion about the fiscal responsibility of each agency (cost sharing).

Figure 19d shows a sample list of control objectives developed from the Figure 19c example. In the incident in Figure 19d, as at

Control Objectives

1. **Firefighter safety gets top priority**
2. **Protect structures in the wildland/urban interface of Town A**
3. **Protect structures in the wildland/urban interface of City C**
4. **Keep fire northwest of Forest B**
5. **Keep fire west of the wilderness area**
6. **Be cost effective. Limit suppression costs to $500 per acre.**

Figure 19d

any fire, firefighter safety should be the first priority.

The next three control objectives are agency specific and the unified commanders must agree on their priority ranking.

A. Protect structures in Town A
B. Protect structures in City C
C. Protect forest lands (B)

The operations chief (who is probably from Town A, but could well be from any of the three agencies) will apply personnel and resources to, hopefully, accomplish *all* the priorities. However, if there is a problem or shortage of resources, priorities are ranked (A, B, C). The ranking can also assist in another very important area; fiscal responsibility. Believe me, you can't start cost sharing too early. It's not an easy subject to just throw out on the table, but you must. It's not practical to wait until the incident is over and then bring up costs. Either have that discussion when the unified commanders first meet or order a finance chief. Each agency will bring into the incident expenditure limitations, paperwork processes and purchasing procedures it must follow. These policies, procedures and limitations need not create problems and delays if addressed early and jointly respected when control objectives are developed.

In Figure 19d, the second priority was to protect structures in Town A. Let's assume that, in addition to the structural engines that Town A needed, several air tankers are necessary to assist the engines. Cost sharing options for Town A are:

A. Air attack supervisor or operations chief keeps track of total drops and/or gallons of retardant and bills Town A directly. (Pre-incident agreement must be in place.)

B. Town A offers assistance in form of engines, personnel, hand crew and dozer to Forest B once Town A is not threatened, in exchange for all drops made in Town A. The incident finance chief writes up this mutual agreement and both parties agree to sign. Obviously, it's hard to absolutely equalize the cost to each agency, however, and if Town A only uses two drops and one hour of flight time it will not want to send five engines plus personnel to the forest for 12 hours as a trade off.

C. Order a finance chief immediately. Unified commanders agree on pro-rata cost-sharing once incident costs have been determined (post incident).

D. Town A protects its structures with help from City C. City C gets assistance from Town A in the form of structural engines. Town A and City C each pay Forest B for all drops made in their areas. Forest B bills Town A and City C directly. (Once again, pre-incident agreements must be in place.)

E. Town A provides logistical resources for the incident (food, fuel and sleeping accommodations). City C provides structural engines for forest land protection and to assist Town A. Forest B provides air support/retardant to Town A and City C. No billing or cost recovery is involved.

The important points to remember about unified command are:

A. Start early (during initial attack, if the incident has potential to develop and spread into other jurisdictions)

B. Co-Locate (Stick together)

C. Develop one common set of control objectives

Each jurisdiction will bring some concerns, needs and priorities to the incident. Prioritize on ICS Form 202.

D. Decide how to make decisions

This sounds easy, but may be the hardest thing to agree on. How are we, as unified commanders, going to make our decisions? I endorse the concept described in Figure 19c, where you have one spokesperson (incident commander) at any given time, but, this can, and will, change as priorities change. Some other important decisions:

1. **Media policy** (news release)
2. **Accident investigation policy**
3. **Fire investigation policy** (arson)
4. **Demobilization policy** (who goes home first)
5. **Cost-sharing agreement**

E. There should be *one* ordering, demobilization process (single-source ordering)

F. There should be *one* planning process

G. There should be *one* incident command post

H. Eliminate duplication

I. Promote open communication between agencies

J. Allow each agency to maintain authority and responsibility for its own jurisdiction

K. Allow coordinated application of resources and personnel to accomplish operational needs

L. Promote cost effectiveness

M. Use unified command for collective problem solving and better decision making

JOINT COMMAND

Another, more-widely-used, application of unified command is joint command, which is employed when two agencies are involved at an incident (Figure 19e). The key points of joint command are about the same as unified command, with these additions:

A. Initial-attack incident commander (in example, Raybould Fire

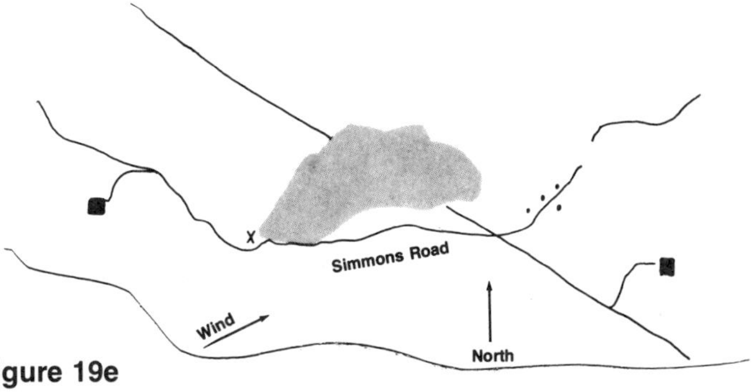

Figure 19e

Department) should meet with initial-attack officer (East Fire District). Generally, company officers should meet early and jointly develop an ICS 201. If the incident is a developing one, this jointly-crafted form will serve as an important tool for expanding the incident action plan.

3. If the incident is still in the initial-attack phase and will probably not burn for over one burn period, ICS 201 can serve as a tool to develop and establish control objectives and priorities. Initial-attack company officers from both jurisdictions should meet and quickly agree on some basic control actions and objectives to satisfy the needs of both jurisdictions (Figure 19f). In this situation, company officers assume responsibility for fiscal accountability and commitment.

Summary of Control Actions
Simmons Road Incident

1. **Raybould Fire Department continue to flank fire, hold fire north of Simmons Road.**
2. **East Fire District will protect structures in Jones Canyon.**
3. **East Fire District will keep fire west of Jones Canyon Road.**
4. **Continue using air tankers to slow head of fire.**

Figure 19f

Chapter 20

Problem Solving

In order to apply some of the principles posed in this text, I have included a problem-solving section. This is intended to help the reader develop a systematic checklist for dealing with wildland fire situations.

The answers offered are the author's and do not reflect an absolute solution, but, rather, one of many possible solutions. The reader should apply his or her agency-specific or regional policies to each problem.

Situation Number One
Lightning Strike in Timber Mix

CONDITIONS: It is 1700 hours in mid-summer. A dry storm frontal passage passed over a drainage three hours ago. Topography in the area is steep, to 60 percent. There is light down-dead fuel loading. After ignition by lightning, a fire is confirmed by an air-attack supervisor. It is presently confined to a single tree and a six-foot-diameter circle around the base of the tree.

No air tankers are available for response. You and two additional firefighters (engine company) are the only personnel available. The nearest access point is three miles away, south of the fire (Figure 20a). The air-attack supervisor reports that the fire spread rate is slow. Your engine has a typical wildland fire tool inventory.

Weather data estimated from the access road on arrival includes 78-degree F, 29 percent relative humidity, southwest wind at 7 mph (20 foot height), 7.0 fine fuel moisture level.

QUESTIONS

1. What are some safety concerns you and your crew should consider?

2. What thoughts do you have about access to the fire?

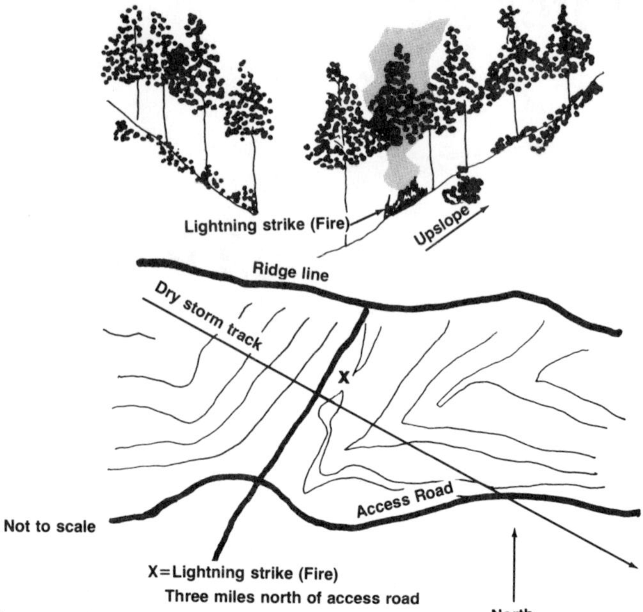

Figure 20a
Lightning strike. Dry storm Ponderosa pine stand

3. Reviewing the above weather data, what are some comments and concerns?

4. What are your predictions about fire behavior?

5. What are some key firefighting concerns?

Situation Number Two
Mid-Morning Grass Fire

CONDITIONS: 1030 hours, summer. A grass fire has started 150 feet off a road. Topography is level. Weather is characterized by no wind, 79-degrees F, 40 percent relative humidity. Fine-fuel moisture is estimated at 9.0.

The fire has burned two acres by the time you arrive (Figure 20b). You are a company officer of a three-person, Type 2 engine company. Two additional engine companies (both Type 3) are scheduled to arrive in 10 minutes after your arrival. No air tanker is available. This is an area that has experienced incendiary fires before.

QUESTIONS

1. What are the problems associated with a wildland fire such as this that can't be anchored to a road, natural barrier or stream?

2. How do you protect the area of origin?

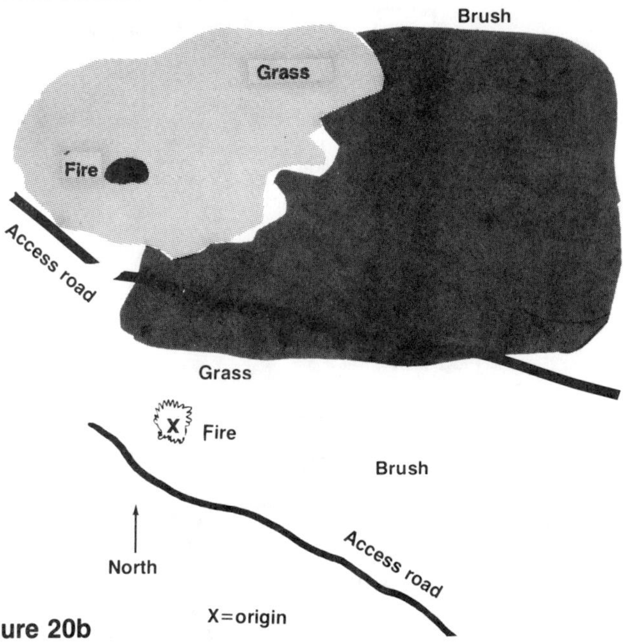

Figure 20b
Mid-morning grass fire (cured annual grass)

3. How do you establish control objectives on a no-wind, no-slope fire?

4. What about safety?

Situation Number Three
Nighttime Fire (2110 hours)

CONDITIONS: A careless camper has left an unattended campfire that has spread outside the campsite and into the fuel bed. Other near-by campers have tried without success to control the fire.

Weather data: 72-degrees F, 35-percent relative humidity, FFM 7.0, winds southeast at 04 mph, no fronts projected. Stable high pressure is present over the region. Winds will shift to downslope after 2230 hours.

You arrive in a Type 2 engine with three personnel at 2125. You stimate the fire is three to four acres in size. Rate of spread is slow. he campground has 25 sites, 10 of them occupied by a total of 25 eople. The campground is located in a 10,000 acre fuel bed that has ad no major fire history in the past 20 years.

The fire is moving upslope toward the ridge line (Figure 20c). lopes above the campground average 40 percent. Access and egress or the road are on a winding, narrow two-lane dirt road.

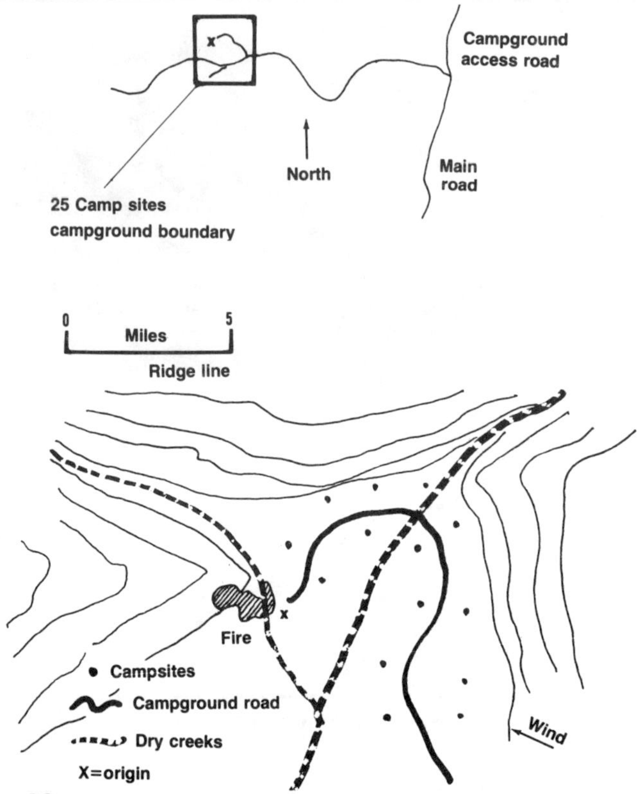

Figure 20c
Nighttime fire — recreational area

Other responding resources and their estimated arrival times ar engine (Type 2) – 2140 hours; another engine (Type 2) – 2150 hour hand crews (Type 1) – 2250 hours; dozer (Type 1) – 2200 hour Each engine carries 500 gallons of water and a complement of on inch hose and hand tools.

QUESTIONS

1. What are your initial concerns about safety-related issues

2. What about road access?

3. How will you make tactical assignments for incoming r sources?

4. What about additional personnel and resource needs?

5. If you were to develop a fire-behavior forecast for this i cident, what key points would you cover?

6. How will you make your assignment (including your crew)

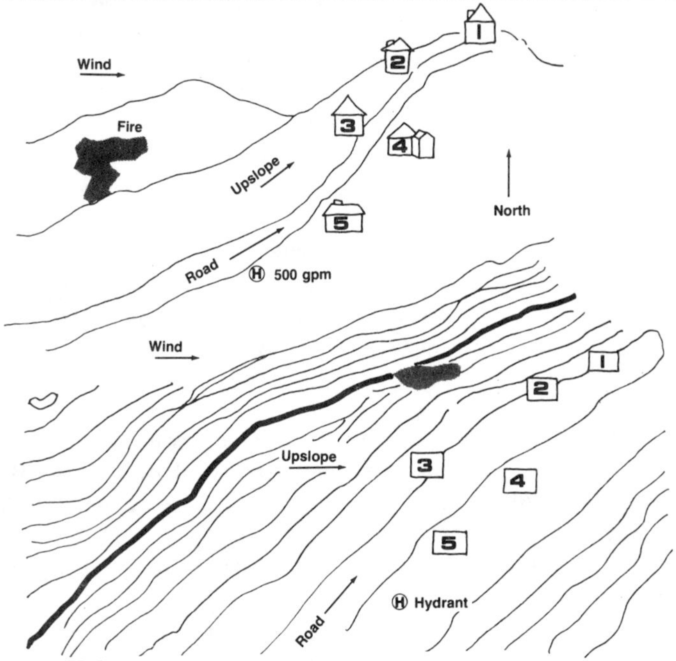

Figure 20d
Wildland subdivision threatened by brush fire.

Situation Number Four
A Wildland Fire Threatening Homes Along a Steep Canyon Ridge Line

CONDITIONS: It's 1040 hours on a Saturday during peak fire season. The weather at 1000 hours was 78-degrees F, 29 percent relative humidity, winds from the southwest at 6 mph. Skies are clear, air mass stable. No frontal activity is projected.

The fire was started by an unknown source in the canyon bottom (Figure 20d). It is estimated at two acres in size when you arrive at the homes, which are about one-fourth mile apart. The fire is a slope-driven one, with slow spread. There is no vehicle access into the canyon (area of origin). A hiking trail does access the area of origin. Canyon slope averages 50 percent.

Fuel bed is medium to heavy brush with good continuity. Fuel age class is 20 years.

The fire is three-fourths of a mile away from structures one and two on your arrival. It is burning three-quarters of a mile off the 20-foot-wide access road.

In addition to your Type 2 engine with three personnel, which arrives on scene at 1040 hours, a Type 2 engine with three personnel will arrive at 1045 hours, a Type 2 engine with three personnel at 1055 hours and a Type 2 engine at 1059 hours. A Type 1 hand crew will arrive at 1100 hours. Two dozers (both Type 1) are responding and will arrive at 1125 and 1140 hours respectively, A chief officer is responding but will not arrive until 1200 hours. Two Type 1 air tankers are available on special request, both 20 minutes away. A re-load, if needed, will take 20 minutes also. One air-attack supervisor will respond, on request, within 15 minutes.

No other ranches or homes are in the fuel bed. Fuel bed size is 2,000 acres. Homes are wood construction, built 10 years ago. Each is from 2,500 to 3,000 square feet. There is minimal separation of brush from structures.

QUESTIONS

1. There are two very different problems associated with this incident, namely the brush fire and structural protection. How will you deal with each in regards to your size-up and tactical objectives?

2. What structure(s) appear to have the lowest survivability and present the highest risk to firefighters?

3. What about additional resource and personnel needs?

4. What are your safety concerns?

5. Using the above criteria, would you, as first-arriving company officer, attack the fire or go into the command mode? Explain your answer.

Situation Number Five
Grain Fire

CONDITIONS: Weather conditions are 96-degrees F, 18-percent relative humidity, west winds at 20 mph. Time is 1330 hours. Topography is gentle and rolling to level. The grain field has no natural breaks.

The fire was started by a harvesting machine at the beginning of harvest (Figure 20e). Two isolated ranches to the east of the ranch are threatened.

The fire is 30 acres on your arrival at 1330. Rate of spread is high. The fire has started some short-range spotting in front of the head. No adverse weather fronts or wind are predicted in the next 24 hours. The fuel bed is 5,000 acres in size.

You arrive in a Type 2 engine with three personnel. An additional Type 2 engine with three personnel arrives at 1400. Another Type 2 engine shows up at 1410 with three personnel.

On your arrival, you talk to the rancher who was at the area of

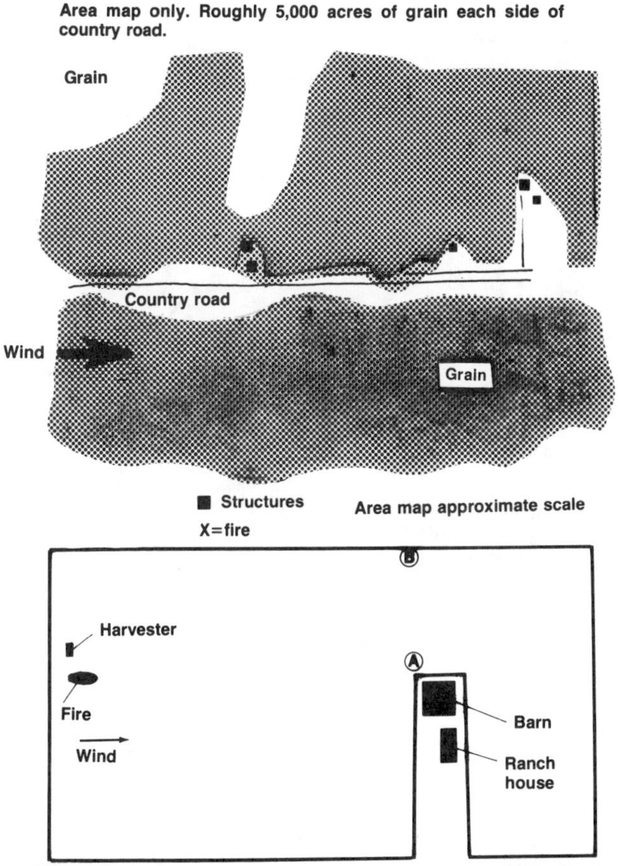

Figure 20e
Grain fire

origin. He indicates he has a ranch dozer (Type 2) available. The harvester is not burning but is an exposure should winds shift.

No other resources are available. The ranch has a 5,000-gallon water storage tank (near the barn) with fire department connections.

QUESTIONS

1. **What are your basic control objectives?**
2. **Would you use the ranch dozer? If so, how? If *not*, why?**
3. **What are some safety concerns associated with grain fires and this incident?**

Situation Number Six
Timber Fire

A careless backpacker has started a fire in a ponderosa pine forest.

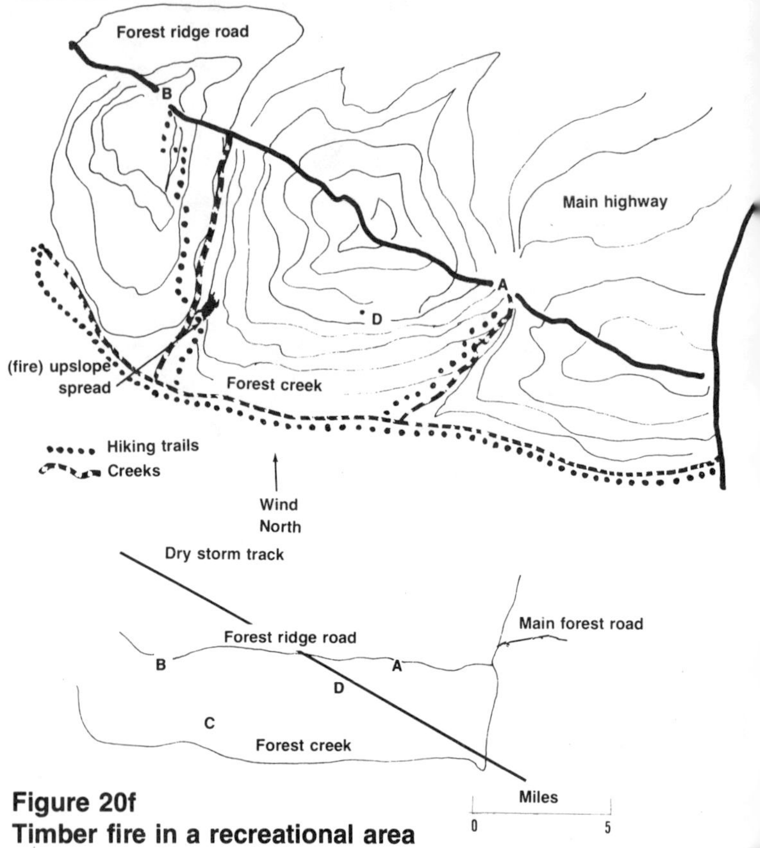

Figure 20f
Timber fire in a recreational area

The stand is mature, with a closed canopy. The down-dead varies fror light to moderate. The fire started at 1135 hours and burned for 2 minutes prior to discovery. It is located in a remote section of th forest.

You are a one-person patrol, and first-in on the fire. You cann access the area of origin but can view the fire from Point A (Figu 20f). At 1200 you estimate the fire at five acres with an upslope spread **CONDITIONS:** Weather data are 85 degrees F, 25-percent relativ humidity, south winds at 10 mph. It is August. Topography is rollir with slopes to 40 percent. A dry lightning storm is approaching fro the north and due to arrive at 1400 hours.

The dispatcher has advised you of the following resources ar ETAs:

Brush Truck (Type 4) 3-person: **1215**
Brush Truck (Type 4) 3-person: **1215**

Hand Crew (Type 1) 15-person:	**1220**
Dozer (Type 1):	**1225**
Dozer (Type 1):	**1230**
Hand Crew (Type 1) 15-person:	**1230**
Brush Truck (Type 4) 3-person:	**1235**
Air Attack (AA01):	**1220**
Air Tanker (Type 1):	**1225**
Air Tanker (Type 1):	**1235**

By 1210 hours, you have plotted the fire at one mile south of Point B on Ridge Road. At 1215 hours, dispatch advises that four additional Type 1 crews (15 persons each) are available plus two additional Type 1 dozers. The hand crews will arrive one hour from dispatch time, the dozers 35 minutes. Two 3,000-gallon water tankers are also available. Each water tanker will take 35 minutes to arrive, once ordered.

Ridge Road and Forest Road are two-lane dirt access roads in good shape. The forest creek is almost dry.

QUESTIONS

1. What are some safety concerns to evaluate prior to deployment?

2. How will the dry storm prediction affect your initial attack deployment?

3. What will the direction of fire spread be after the dry storm front passes point "D" on the dry-storm track?

4. How will you deploy initial-attack personnel and resources (crews, dozers, air attack, brush trucks)? Explain.

5. What are your attack options? (Use the figure to reference points.)

Situation Number Seven
Protecting Threatened Structures

CONDITIONS: It's 1300 hours on a Saturday in mid-summer. A brush fire has started in a fuel bed adjacent to a subdivision. Topography ranges from level to a 20 percent slope. Weather is 90 degrees F, 20 percent relative humidity. The wind is northwest at 15 mph.

The access road is a 25-foot-wide paved surface with a 40-foot cul-de-sac. Fuel is medium brush mix, four to six foot in height. Fuel loading is seven to ten tons-per-acre. Continuity is uniform. The fuel age class is 20 years.

Each of the seven structures is approximately 2,000 square feet. Their construction is wood and stucco with composition shingle roofing material. There is no flammable vegetation within 30 feet of any structure. They all sit in a fuel bed of approximately 3,000 acres.

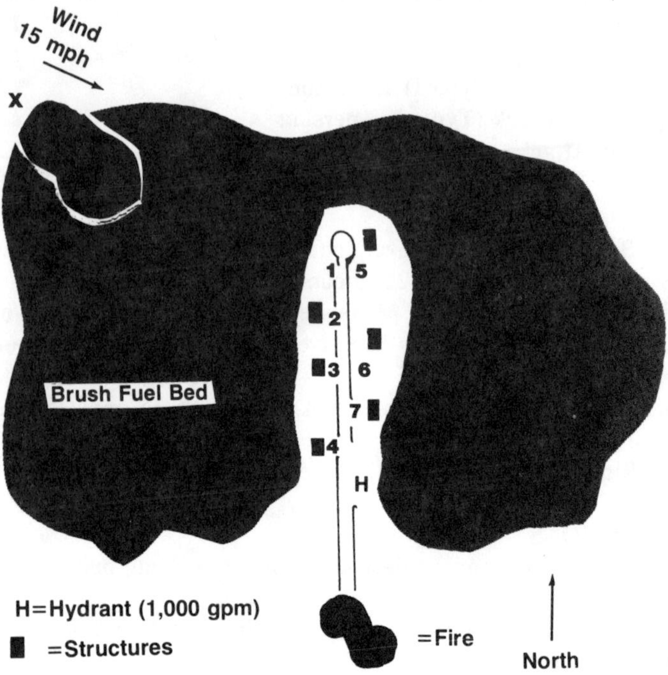

Figure 20g
Protecting structures in the wildland/urban interface

A 1,000 gpm hydrant is south of structure number seven.

You have been assigned four triple-combination engines, each with three personnel, to protect the structures (Figure 20g). Your division supervisor has advised you the fire will threaten structures two and three within 30 minutes. Each engine has 1½-inch hose paks (150 feet) and 1,500 feet of 2½-inch plus a full complement of tools and equipment.

QUESTIONS

1. Should you force evacuation of residents? If your answer is yes, how would you acomplish this? If your answer is no, how would you evaluate residents' safety?

2. What would you cover in the briefing for your engine company personnel prior to deployment?

3. What are your personnel safety concerns?

4. How would you tactically position the four available engines?

5. How and when would you deploy attack lines?

6. You are the company officer from one of the engines in the

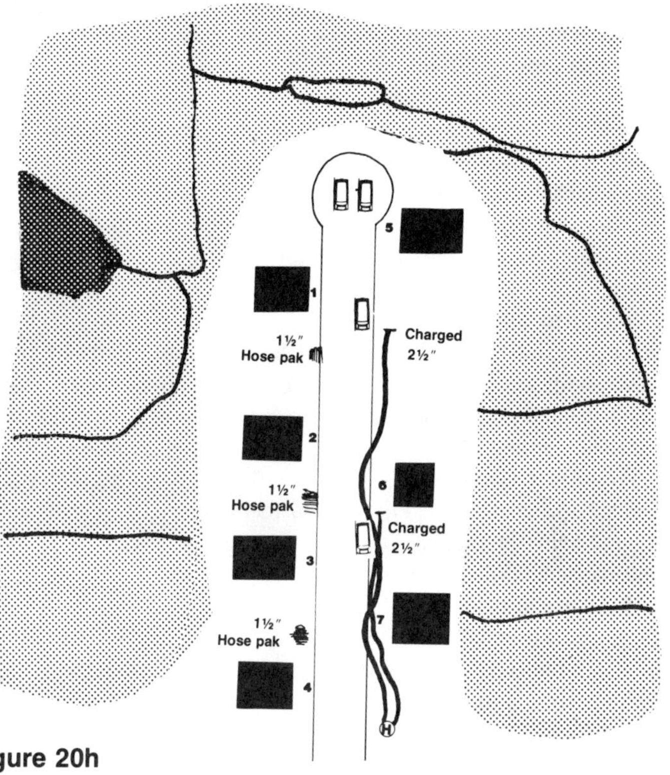

Figure 20h
Tactical deployment of engines to protect personnel and structures.

cul-de-sac (Figure 20h). The division supervisor has left you in charge of the resources and personnel. How would you manage them?

ANSWERS
Situation Number One

1. Safety Concerns

Access routes and *distance* are important. What is the footing like? Does your access route cross into a potential fire-spread area? How long is it going to take personnel to get into the fire? Will the weight of tools and equipment, coupled with slope percentage and footing, cause fatigue, which might limit ability to sustain an aggressive initial attack?

Safety zones. Where can we establish them? What will our escape route(s) be in the event of a change in fire behavior?

Potential injuries. What first aid equipment will we need? Think about injuries associated with sprains, fatigue, heat exhaustion, headaches and tool cuts.

Communications. Extra radio batteries for portable. Extra flagging in case you need to use air-ground signaling for help or assistance or to mark a trail. Keep in constant communications with the dispatch or the air attack supervisor.

Compass, topography map references. Timber height might make it hard to navigate into the fire. Use topography maps and compass directions.

2. Access to the fire

Direct access into the fire may not be the safest. I would utilize the drainage for access in this situation. It may provide easy egress (escape route) and access into the fire area. As you walk into the area, look for safety zones.

3. Weather Concerns

A weather concerns checklist should include:

- Are wind shifts predicted?
- Nighttime winds (downslope)
- Is this a thermal belt region?
- Is there good relative humidity recovery?
- Note any additional cumulus/frontal passages predicted.
- Does tomorrow's forecast predict more cumulus or frontal passages?

4. Concerns about fire behavior

- What will the likely size of the fire be on arrival?
- Will nighttime conditions modify spread, spread direction and fire behavior?
- Will current weather conditions and fire behavior (flame height, thermal intensity) allow firefighters to direct-attack the fire?
- Think incident potential.

5. Key firefighting concerns

- Are there other strikes in the area that have not spread yet, but may by the time you arrive?
- All firefighters should commit to an extended attack.

  Ensure:

  a. Double tool up

  b. Extra water (drinking)

  c. Extra food (rations)

  d. Files for sharpening tools
- Pace yourself when walking into the area.
- Make sure an anchor point is established.
- Make sure you take in a cutting tool in case the tree must be felled Use caution in felling the tree.

Situation Number Two

1. Problems associated with a wildland fire that can't be anchored to a road, natural barrier or stream

- Any time you start an attack without an anchor point, you risk being outflanked should weather conditions (winds) change. This is especially important in grass fuel types.

2. Protecting the area of origin

- Try to estimate when the fire started and the spread to this point (e.g., a 10-minute response time plus two-to-five-minute discovery time). As you start your attack, try to minimize equipment driving into the black area. Make sure you remind other responding resources.

3. Establishing control objectives for a no-wind, no-slope fire

- Keep the fire in lightest fuel type possible. Attack the fire on the brush side first.
- Knowing your first-in district, if winds were to start what is their likely direction? Attack the fire so as to hit the likely hot flank and head first.
- Keep the fire out of areas of down-dead fuels.

4. Safety

- Don't take the small fire for granted. This scenario has been responsible for many injuries and fatalities.
- Establish an anchor point using criteria discussed in Answer 3.
- Use the black (burned-over area) as a safety zone.
- Be alert to fire-behavior changes.
- Have personnel pace themselves while working. Remember SQQT!

Situation Number Three

1. Initial concerns about safety

- Firefighter footing
- Campground occupants' safety, possibility of evacuation
- Campers fleeing area creating a hazard for incoming resources
- Dozer deployment

2. Road access safety

- High potential for a vehicle accident.
- Request law enforcement or road department for traffic control. Emergency vehicle access only (camper egress okay).
- Warn each evacuating camper that fire vehicles are accessing this location, so drive slowly.

3. Tactical assignments for incoming resources

- Have all resources except the dozer respond to the campground (safety zone).
- Advise dispatch to have dozer operators contact you when five minutes from the campground. This will allow you to monitor fire behavior and determine the best access.

• Establish a good anchor point; direct attack from the campground (area of origin) up flanks. Use a progressive hose lay (wet line). The anchor must be secure enough to hold when winds shift to downslope (2230 hours).
• Stress quality line, minimum 10-foot wet-line width.
• The predicted wind change should slow the head. Concentrate on flanking action. Watch for signs of wind shift.
• Make sure all personnel practice safety. Talk about the likely wind shift. Plan for escape routes and safety zones.
• If the dozer(s) is deployed, use drainage (east of fire) or slope west of the incident to keep dozer away from personnel while accessing the fire. Alert personnel to possible rolling materials from the dozer.
• Utilize hand crew to follow up engine personnel on flanks. Start to work on the head of the fire in conjunction with the dozer.

4. Additional personnel and resource needs

• Will you need a water supply for an additional engine (Type 1 or 2) or water tanker for overhaul?
• Request a fire investigator.
• Call in additional law enforcement to assist in evacuation of the campground.

5. Fire-behavior forecast

• Realize that relative humidity recovery should continue to slow fire spread.
• Downslope winds may change fire behavior on flanks. Prepare for a wind shift.
• If downslope winds do not develop, upslope spread will be slow.

6. Making an assignment

• Assist in evacuating campers.
• Assess wisdom of using campground as a staging and safety zone should downslope winds materialize.
• Start progressive hose lay/wet line establishing an anchor point.
• Give updated size-up to dispatch.

Situation Number Four

1. Size-up and tactical objectives for the brush fire and structural protection

• **Brush fire**

a. Hand crew, dozer show.
b. Is it too steep for dozers?
c. Order two Type 1 air tankers, one air attack supervisor.
d. Order two additional Type 1 hand crew strike teams.
e. How about constructing a road along hiking trail for brush truc

access? Would this be a rehabilitation nightmare? Order an environmental technical specialist if you construct a road.

f. Consider safety of crews walking into fire. Plan safety zones, escape routes.

g. Make sure crews and dozers are aware of aircraft drops.

h. Make sure crews, dozers work safely together.

i. Radio communications

j. Keep in mind that peak burning conditions are still to come (1200-1600)

k. It may be hard to get water into the fire area.

- **Structures**

a. Dead-end road

b. Limited water supply

c. Poor access, turnarounds for resources

d. No separation between structures and brush.

e. Older wood construction.

f. Not much time to set-up, pre-position resources.

g. Back resources up road. Pre-positioning is important.

h. More engines may congest the egress route.

i. Thermal outputs may be untenable for firefighters.

j. Structure one is in the "path of least resistance."

k. Fire is likely to make several "runs" at houses.

l. Law enforcement is needed to assist in evacuation.

m. Contact law enforcement or road department for traffic plan. Think access for fire equipment, egress for residents.

2. Structures that have the lowest survivability and safety risk

- Structure number one is in the path of least resistance, with a low survivability factor and high risk to firefighter safety.
- The fire will probably make several upslope runs at structures. Structure number two has only moderate survivability in this situation. It poses a moderate risk to firefighter safety.
- The key to protecting structures number one and two is to pre-position hose lines (dry). Make sure houses are secure (window and doors). Discuss possible tactics with firefighters. Position fire apparatus out of path-of-least-resistance corridor. Discuss safety and egress plan if conditions become untenable.

3. Additional resource and personnel needs

- I would immediately call for another alarm, with a minimum five engines (Type 2). I would also request a Type 1 hand crew strike team. I would ask for immediate dispatch for both Type 1 air tankers and the air attack supervisor. Stage the engines away from the canyon until it is feasible to pre-position resources onscene. Keep egress route open. Advise the incoming chief officer of the developing situation and need for additional command staff.

4. Safety concerns

- Protecting structures in path of least resistance from heat, smoke and lack of oxygen.
- Safe egress of personnel if conditions worsen.
- Downhill fireline construction once main flame front passes. The fire will likely make several upslope runs at structures.
- Crews and dozers walking into area of origin.
- Safety associated with air tanker use (drops around personnel).
- Good radio communications between crews, dozers, aircraft and engines.

3. Whether *you*, as first-arriving company officer, should attack the fire or go into a command mode.

Base this on:

- The fact that the incident is a developing one. (An additional commitment to the incident will not change the situation.)
- The peak burning period is yet to come.
- This is not an initial-attack-size incident, as you can't easily get to the area of origin.
- Incident complexity. Brush fire and structures are threatened. Coordination of personnel and resources is important.
- The first chief officer will not arrive for over one hour.

Situation Number Five

1. Basic control objectives

- Protect structures (ranch structures).
- Evacuate ranches to east of incident (law enforcement).
- Construct extra control line around ranch structures (ranch dozer).
- Flank fire with engines.
- Protect harvester.

2. Using the ranch dozer

- I would utilize the dozer to widen the separation between ranch structures and the grain field. If time still allowed, I would have the dozer start a control line from Point A to B and back (a double-width line). If time still allows, repeat the same routine.

3. Grain-fire safety concerns

- High rate of spread
- Resist temptation to hurry (driving speed) on flanks.
- Spotting
- Wind speed
- Wind shifts (change in fire-spread direction)

Situation Number Six

1. Safety concerns prior to deployment

• Arrival time of personnel and resources versus time that dry lightning storm will influence fire behavior
• Safe deployment of hand crew using hiking trail (direct attack)
• Safety of using Ridge Road to stop the head of the fire
• Gusty erratic winds and the use of air attack
• Safe deployment of dozers
• Peak burning conditions yet to arrive. Spotting potential
• Safety zones for Ridge Road
• Evacuate (if possible) any other hikers and campers in the area.

2. How the predicted dry storm will affect initial-attack deployment

• Clockwise wind shift (northern hemisphere)
• Rate of spread change, potential for spotting
• May threaten use of Point A hiking trail for access.
• Will impact air resources with gusty, erratic winds. Winds will affect effectiveness of fire retardant.
• Potential for additional fires due to lightning strikes
• Hand crews, dozers may not be able to establish a good anchor point prior to frontal passage.

3. Direction of fire spread after dry storm front passes Point D

• East or southeast

4. Deploying initial-attack personnel and resources

• I would utilize the air attack supervisor to assist in monitoring safe deployment of personnel and resources and to monitor fire behavior. Start walking the dozer in along the forest creek hiking trail access off the main forest road. I would start walking the hand crews in along the forest creek hiking trail with the dozers. Stage brush trucks along the ridge road near Point A.

The goal is to have dozers and crews reach Point C on the hiking trail (anchor point) prior to the dry storm frontal passage. Air tankers may be most effective in establishing a good anchor point.

Crews and dozers should establish safety zones upon their entry into the fire.

5. Attack options

• Direct attack

a. Crews and dozers access hiking trail from main forest highway; air attack supports crews. Establish an anchor point at Point C on the hiking trail. Then flank attack. Caution on right flank: It will become a head as the front passes over fire area.

b. Air attack may not be effective on the head because of the canopy effect on retardant dispersion. However, some effort should be made to evaluate this first priority. Dozers may have difficulty climbing slopes on upper flanks. Keep in mind secondary air-attack priorities to support crews and dozers.

c. Brush trucks should be staged along Ridge Road near Point A. They can be used off Ridge Road once the head is stopped and flanks are tied into the Ridge Road.

- Indirect attack

a. Order the four additional Type 1 hand crews and two additional Type 1 dozers. Also, request both water tankers.

b. Deploy initial attack crews and dozers to widen hiking trail and creek from main forest highway to Point C (area of origin). The line should be wide enough to hold a backfire and free of jackpots of down-dead fuels. Post-fire rehabilitation will be important. Order an environmental rehabilitation technical specialist *prior* to starting the operation. (That doesn't mean you must wait to start your widening effort, just order one.)

c. Send in a brush truck (Type 4) to support the crews and dozer. Its objective will be to establish a good anchor point at the main highway and another at Point C. Once at Point C, one Type 1 crew and one Type 1 dozer can tie in Point C to Point B. Next, fire Point B to Point C. When the time is right, a firing operation will take place from Point C back to the main forest highway.

d. The four additional Type 1 hand crews and two brush trucks will report to Point B on Ridge Road. Ridge Road will be fired on the south side from Point B back to the main forest highway.

e. Water tankers should be staged at the main forest highway and forest road.

Firing will not take place until:

- The front has passed over fire area (after 1400 hours)
- All control lines are tied in.
- Winds have stabilized.

The firing sequence:

- B towards A
- B towards C
- C towards forest highway
- Forest road to forest creek

Situation Number Seven

1. Whether you should force evacuation of residents/evaluating their safety

I would like to force evacuation, for these four basic reasons:

- The fire will arrive prior to guaranteeing all residents could safely evacuate.
- Forced evacuation is very controversial, and, unless a strict policy is well established, most law enforcement agencies are reluctant to force residents to evacuate, especially on a short lead time.

NOTE: Be alert to the survival needs of law enforcement officer(s). Be aware of their lack of safety clothing and training in firefighting. Do not put them in possible extreme-fire-behavior situations.

• In this scenario, the street dead ends into a cul-de-sac. You will be very busy positioning resources and equipment. Maintain a clear egress route so personnel and resources can leave without delays, should conditions warrant.

• I would quickly advise residents of conditions and recommend they stay indoors and close all windows and doors. Able and willing adults can assist by removing flammable combustibles from decks next to their homes. They can secure all automobiles. Advise them not to waste water.

You should also note any residents who are sick or non-ambulatory. Question residents about whether their children are accounted for. Reassure those who stay that you will be in the area and available until the threat passes.

2. Briefing Engine company personnel prior to deployment

• All personnel

a. Make sure all safety gear is used.

b. Remind everyone the engine cab provides safe refuge if smoke conditions get thick. Breathing apparatus may also be utilized. If a law enforcement or road department employee is manning a critical road block make sure he/she is aware you have breathing apparatus.

c. Don't panic; stay together; stay close to the engine until ordered to deploy.

d. Do not overreact to panic-stricken homeowners who plead with you to assist in fighting their fire. Follow your control objectives.

e. Keep mobile and flexible in your attack. The attack should be a coordinated one, looking at each problem from the "task-force" attack concept, *not* individual engine-company goals. Pre-position dry hose paks and supply lines.

f. Allow the main flame front to pass or hit prior to charging lines and deploying.

g. It will be very smoky, so use caution and don't waste water on smoke.

• **Engineers**

a. Position resources facing downcanyon (or egress direction).

b. Keep resources running (watch temperature gauges).

c. Be prepared to disconnect hose line(s) on officer's order.

d. Drive cautiously through smoke. (Keep headlights on.)

e. Park the apparatus to gain maximum distance from radiant heat.

f. Keep hose line(s) out of street, where possible.

g. Keep windows rolled up and cab doors closed, when possible.

h. Watch hose bed for embers and burning material.

i. If, and when, you attack, advise the officer when the water tank level is down to one half.

- Firefighters

a. Quickly survey in and around structures one, two, three and four for hazards and problems. Double check for open doors and windows.

b. Pre-position dry hose paks in a safe location (not dry grass).

c. Envision likely area first flame front will hit and problems you might face.

d. Utilize street, lawns or cab as safety zones.

e. Allow the first flame front to hit prior to charging hose line(s). (A dry line is easier to re-position than a charged one.)

3. Personnel safety concerns

- Situations will accelerate very quickly once the flame front hits. Multiple problems may develop, so evaluate each prior to using water. Keeping all aspects of safety in mind while making an aggressive attack.
- Exposure of personnel to heat and smoke. Possibility of heat exhaustion and fatigue.
- The fire may make several intense runs. Keep alert and flexible to changing fire behavior.
- Keep personnel together so they can leave the area, if necessary, in a timely fashion.

4. Tactically positioning the four available engines

See Figure 20g for tactical deployment of engines to protect personnel and structures. I feel it is important to spread out resources for several reasons:

- The cul-de-sac is a perfect safety zone and is north of the main fire front so resources can ''drop into'' the problem area once the flame front passes.
- The other two engines are spaced out in close proximity to the area likely to be threatened. They are positioned to allow maximum distance from radiant heat, yet close enough for quick connection of hose paks once deployment is ordered.
- By positioning resources in several areas, it is unlikely any egress problems will result and personnel are never far from an engine in an emergency.

5. Deploying attack lines

- Pre-position dry hose paks (1½-inch) or flake out 150 feet of 1½-inch hose with nozzles. I would do this between structures likely to be exposed.

• Lay out hose on grass, pavement or a driveway. Keep the street as free as possible of hose.lines.

• Pre-position dry 2½-inch hose off the hydrant. Two engines can lay dry hose as they move up the cul-de-sac. As with the 1½-inch hose paks, estimate where these lines might be needed. Charge and clamp the two 2½-inch lines. These can serve as a supply source, or they may be connected directly to the 1½-inch hose paks. The key is to remain flexible and flow with the fire, only deploying for problems that can be quickly knocked down. In this situation, I have established two supply lines in front of structure number six and one near structure one.

6. How you, as company officer, would manage personnel

• Make sure each resource is in radio communications with others. (Put engineer in charge of listening to radio traffic.)

• Make sure each company officer understands control objectives.

a. Personnel safety first

b. Remain flexible. (Think task force objectives.)

c. Keep mobile.

d. Do not deploy until the flame front hits.

e. Keep all personnel ready to leave area if need be.

f. Conserve water.

• Be visible and available to the other officers and personnel.

• Be alert to any rescue problems with residents.

• Keep dispatch/division supervisor updated on your progress and situation.

CHAPTER 21

The Major Incident

Since the majority of wildland fires (over 90 percent) are controlled at under 10 acres it is unlikely a majority of the nation's wildland firefighters will get a chance to gain experience associated with a major incident. However, as growth continues in the wildland/urban interface or intermix, the definition of major incident may well change. The "traditional" major incident used to be described in terms of a multiple-day incident burning in a large fuel block. However, with the addition of more development (structures and people) in the wildland fuel beds, it may create a new definition of major incident. Because of the different firefighting needs in a wildland/urban interface or intermix (structure protection-evacuation) fire, a major fire could well be defined as 100 or less acres of fuel if structures are intermixed in that fuel bed. Or in the case of a rural volunteer fire company protecting a 300 person township with 1 or 2 structural engine companies, a five acre fire threatening the town could be a major incident.

What makes a fire a major incident? How do you evaluate your jurisdiction in terms of having the possibility of "hosting" a major wildland fire? Some key factors include:

☐ A major fuel block of 100 or more acres of grass, brush, or timber. Good continuity, good fuel transition, and old age class vegetation. It could well be a dedicated open space or natural open space park. It could be a parcel of land protected by a natural conservancy.

☐ Large area of down-dead fuels (bug, snow or drought kill). Large area of poor timber harvest slash could also create major concerns. Fuels on the ground that could preheat aerial fuel canopies and intensify fire behavior.

☐ Structures in a fuel block that do not have defensible space. Structures which have combustible roofs and/or siding.

☐ Personnel and resources which have long response time to major fuel blocks and structures (outside urban limit line).

☐ Inadequate road system (access-egress).

☐ Special problem areas – weather – areas which have frequent adverse wind patterns or frontal activity.

Typically these factors are evaluated annually prior to fire season by engine company personnel and chief officers. In conjunction with this field survey additional activities should occur:

1. Department fire chief should take the **political structure** on a field tour of key areas or if their schedule is too busy, a detailed letter should be written outlining hazards and fire protection concerns. This letter should be frank about the fire departments concerns and ability to protect structures or watersheds at risk. If necessary, prefire season workshops should be held to discuss problems and outline emergency plans.
2. Develop a **fire model** on the key area(s) and utilize it during a pre-fire season full scale exercise. This can also serve as a valuable tool during homeowner association meetings to illustrate potential fire behavior.
3. **Homeowner association meetings.** You might end up "preaching to the choir" because those attending meetings are generally people well informed on wildland fire hazards and those who fully comply with fire safe requirements. However, it's good to review your concerns on issues related to arson, evacuation and fire behavior.
4. Well planned and timed **media releases.** These releases should stress realistic problems and concerns.
5. Review and update emergency **response plans** and **mutual aid** procedures. This should include coordination with law enforcement and political subdivisions. Make sure all chief officers are clear as to how the fire department operations compliment and support the city or county emergency operation center. This should include reviewing how the fire department fits into a local emergency situation where the political structure gets deeply involved in incident management from an E.O.C. setting.

As previously mentioned, growth into the wildland areas coupled with more growth outside traditional urban limit lines has changed the dynamics associated with a developing wildland fire. If we graph out a developing wildland/urban interface incident it might look something like the following:

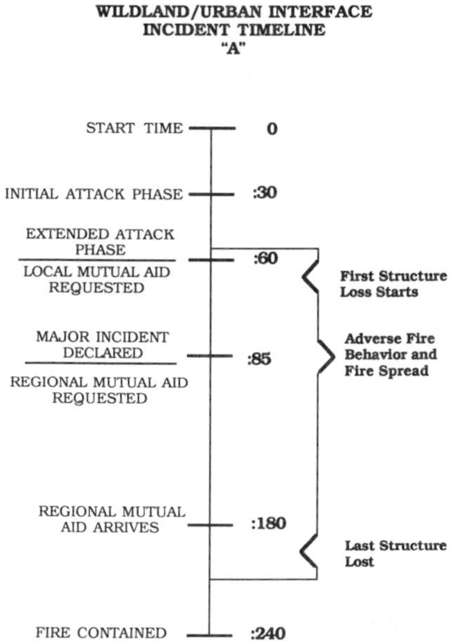

In the above timeline the initial attack phase is shown as the first thirty minutes of the incident but this could vary by specific agency. In traditional initial attack operations 2-4 engines or brush trucks are coordinated by a chief officer. The resources and personnel deployed on an initial attack face few key decisions once size-up and initial tactics have been accomplished. Over 90% of incidents are controlled in this phase.

However, if the fire escapes initial attack, the size-up and initial actions must be evaluated and modified to conform to the expanding organizational needs and decision process. The key point here is in most cases the initial attack company officer is required to make a limited number of key decisions (arrival, size-up, deploy). If the incident escapes initial attack the company officer would pull out his/her ICS-201, complete it and prepare for a transition of command (with the incoming chief officer). Prior to the increased growth in the wildland/urban interface the fire could burn for some time in isolated fuel blocks before threatening urbanized areas.

The 1985, 1987, 1988 and 1990 fire seasons produced more fires which escaped initial attack, threatened structures and developed quickly into major incidents. This often meant structures were threatened during the initial attack phase. The western states also found that the prolonged drought critically stressed all fuel types which adversely influenced fire behavior. Initial attack resources and personnel faced abnormal rates of spread and fire intensity which limited tactical deployment options.

The previously discussed timeline has in this author's opinion been modified somewhat as a result of the previously mentioned factors:

WILDLAND/URBAN INTERFACE
INCIDENT TIMELINE
"B"

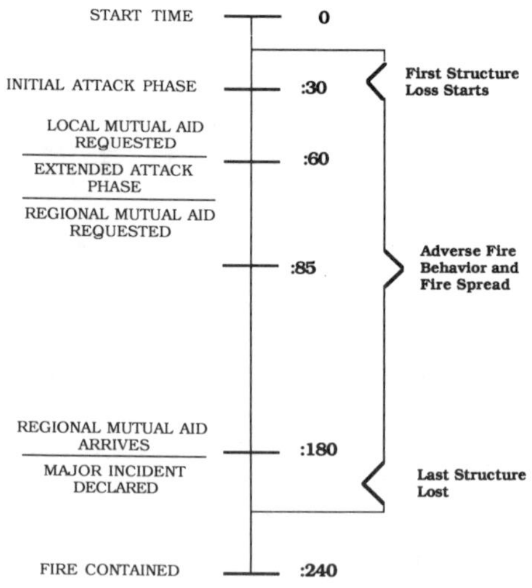

You will note that structures are lost or threatened during the initial attack phase often just after arrival on scene. The key point

here is that first arriving company officers are facing many more key decisions early on in the incident. These include:

- Structure(s) threatened?
- Access-egress problems?
- Evacuation needed?
- Additional resource needs?
- Initial control objectives (priorities).
  - Life
  - Property
  - Resource value
- Incident potential (how big & bad can it get?).
- ICS organization needs (operations chief, division supervisors, etc.).
- Fire behavior forecast.

The decisions facing a company officer when structures are involved or soon will be, come hard and fast. If the officer does not ''quickly'' evaluate the incidents potential it will overwhelm him/her. Unfortunately, recovery is difficult at best which often leads to confusion and freelance firefighting, poor fireground communication management, little or no divisional supervision and increased risks for firefighters (safety).

To help illustrate how rapidly things can happen and how quickly complex decisions can arise, let's review one of the nation's largest and most destructive wildland/urban interface fires, the June 1990 ''Paint Conflagration'' in Santa Barbara, California which damaged or destroyed 648 structures causing an estimated $400 million damage.

As previously discussed, it is very important to conduct pre-fire season public education efforts to prepare the public and political structure for fire season. In March of 1990, before declared fire season, the Santa Barbara County Fire Chief issued a detailed executive briefing for the County Board of Supervisors based on several key concerns including (A) 4th year of drought, (B) abnormally low live fuel moisture levels, (C) Palmer Drought Index (record low), and (D) chaparral dieback. Homeowner association meetings were conducted and a detailed letter was sent to the Board of Supervisors outlining the fire departments concerns and potential limitations.

On June 25-26, 1990, based on National Weather Service Data and local weather conditions, the wildland fire agencies in Santa Barbara County started sharing mutual concerns and thoughts about the weather conditions. As previously mentioned, the drought has lasted four years in the county, and since fire season was declared on May 1, agencies were very concerned about what 1990 would bring.

It is also important to state here that, since the previous three years were also scary in terms of incident potential, public information and agency administrators were worried that the annual "gloom-and-doom" news releases would be shrugged off by both the public and the media, since few extended-attack fires had actually taken place so far. This is an important consideration for information officers charged with preparing annual fire season media releases.

The focus for 1990 would be the Palmer Drought Index (soil-plant moisture), and the fact is that 1990 conditions were, and are, the worst ever in the history of the index (Fig 3h). Additionally, live fuel moisture level climax points were very low, and even without an adverse wind model, fires would be very hard to control.

Public information and education groups had been focusing on homeowner association meetings. The county even held a simulation of a major wildland/urban interface fire in the Santa Barbara front country (Mission Canyon) to illustrate how homes would be lost even with mass mutual aid given the fuel moisture and weather conditions.

On June 26, Santa Barbara County fire agencies were on a red-flag alert status as Santa Barbara front country was hit with peak temperatures of 109°F with relative humidity of 9% and a fine-fuel moisture of 2.3. Live fuel moistures were near 60%, and critical.

No major fire activity took place on June 26. By the 27th, chief officers from the fire agencies determined a need to activate the County Fire Coordinations Center in Santa Barbara and to beef up the staffing and resources.

A bulldozer (D-7, Type 1) and strike team of brush trucks (Type 3) were pre-positioned in the front country, along with an extra chief officer. Many of the fire agencies were starting fire patrols in their own jurisdictions. The fire coordination center took the radio traffic and activity coordination away from the dispatch center so they could devote their full attention to incident dispatching.

The battalion chief who would serve as strike team leader for the aforementioned pre-positioned strike team was en route to the strike team staging area at San Marcos Pass Summit when the Paint Fire broke. He helped to quickly assess fire behavior potential and speed up mutual aid requests. He also quickly helped to set the tone for extra personnel safety needs, because of observed erratic fire behavior.

Actually, the fire activity started at 1513 hours on June 27 at the county dump transfer station near the base of San Marcos Pass. Spark from a forklift ignited the cardboard debris. It quickly spread from the transfer station into surrounding grass and oak woodland

Fanned by gusty winds it soon threatened a nearby subdivision.

Mutual aid was quickly requested for the dump fire from nearby Santa Barbara City, Montecito, Carpinteria and Ventura County fire departments. Also, two of the five brush engines assembled for red-flag alert standby were diverted to the dump incident.

The dump fire was still being fought when the Paint Fire began just 1.5 miles to the north. The Paint Fire was the result of an arsonist's handiwork near the intersection of Highway 154 and Painted Canyon Road (Figure 3).

Weather conditions at the time of the incident consisted of 97°F. temperature, 10% R/H, wind from the north at 12 to 15 m.p.h. and an estimated fine-fuel moisture of 2.3(4.0 or less is critical).

The fire was set in a well-defined steep drainage at the head of Maria Ygnacio Creek. Vegetation there was heavy chaparral, estimated at 25 to 40 tons per acre. Its age class was about 40 years, so there was a tremendous amount of decadent material in the understory and subcanopy.

The incident fire behavior the first two-plus hours can only be described as **awesome** – far beyond merely adverse. Personnel estimated the rate of spread at 208 chains per hour (a chain equals 66 feet), with 40-feet flame lengths taking out 75 percent-plus of the canopy cover first flame-front passage.

During the first flame-front passage, vertical flame models were pushed to horizontal, quickly pre-heating large areas within the canyon and contributing to massive spotting. To best illustrate the rapid spread of this fire, here are a few key radio transmissions given to fire Coordinations (remember, the fire started around 1800 hours):

1802: *Brush 24 reports nearly on scene – smoke showing.*

1805: *Brush 24 reports two to five acres in heavy brush, 15 to 20 m.p.h. winds – major fire potential.*

1810: *Fire is declared major incident – spotting occurring.*

1814: *Battalion Chief on scene reporting fire is a threat to Trout Club and Painted Cave subdivision. Battalion Chief assumes Paint Command.*

1820: *Los Padres Forest National command team (incident commanders Chief Simmons – SBCo and Vincent – LPF) transition into command to manage the incident. Initial Paint commander assigned as Paint Operations.*

1827: *County Fire Chief surveying the situation and reports winds 50 to 60 m.p.h., major spotting and fire heading into structures.*

Within the first 45 minutes of burning, the fire would travel downslope and over 1.89 miles from its origin, indicating a rate of spread of over 200 chains per hour (this equates to a 2.5 m.p.h. rate of spread).

It is estimated that the fire crossed Highway 101 (Figure 3) at approximately 1930 hours. The fire produced flame lengths estimated at 40 feet; spotting was estimated between one-quarter and one-half mile ahead of the fire. The fire's southernmost run occurred by 2100 hours on June 27. The major activity on Day Two of the incident was on the north end and the open flanks. Fire behavior was greatly reduced in both rate of spread and intensity as fire spread shifted from downslope to upslope. By the end of the second day, the fire had burned an estimated 4,200 acres of watershed. The final acreage burned at time of containment on June 30 at 2000 hours was 4,900.

On June 29, at approximately 1100 hours, fire officials had the grim facts of the destruction verified as the Red Cross Damage Team released its preliminary report. The loss included:

- 28 apartments – damage: $16,775,000.
- 15 businesses – damage: $3,037,000.
- 2 farms – damage: $200,000.
- 1 mobile home – damage: $50,000.
- 10 public buildings – damage: $1,611,500.
- 570 single-family dwellings – damage: $215,373,000.

Total units damaged or destroyed: 648.

NOTE: These damage figures do not include approximately 20 new vehicles burned at the county road yard or damage to utility service lines and facilities. Eventually damage estimates would reach $400 million.

At the height of the incident approximately 1,795 personnel were assigned, including 120 engine companies, 34 hand crews, nine bulldozers, five fixed-wing air tankers, four helicopters and 69 overhead. Suppression costs are estimated at $3 million.

Mutual aid support for this incident could only be described as tremendous. With eight major incidents going on in Southern California and critical fire weather everywhere, the California fire agencies once again demonstrated why California has the best mutual aid system in the world, and why we utilize the FIRESCOPE Incident Command System (ICS) to manage all risk incidents.

The fire agencies in Southern California looked past their own situations and jurisdictional boundaries and put engines on the road immediately. This was a key factor as to why more structures were not lost.

A key to successful operations in a developing wildland/urban interface or intermix fire is having adequate strike teams to preposition and deploy for "rolling" tactics. Incremental ordering (or an engine here or there) doesn't provide enough personnel, water or safety to protect large numbers of structures.

Another key point in a rapidly-developing incident is maintaining personnel safety as the highest priority. When mutual aid resources are being used in steep, winding mountainous terrain, or in subdivision areas, the conflict between access and egress can often lead to accidents and injuries. Getting safety officers briefed and in the field is important.

Additionally, the transition from initial attack to a local fire team to a national fire team occurred so rapidly it would have been understandable to have a loss of coordination between safety officers and team member briefings. But this didn't happen. Teams were briefed and transitions were completed with only few problems or distractions.

Incident commanders were commended on the high safety standard of the incident. Only nine minor injuries were incurred between June 27 and July 4. These included a helicopter crash where the pilot miraculously walked away with just minor injuries. The helicopter was not so lucky, however. A critical incident stress team was provided for the hand crew and helitack crew that witnessed the helicopter crash.

In terms of cooperating agencies and safety records, most notable was the effort by law enforcement agencies that were responsible for evacuation, road blocks, and, in some cases, checking to see if persons were trapped by the fire. Only one officer was injured, when a motorcyclist tried to crash a roadblock to gain entry into a secured area. The officer suffered a dislocated shoulder.

Yet another successful facet of the incident was the close working relationship between agency administrators and chief officers. Neither the Fire Chief nor Forest Supervisor required what some would term a "mating dance" to get up and running. The close day-to-day relationship paid off tremendously in trust and commitments.

The incident did not get hung up transitioning from a local team organization to a national fire team level organization. Joint control, planning, logistics and fiscal cost apportionment started early and rapidly. Some examples of this included:

:20: The ordering process shifts from County Fire Coordinations to a unified ordering point at the Forest Service expanded dispatch.

00: Initial ICS-201 is used to develop Joint Incident Objectives ICS-202. They include:

- Personnel safety.
- Structure protection – prevent further involvement.

• Keeping fire west of Mission Canyon.
• Keeping fire east of Las Vegas Creek.
• Keeping fire south of Camino Cierlo Road.
• Minimizing damage to San Marcos watershed.
• Maximizing cost effectiveness.

2100: Forest Service District Ranger and County Fire Deputy Chief developed Escape Fire Situation Analysis (EFSA, and briefing for incoming national fire team).

This document was reviewed and approved by agency adminis-trators from the Los Padres National Forest and Santa Barbara Fire. The EFSA and the written delegation of authority form the "con-tract" between agency administrators and the national fire team (Incident Commander). The EFSA lists fire behavior and environ-mental, cultural, social and fiscal concerns and limitations.

The local forest team is interagency in makeup (Santa Barbar County – Forest Service) and both joint commanders were on scen within minutes. They utilized on-scene personnel to quickly fill ou necessary overhead positions and start mass mutual-aid strike tean requests through Fire Coordinations and, eventually, the unified or dering point.

As the incident continued to unfold, the agency administrator (Fire Chief and Forest Supervisor) assembled to evaluate the nee for even greater commitment. The key here was that it would hav been easy with all the structures being lost, and the speed of thi incident, to stay with oral objectives and directions without using th writing ICS-201, ICS-202, EFSA and Delegation of Authority. Bu the written documentation was important for setting the tone fo safety, environmental protection, and operational priorities and fisc management. Even though the fire was still developing, the concer for possible fire/flood problem months after this fire were concern being evaluated.

Along with initial control objectives, E.F.S.A. and delegation authority, a list of political considerations were developed. This w done because local, state and federal political subdivisions we involved along with many special interest groups. The list of co siderations included:

• Outright loss of hundreds of homes.
• Outright loss of numerous businesses.
• Threat of life loss.
• Significant impacts to urban infrastructures and utilities.
• Very hot fire likely causing hydrophobic soil conditions watershed above urbanized area could cause significant threat of fir

flood sequence.

- Sundowner weather conditions could last for several days.
- A local emergency declaration has occurred. A formal request has been made to the state for a state of emergency declaration.
- Main railroad shut down both directions.
- Highway 101 closed.
- Local, state and national media exposure.

Two additional key activations which proved important were getting environmental technical specialists (fire/flood sequence concerns) in there early so that they could tell us where to, or more importantly, where not to, use bulldozers.

The activation of a damage-assessment team to start an initial count of structures lost or damaged while the fire was still burning was also important. The American Cross team provided the first detailed damage survey. Field observers helped give accurate intelligence on fire damage and perimeter extension. This early evaluation helped provide information officers with accurate totals, and helped law enforcement secure areas from looters or ''lookie-loos.''

As is often the case in a rapidly-developing incident involving many assisting and cooperating agencies, some things fall through the cracks. The Paint incident had 30 assisting and cooperating agencies assigned to it. Some areas that could have come off better included:

• Keeping local government officials closer to the incident command post (ICP) for quicker access and frequent briefings. Traveling between the ICP and city and county EOC's takes too long and is logistically difficult because of traffic. Better briefings keep rumors down and political structures happier. Media releases issued from 2-3 different release points are difficult to coordinate and manage (FAX machines help if you don't lose power).

• Making sure the liaison officer position is staffed early in the incident and that he or she is touching bases with each assisting or cooperating agency (the importance of this position cannot be stressed enough).

• Keeping law enforcement agencies well involved in discussions about traffic plans, roadblocks and evacuation. Since they are generally charged with this responsibility, they need to be involved in the planning **prior** to decisions being made.

• Communication plan and radio frequency management. It's difficult to develop one that will fit all responding agencies, and getting frequency management is harder on immediate-need deployments. The strike team leaders did a fantastic job in keeping abreast of assignments and requests.

• Incident check-in points. The initial two hours were strictly immediate-need and immediate-deployment tactics; no formal check-in was occurring. This made it difficult to estimate logistical needs for the next six to eight hours, and undoubtedly some media releases were also inaccurate because of same.

• Logistical support. Early in the incident, until about 8-12 hours after it began, the meals and drinks did not reach all assigned personnel. This is a critical issue, and cannot be stressed enough. You almost need to assign a quality control person to float around to check on who's getting fed and who isn't.

• Losing control of the incident information releases. It is best to keep the information release point at the incident and bring in the interested agencies. If individual EOC's want to set up information releases, hard copy releases can be provided. Otherwise, the information quality and accuracy drop off.

• It is also necessary to provide support to dispatch facilities to answer the thousands of telephone calls from local and national media. A key concern of dispatchers was that no one briefed them or updated them on the incident or for the most part checked on their well being. Some needed de-briefing as they took thousands of calls for help from panic stricken residents.

• Critical incident stress debriefing sessions for personnel. The incident started on June 27 and things were still hectic a week later. This made it very difficult to debrief those who witnessed and struggled to save many structures and businesses. Many personnel did not get the debriefing.

Figure 3

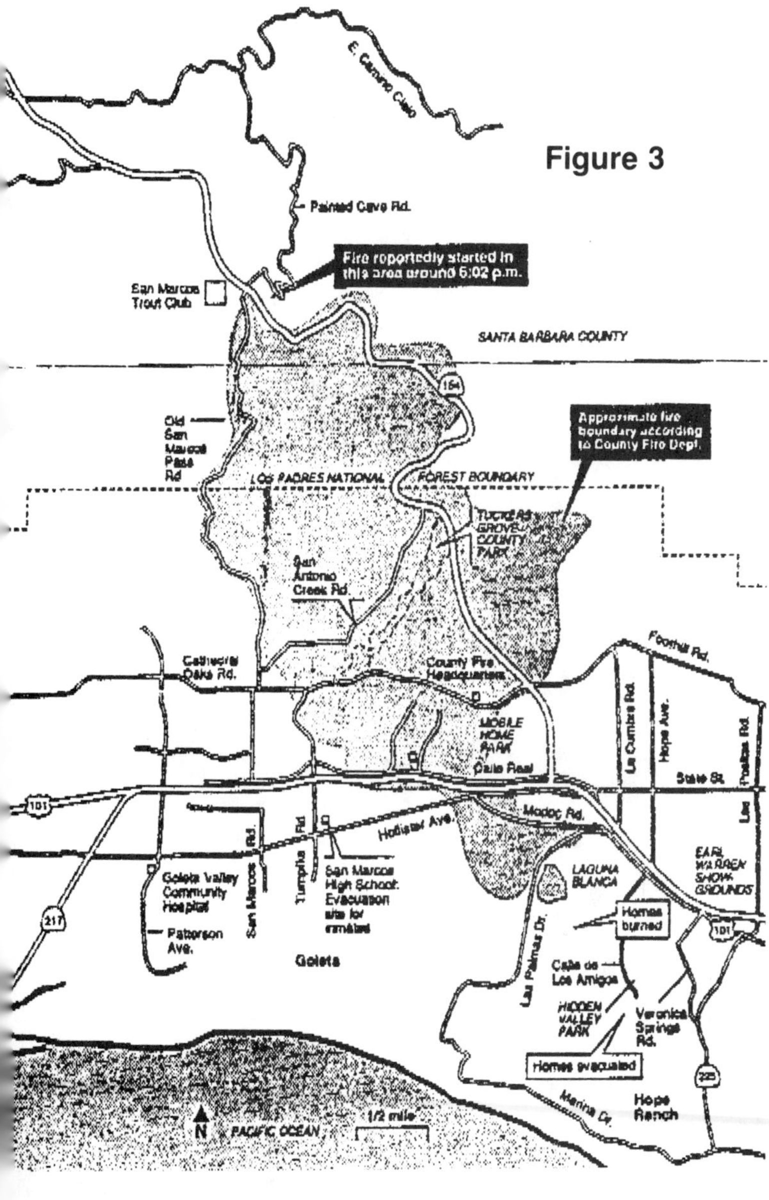
E. Camino Cielo
Painted Cave Rd.
Fire reportedly started in this area around 6:02 p.m.
San Marcos Trout Club
SANTA BARBARA COUNTY
154
Old San Marcos Pass Rd
Approximate fire boundary according to County Fire Dept.
LOS PADRES NATIONAL FOREST BOUNDARY
San Antonio Creek Rd.
Cathedral Oaks Rd.
County Fire Headquarters
MOBILE HOME PARK
Calle Real
Foothill Rd.
La Cumbre Rd.
Hope Ave.
State St.
101
Modoc Rd.
Hollister Ave.
San Marcos Rd.
Turnpike Rd.
Goleta Valley Community Hospital
Patterson Ave.
San Marcos High School. Evacuation site for animals
Goleta
217
LAGUNA BLANCA
EARL WARREN SHOW GROUNDS
Homes burned
Las Palmas Dr.
Calle de Los Amigos
HIDDEN VALLEY PARK
Veronica Springs Rd.
Homes evacuated
225
Hope Ranch
Marina Dr.
N
PACIFIC OCEAN
1/2 mile

Bibliography

Albini, Frank, *Estimating Wildfire Behavior and Effects,* Technical INT-30, U.S. Forest Service, 1976.

Anderson, Hal, *Aids in Determining Fuel Models,* Technical Report INT-122, U.S. Forest Service, 1982.

Brown, A., and Kenneth Davis, *Forest Fires,* McGraw-Hill, New York, 1973.

Burgen, Robert, *Estimating Live Fuel Moistures National Fire Danger Rating System Research Paper INT-226,* U.S. Forest Service, 1978.

Clar, C. Raymond and Leonard Chatten, *Principles of Forest Fire Management,* State of California, 1966.

Countryman, Clive, *A Study of Mass Fires and Conflagrations,* Technical Report PSW-22, U.S. Forest Service, 1963.

------, *Carbon Monoxide: A Firefighting Hazard,* Technical Report, U.S. Forest Service, 1971.

Davis, James, *Building Professionalism Into Forest Fire Suppression,* Journal of Forestry, July, 1977, pp. 423-426.

Field Operations Guide, ICS 420-1, Incident Command Publication, FIRESCOPE Products, Riverside, California, September, 1983.

Gaylor, Harry, *Wildfires: Prevention and Control,* Robert Brady Publishing Company, Maryland, 1974.

Greenlee, John, *Wildland Fire Modeling and Strategy Assessment,* Fire and Land Management Enterprises, August, 1982.

Hafterson, John, *Escape Fire Situation Analysis,* Missoula Intermountain Fire Council, Missoula, Montana, 1980.

International Fire Service Training Association Ground Cover Firefighting, Second Edition, Oklahoma State University, Stillwater, Oklahoma, 1982.

Introduction to the Fundamentals of Fire Behavior, Technical Study Guide 725-565, U.S. Forest Service, Washington, DC, 1964.

National Wildlife Coordinating Group (N.W.C.G.) Fireline Handbook 410-1, Washington, DC, March, 1984.

Pyne, Stephen, *Introduction to Wildland Fire,* Wiley Publishing Company, New York, 1984.

Rothermel, Richard, *A Mathematical Model for Predicting Fire Spread in Wildland Fuels,* Technical Report INT-115, U.S. Forest Service, 1972.

------, *Fire Behavior Systems for Fire Management,* U.S. Forest Service, 1980.

Schaefer, Vincent, and John Day, *A Field Guide to the Atmosphere,* Houghton Mifflin Company, Boston, Massachusetts, 1981.

Schroeder, M.J., and Charles Buck, *Fire Weather Handbook,* U.S. Forest Service Handbook 360, 1970.

Swanson, D.H., *Air Tanker Performance Guides,* Technical Report INT-27, U.S. Forest Service, 1976.

Wilson, Carl, *Fatal and Near Fatal Forest Fires,* Published Report, International Fire Chiefs Association, August, 1977, pp. 9-15.

Subject Index